THE
MICROBREWERS'
HANDBOOK

Ted Bruning

First published in Great Britain 2007 by Navigator Guides
www.navigatorguides.com
Reprinted 2008 (twice)

This revised edition published in 2009 by
Paragraph Publishing, St Faiths House, Mountergate, Norwich, NR1 1PY
www.paragraphpublishing.com

A catalogue record for this book is available from the British Library.

The publishers have made every effort to ensure the accuracy of information in the book at the time of going to press. However, they cannot accept responsibility for any loss, injury or inconvenience resulting from the use of information contained in this guide.

Acknowledgements: The publishers would like to thank all those microbreweries who provided information for their case studies and to Ted Bruning for all his hard work and constant enthusiasm for the project.
Photo credits cover: Copyright © mash tun photo Black Sheep Brewery

Publisher: Damian Riley-Smith
Cover Design: Alicia Alexandrakis
Publishing consultant: Navigator Guides
Printed in Great Britain by JF Print Ltd

Contents

Foreword

By Carola Brown, Past President of the Society of Independent Brewers

This book rings bells that take me back 27 years to when my husband Mike and I went to the Great British Beer Festival at Alexandra Palace, where we first met "micro" brewers and were inspired to join their number. We were lucky in already owning a building we could use on our farm in West Sussex, an area with plenty of free houses – no pub companies then! – and we started brewing in the old cowhouse in July 1980, with four pubs taking Ballards Best (and then only) Bitter. Many visitors found their way through the lanes to our farm and brewery, sometimes arriving via the chicken run! Every time someone bought a polypin of beer we were so thrilled we'd have some, too – luckily we didn't have to drive home as we were there already.

Outlets built quickly, and by 1985 we moved to a larger building because we were selling our, by then, two beers to about 40 pubs. Nowadays we produce six draught and four bottle-conditioned beers all year round; we've moved again to larger premises (avoid moving if possible – it's very traumatic!); and we're supplying around 80 pubs and numerous shops and off-licences.

I've been involved in brewing for over 26 years; I ran our pub for three years; and I have sat on the council of the Society of Independent Brewers for 18 years. It was all a complete surprise, and I've loved almost every minute of it. There have been some tough times, and it's hard work, but you have a very good chance of papering the walls of your brewery with awards won in numerous brewing competitions and beer festivals. You may receive letters from complete strangers saying your beer is the best they've ever tasted and where can they get more of it? Best of all, you will have the everyday satisfaction, denied to most of the population, not only of making a product with your own hands, but making a product specifically designed to give pleasure to you, and everyone who drinks it!

Ted Bruning has been well known for many years as a beer enthusiast and beer writer. In this excellent book his love of his subject and his experience come together to provide an agreeable and amusing routemap to becoming a fully-fledged commercial brewer.

This book will prove invaluable in helping you make up your mind to go for it, and guiding you towards success. I raise a pint to Ted Bruning, and to you!

Ballards Brewery
The Old Sawmill
Nyewood
West Sussex

The world of beer has become more diverse and full of flavour over recent years, and *Beers of the World* is excited to be a part of these changes. This growth in variety and intensity has been best exemplified by the world of the microbrewer, where craft and production meet to create some of the finest beers in the world. *Beers of the World* is delighted to be involved in this second edition, written by Ted Bruning former editor of *What's Brewing*, in which all aspects of the process are explored in detail.

We have updated the book and included illustrations to explain the process in more detail, and at the back we have introduced a directory of every microbrewery in the UK at the time of publication. So should you want to taste some of the great beers brewed by your local microbrewer, or ask them some pertinent questions, then you can now find them here.

Sally Toms,
Editor, Beers of the World
www.beers-mag.com
June 2009

Author's Preface

I f you've picked up this book, chances are you're contemplating a dramatic change of life. You may be a licensee wanting to add a small brewery to your pub; you may already be working as a brewer and looking to strike out on your own; you may be a home brewing enthusiast hoping to turn your passion into a living; you may be none of the above. You may be a "civilian" fed up with the rat-race, perhaps with equity in your house or a redundancy cheque in your pocket that you're looking to convert into a whole new life. If so, microbrewing might be for you.

Every time I ask an established microbrewer for a word of advice for the aspirant, they have the same one: "Don't!" Maybe they're remembering all the struggles and frustrations of making a success of their chosen line of business. Maybe they don't want the competition. But I don't know one of them who isn't happy with his – or, in a few cases, her – lot, or who would trade it for a steady office job. That goes for even the most inveterate moaners among them – and believe me, there are a few!

But before you read any further, ask yourself this question: have you got what it takes? Have you got the grit it takes to jump the bureaucratic hurdles? Have you got the painstaking, near-obsessive character it takes to brew a cracking pint day in, day out? Have you got the ready wit, winning charm, and bloody-minded ruthlessness it takes to get out there and sell? Have you got the imagination, intuition and insight it takes to spot and seize new opportunities? If so, you're halfway there. Add a single-minded attention to administrative detail and faultless form-filling, an accountant's grasp of sums, and a bottomless well of energy, and you might yet make a microbrewer.

Most of these personal qualities, though, are the basic requirements for any sort of business. In microbrewing, there are compensations. One is that everyone will love you because everyone loves beer – and even those who unaccountably don't will be captivated by your story and, at heart, on your side. Another is that you'll be operating in an almost uniquely successful sector of manufacturing. Don't believe me? Just go out shopping and look for widely available brands of cosmetics, confectionery, meat and fish products, biscuits, condiments, shoes, pharmaceuticals or power tools from small independent makers. You may find a few, but mostly in small independent retailers. Microbrewers, though, have torn themselves a niche in the national retail markets, both on-trade and take-home, that few other small manufacturing industries can rival. Depending on your choice you can operate in the warm bosom of your local community or the cold limelight of the national stage, or both. There may be trouble ahead – okay, there will be trouble ahead – but in choosing microbrewing you are giving yourself a far, far better chance of success than, say, the putative restaurateur.

And the good news from the Society of Independent Brewers, which represents the majority of Britain's smaller producers, is that this seems to be holding good despite the recession. Its Local Brewing industry Report 2009 records an impressive 10% overall volume growth during 2008, with the average number of pub accounts per member increasing from 79 to 94 and throughput per pub account growing by 9%. Members' bottled sales were also up 20%; and all this in a year when production by the bigger brewers was down by 8.3%. So while it might be overegging the pudding to claim that microbrewing is recession-proof, it certainly seems to be a better bet than, say, electrical retailing. Or construction. Or banking.

This book is more of a road atlas than a street map. It will, I hope, direct you up the motorway of hardship to the edge of Success City while leaving you to find the precise route to Fulfilment Avenue for yourself. More prosaically, it aims to set out the challenges and rewards of a new life in small brewing clearly enough for you to make up your own mind whether it's for you and you're for it. All I hope is that I have supplied you with a good long look before you decide whether to leap.

This book would not have been possible without the help of many people. I particularly thank the 15 brewers who submitted themselves to interrogation to provide the case histories you will find within. Others who have given their time and patience include David Smith, David Porter, Keith Thomas, Brendan Moore, Lucy Hunter, Carola Brown, Chris Garrett, Paul Corbett, Richard Shardlow, Peter Amor and Nina Bates. I have also been helped by the planning and licensing officers of South Cambridgeshire District Council, who not only explained the arcana of their crafts but also offered their best wishes to all would-be microbrewers; their names, alas I did not record. To them all, my thanks. To those I have forgotten, my apologies as well as my thanks.

Ted Bruning 2009

Introduction

How it all Started

I N 1965 Peter Maxwell Stuart, the 20th Laird of Traquair, unwittingly started a revolution. He had rediscovered the 18th-century brewhouse that once kept masters and servants alike at his ancestral pile at Innerleithen, Peeblesshire, supplied with ale, and decided to restore it. A period of hard work followed, and before long the beer started flowing again at Traquair House.

Neither Peter Maxwell Stuart, nor anyone else thought at the time that the establishment of the first commercial brewery in Britain in half a century was any more a mere curiosity, a one-off. Then seven years later another former brewery, this time at Selby in North Yorkshire, also recommissioned its vessels. Founded in 1894, Selby had stopped brewing in 1954 to become a licensed trade wholesaler. But, said owner Martin Sykes: "I foresaw a revival of interest in real ale and got in early." In November 1972 the first brew was released; and this time it was no one-off curiosity.

Less than a year later the third of the new wave of "microbreweries" – and the first truly new brewery in over 50 years – was founded by former rocket scientist Paul Leyton at the Miners Arms at Priddy in Somerset. It sounded like a pub but was actually a restaurant, where you could only drink Paul's home-brew with a meal; and all the beer was bottled rather than draught. The year after that a fourth micro – and nobody now remembers who coined the term – was set up at the Masons Arms at South Leigh in Oxfordshire, and the microbrewing revolution was well and truly on.

True, it got off to a faltering start. Nearly all of the country's 55,000-odd pubs were either owned by existing breweries or were loan-tied, having accepted the exclusive supply agreement that came with low-interest brewery loans. Half of the 300 small breweries started in the 1970s and 80s failed, most often for want of free-of-tie pubs to sell their beers to.

Campaign for Real Ale (CAMRA)

But the 1970s was also the founding decade of the Campaign for Real Ale (CAMRA), fomentor of the great consumer revolt against the weak, gassy, keg beers the brewing industry was foisting on the public. CAMRA and the microbrewers were symbiotic from the start – in fact Martin Sykes, the refounder of Selby Brewery, was a member of CAMRA's first National Executive Committee. CAMRA's Good Beer Guide pointed drinkers to pubs that stocked traditional beer, including real ale from new brewers; and the beer festivals staged by its rapidly expanding web of local branches allowed the public the opportunity to try the new brewers' ales for themselves. So, with growing support from enthusiastic beer-lovers and from the handful of publicans who could and would stock their beers, the luckiest and pluckiest of the pioneers clung on. Slowly their numbers grew, and within a decade local independent brewers had become an established, if often penurious, fixture of the nation's beer and pub scene.

Who were they, though, these pioneers? Not the counter-cultural hippy good-lifers you might suppose. Most of them, in fact, were already brewers.

Throughout the 1950s and 60s big breweries had been buying up smaller ones and closing them down. This concentration in the industry was the delayed effect of the economic conditions of the preceding four decades: war followed by depression followed by war followed by rationing had left scores of small family breweries hopelessly uncompetitive. Their pubs and breweries hadn't had a bean spent on them in generations and were in many cases near-derelict; and the owners were desperate to sell, sometimes for ludicrously small sums. Bass once recouped the entire purchase price of a brewery it had bought simply by auctioning the contents of the new acquisition's wines and spirits warehouse. In other cases, buyers found that their acquisitions hadn't had their pub estates revalued since before the First World War , and covered their outlay just by sending round a team of surveyors.

That is, perhaps, another story. The upshot, for our purposes, was that hundreds of experienced staff – executives as well as brewers – were thrown out of work as old-established breweries were rationalised out of existence. Most of them simply disappeared into the general labour force; but a few decided to carry on making a living at their chosen trade and, following the lead of Traquair, Selby and the rest set up breweries of their own.

The Pioneers

And some of them were pretty senior figures. Bill Urquart founded the Litchborough Brewery in a barn at his Northamptonshire home in 1974 having been laid off by Watney after 40 years in the business. His last assignment had been to run down the old Phipps Brewery in Northampton, which was earmarked for demolition to become the site of Carlsberg's brand-new lager plant. Part of his job was to decide who would be made redundant and who would get a job at the new plant. At 58, he had a feeling that his own name was on the list for the chop, so he seized the opportunity to acquire the skills he would need to set up on his own. At Litchborough he not only brewed a bitter so popular that his own golf club sold it, but he also helped many other new brewers set themselves up.

Another senior brewer who set up for himself but spent as much time helping newcomers as running his own brewery was Peter Austin, founder of Ringwood in Hampshire in 1978. Peter had just retired as head brewer of the Hull Brewery, but his new life took him all around the world, installing small brewing plants as far afield as China.

Other highly experienced pioneers included Simon Whitmore, managing director of Courage's western region who founded Butcombe Brewery in Somerset in 1978 after being made redundant. Peter Mauldon, who in 1982 refounded his family brewery in Sudbury, Suffolk (established by his great-grandfather in 1795, bought and closed by Greene King in 1960), had been a senior brewer at Watney in Mortlake, Surrey. David Bruce, who opened the first of the Firkin chain of brewpubs in 1979, had worked in management and brewing at both Courage and Theakston's. Martin Ayres, Ted Willems, John Bjornsson, Chas Wright, Pat Glenny, James Johnstone, Gerry Watts, Roger Catte, Geoff Mumford, Bruce Wilkinson, Tony Allen, Peter Yates, Peter Amor, Bryan Wilson and John Gilbert were other industry veterans who set up on their own in the 1980s and whose ventures are still going strong today, often under second- or even third-generation ownership.

Despite the newcomers' resumés, the established brewers – both the surviving older-established family firms and the new Big Six national brewers – were at first rather scornful of their potential. It was hard to believe they could produce anything decent on brewing plants thrown together from scraps of old dairy equipment and the like; and the older firms were armour-plated, or so they believed. Their tied estates, and the number of free houses they controlled through low-interest loans, surely meant that the upstarts would never gain more than a toehold in the retail trade and could never become a threat. A semi-cordial relationship based on amused condescension soon developed. Pitfield Brewery used to get its fresh yeast from Charles Wells of Bedford, turning up at the back gate with a galvanised bucket which a worker would obligingly fill with barm scooped straight from the fermenter. No-one saw Pitfield as anything but a harmless eccentric – until 1987, that is, when its Dark Star strong old ale became the first microbrewer's beer to win the Campaign for Real Ale's Champion Beer of Britain competition.

For these chaps could brew, whatever the mainstream thought. Brewing is, after all, not that complicated a process (although brewing consistently good-quality beer is extremely painstaking and demanding). A chef-turned-microbrewer I know tells me it is far easier than cooking in a restaurant. Nor does the equipment itself have to be expensive and gleaming, so long as it's well-maintained and only has the holes in it that you actually want. And anyway, most of the new wave had actually been brewing all their working lives, so to find them consistently turning out beers of seriously commercial quality should have come as no surprise.

Actually, in terms of quality they had some key advantages over their much bigger competitors. With no accountants counting the farthings, they didn't have to skimp on the raw materials they used. With no tied estates to guarantee a base level of sales, they could only survive by brewing consistently better beer. And with no marketing departments telling them what the public supposedly wanted, they were free to brew whatever they fancied. Some rifled the recipe books of the past and reinvented vanished beers such as porters and old ales (like Dark Star); others experimented and came up with entirely new styles. The cumulative effect was to arouse in the beer-drinking public an appetite for novelty and variety (and, paradoxically, so far had mass-produced beer fallen by then that a thirst for the traditional and a thirst for novelty were virtually identical) that older, more staid, breweries couldn't or wouldn't satisfy – or in many cases even acknowledge.

Throughout the 1970s and 80s the trickle of newcomers accelerated thanks to a house-price boom that gave most middle-aged people the equity to invest in a new life of their choice, and an economic recession that left many middle-aged people with no choice but to invest in a new life. Fewer and fewer of the second wave came from within the brewing industry itself; but many of them were experienced businesspeople of considerable acumen, so although the retail trade remained largely closed to them, the rate of business failures slowed even as the rate of start-ups increased. By the end of the 1980s the number of new breweries had reached three figures.

Society of Independent Brewers (SIBA)

But while the older brewers stubbornly defended their position – and the Big Six between them owned well over 30,000 pubs – the moderate success the microbrewers had achieved only made them more frustrated. It was this frustration that transformed them from an assortment of very different people with very different backgrounds and ambitions into a movement. SIBA, the Small Independent Brewers Association (now the Society of Independent Brewers, but maintaining the original acronym), was formed at a meeting at a pub in Wiltshire in 1980 after the Brewers' Society (BS) had refused to admit new members who brewed less than 200 barrels a week. (This was regardless of the fact that perhaps a dozen existing BS members brewed nothing like that amount.) It was run from a ground-floor flat in Highbury by a couple of enthusiasts, Elisabeth Baker and the late Tony Williamson, who as well as scraping a living from running the small brewers' magazine, *The Grist*, were SIBA's occasionally-paid. And if SIBA was a ramshackle, cash-strapped organisation, it included some surprisingly high-powered people. Dave Roberts of the Pilgrim Brewery of Reigate, for instance, was a former senior civil servant in the Welsh Office who knew intimately how government worked; and so SIBA soon became a potent lobbying force.

Monopolies and Mergers Commission

In 1988, as a result of pressure from SIBA, CAMRA and licensees' associations, and with the help of a handful of supportive MPs, the Office of Fair Trading ordered a Monopolies and Mergers Commission (MMC) enquiry into the supply of beer. The mainstream brewers had been here before and had always escaped with no more than cosmetic changes. But this time their complacency proved ill-founded, for much to their surprise the MMC found there was a "complex monopoly operating against the public interest" and recommended measures to smash it. To the brewers' even greater surprise and indeed fury, the then Trade Secretary Lord Young proposed to implement measures in full. He quickly disappeared in a reshuffle, and although his successor, Nicholas Ridley, watered down the MMC's proposals considerably, the 1990 Beer Orders still had the desired effect.

The Beer Orders

The Beer Orders contained two key clauses. The first was that the Big Six (Bass, Allied, Grand Met, Whitbread, Courage, and Scottish & Newcastle) must either sell or lease free of tie half of their pubs above a 2,000 ceiling; the second was that their tenants should be allowed to stock one guest real ale of their choice. The first measure led, eventually, to the demise of the Big Six

– only the smallest of them, Scottish & Newcastle, survives in anything like its 1980s form – and the emergence of giant non-brewing pub companies such as Punch Taverns and Enterprise Inns. The second led to a huge increase in the number of microbreweries, thanks to the opportunities it opened up in the retail trade.

The early 1990s were halcyon days for the micros as they saw their beers go on sale in pubs owned by the Big Six (and served, to add insult to injury, through handpumps and beer engines also owned by the Big Six, much to the Big Six's disgruntlement). One of the country's most successful local brewers, Wickwar of Gloucestershire, was founded in 1990 by Courage tenant Ray Penny expressly to supply himself and fellow tenants with guest ale. It wasn't long before Ray got rid of his Courage tenancy to concentrate on running his brewery, which has since moved to bigger premises and supplies around 350 free houses in the region. He is also developing a small tied estate of his own.

End Product Duty

Small brewers were boosted still further three years later when the archaic system of levying duty on the unfermented wort was scrapped. This system, which dated back to Gladstone's introduction of malt duty in 1880, put the smaller brewers at a serious disadvantage. All brewers – however large – were allowed 6 per cent duty-free wastage allowance, which meant that the more efficient big brewers were in effect selling 4 or 5 per cent of their beer tax-free, whereas smaller brewers were sometimes charged duty on beer they couldn't actually sell. In 1993 this system was replaced by end-point duty calculated according to the beer's percentage alcohol by volume. It meant there was no longer any need for a wastage allowance: brewers were only charged for what they had actually sold, and could even claw back the duty on beer spoiled or returned as unfit for consumption. So end product duty meant a more level playing-field as fas as prices were concerned.

The party didn't last, though. By the late 1990s the Big Six had disappeared, and the guest ale market had disappeared with them. But the microbrewers had made plenty of hay during the brief period of sunshine. Consumers had got used to the idea that Courage pubs didn't only stock Courage beer and Whitbread pubs didn't only stock Whitbread beer. Choice had been put in front of them, and they liked it. The new non-brewing pub companies saw this and started stocking cherished traditional ales from big-name family brewers such as Adnams, Fuller's and Young's alongside national brands such as Bass and Tetley. Once the idea of choice had caught on it gradually became easier for microbreweries to find outlets, and by the time the Beer Orders were finally scrapped in 2002 as no longer relevant, they had trebled in number.

Progressive Beer Duty

The scrapping of the Beer Orders was mourned by CAMRA but not by anyone else. For as luck would have it, the very same year saw the next great legislative boost for microbrewing in Britain when after years of hard lobbying by SIBA (aided by CAMRA) the chancellor introduced the same system of progressive beer duty that was already common in Europe. Progressive beer duty (PBD) or "sliding scale" allowed a 50 per cent duty rebate to producers of less than 5,000 hectolitres or 3,000 barrels of beer annually (a brewer's barrel is 288 pints or 1.63 hectolitres). Brewers of more than 3,000 but less than 18,000 barrels a year got smaller rebates. It was a step that enraged established brewers; and even those few micros that had grown to near the 18,000-barrel ceiling were less than pleased, describing it as a disincentive to growth. But the proof of the pudding is in the eating: PBD has led to a further doubling in the number of micros in Britain, of which there are now approaching 600.

Direct Delivery Scheme

Following the hat-trick of the 1990 Beer Orders, end product duty, and PBD, SIBA scored again with its Direct Delivery Scheme. The withering away of the guest ale market as the Big Six were one by one snuffed out threatened to close the pub trade to small brewers again thanks to the appearance of non-brewing pub companies or "pubcos", as they are inelegantly abbreviated. Most of them were founded with estates of discards bought wholesale from the Big Six. Often they were set up by ex-Big Six personnel, financed by Big Six loans, and stocked only Big Six beers. But one by one they were bought out by aggressive predators funded by venture capitalist houses, in many cases foreign-owned, and very soon the links between the pubcos and the old national brewers were severed. Next, the Big Six themselves were targeted; as we have seen, all of them except S&N have now gone, bought out by Carlsberg from Denmark, Coors from the USA, and InBev, the Belgian-based Stella Artois giant.

At the same time, many old-established regional breweries were succumbing to a fad for separating their brewing operations from their pub estates. The near-universal business model in the industry had always been "vertical integration" – that is, the ownership of both manufacture and retail. One of the effects of the Beer Orders, though, had been the driving down of wholesale beer prices as the pubcos shopped around for their beer. In the light of this, the City of London decreed that brewing was no longer profitable, and that the regionals should become pure retailers. Those that gave in to the siren song and got shot of their breweries – Usher's, Gibbs Mew, Morland, Greenall Whitley, Morrells, Brakspear, Eldridge Pope, Burtonwood and others – have by and large been taken over, either by other pubcos, or by those rival regionals that still believe in vertical integration. For its opposite, as things turned out, has proved to be total disintegration.

Today's big pubcos source their beers more widely than either the national or regional breweries to whose estates they succeeded ever had. But they have always found it difficult to deal with local microbrewers. They own no drays or depots of their own; their pubs are supplied either directly by the brewers themselves or, more commonly, by third-party wholesalers. Micros have generally been too small to deal direct with such giants nationally – Punch Taverns owns 9,000 pubs, and Enterprise Inns has almost as many; and few of the new wave of brewers could supply even a fraction of such vast estates. And even when microbrewers' beers have been listed by a pubco for regional distribution, it has always been galling to have to deliver to a depot 100 miles away or more to get into a pubco-owned pub just down the road – and even more galling to have to return to the depot for the empties!

SIBA's Direct Delivery Scheme has created software that allows local brewers to deal directly with pubco-owned pubs that want to stock their ales. The scheme may appear cumbrous in that it's still the pubco that actually buys the beer from the brewer and sells it to the pub; but the transaction is entirely electronic, and in practical terms it's the brewer who makes the sale, delivers the beer, and collects the empties. (No small matter when the 72-pint firkins most commonly used cost £80 apiece, and the longer they stay out in trade the more you need to own.)

The Future of Microbrewing

In a nutshell, then – rather a large nutshell, granted, but the story of 40 years can't be told in 40 words – that's how we got where we are. The question is:

where do you fit in?

That depends very much on your ambitions and your access to capital. Microbrewers cover such a huge span these days that the very term "microbrewer" is no longer applicable to them all. The biggest of them are very big indeed: Sharp's of Rock in Cornwall brews more real ale than the duchy's established regional, St Austell. Hop Back of Salisbury expanded through two Business Enterprise Schemes and now has a dozen pubs of its own and, in Summer Lightning, a genuinely national brand. St Peter's of Elmham, Suffolk, was founded by multimillionaire John Murphy of Interbrand expressly as an exporter and now sells its beers in their distinctive green flasks all over the world. At the other end of scale there are dozens, if not scores, of publicans who have installed tiny brewplants in their outbuildings just to supply their own pub. And the Jenkins brothers of Bullmastiff Brewery in Cardiff have won award after award but resolutely refuse to expand to meet the huge demand for their beers because they've got things just how they like them.

With such a wide range of sizes and styles of operation, microbrewers have experimented with a number of descriptors that would encapsulate them all. "Craft brewers" was tried and rejected as being too evocative of the kitchen sink. "New brewers" seems out of date when some of them are celebrating their 30th birthdays and have even changed hands as their founders retired. "New wave brewers" is accurate enough, but again, many of them don't feel that new any more. So they have settled on "local brewers". It may not always be accurate when many of them have national and even international distribution, but it feels right. It positions them in the local food movement and creates an identity that separates them from the regionals and nationals.

That's the hope, anyway; it doesn't always work out, but for many local brewers it has come true. It can come true for you, too.

Chapter One
How to Brew

B REWING beer, as I mentioned in the introduction, is not actually all that complicated. Not in theory, at any rate. You simply steep malt in hot water until its starch content turns into sugar and dissolves; you strain off the resulting thin syrup and boil it up with hops; you add yeast; and when it all stops bubbling and foaming, you drink it. (Or, in your case, sell it for someone else to drink.) How hard can it be? But as with any craft, success depends on absolute mastery of materials and processes; and within the simple framework outlined above, the possible variations are almost infinite. So before you can present the public with a product of consistently good quality (and achieving consistency will be one of your key skills), you're going to need a lot of training, both theoretical and practical.

You can learn the brewing skills you will need on courses run by formal training providers such as **Brewlab**. You can learn the basic engineering skills you will need to keep your plant running (if you don't already possess them) from the fabricator who installs it. But before you take either of those risky and expensive steps, you can teach yourself most of what you will need to know about beer by reading, tasting widely and intelligently, visiting working breweries, and by brewing at home. And you can start the reading part of your home-learning course right here.

In nearly 40 years of pub-going, I have never got over my surprise at how little the public actually knows about its beer. Many regular drinkers don't even know what it's made of; and public ideas about alcoholic strength are hopelessly confused. So let's start with a potted description of what beer is and how it's made.

The Basics of Brewing

Most alcoholic beverages have three components. The first is a liquid medium. The second is the sugar that the yeast will digest, alcohol and carbon dioxide being its waste products. Finally, there are the aromatic or flavour components. If you're making wine, all three come in one handy little package – the grape (or the strawberry or blackberry or whatever soft fruit you're using). All you have to do is crush your fruit, add yeast – or let naturally occurring wild yeasts do the job for you – and let it ferment. Hard fruits such as apples and pears are harder to crush – you have to pulp them in a mill before you can press the juice out of them – but the principle is the same. Everything you need is in the fruit. With beer, things aren't so simple. In fact, cereal grains are so hard to ferment it's a wonder that beer was ever invented. For in their natural state, grains contain almost none of the required components: no liquid, no sugar and not much in the way of flavour. All three have to be painstakingly brought together before you can even think about introducing yeast.

Malt

Malt is usually made from barley, but brewers also use other grains, both malted and unmalted. Wheat you will probably already be familiar with as a brewing grain, but oats, rye and even rice are also added for particular purposes. In essence, malt is cereal grain that has been tricked into germinating by being steeped in warm water to mimic spring weather. During germination, enzymes in the grain start to convert its insoluble starch into sugar, which the plant needs in order to fuel its growth. This sugar, maltose, is soluble, and is what you want as your fermentable material. So, soon after the grain has started to germinate, it's dried in a kiln to halt the process before it goes too far. Different kilning times and temperatures produce pale, amber, chocolate, crystal, roast and other types of malt, each with its own properties. You will almost certainly be using blends of malts, so you will need to be familiar with all their characteristics. You may also want to use brewing sugars in some brews: these have flavour characteristics of their own and are perfectly respectable adjuncts in many brewing traditions.

Liquor

Once the little sprouts have been shaken off, the malt is ground into a coarse flour ("grist") ready to be "mashed" in hot water (always referred to as liquor – water, in a brewery, is for washing and cooling). Mashing both completes the conversion of starch into sugar ("saccharification") and dissolves the sugar to produce a thin malt syrup or wort. The mineral content of the water is critical: gypsum-rich water from the artesian wells beneath Burton-upon-Trent produced the classic pale ales that succeeded the darker stouts and porters brewed with London water (well-water, not Thames water!) in popular favour in the 19th century. British ales require hard water while continental lagers require soft water, for reasons that will be explained later on. Some breweries are lucky enough to have their own wells or boreholes; you will probably have to settle for mains water, but you will want to analyse it and alter its mineral content first.

Hops

Next, the boil; and the addition of hops. Hops contain acids that kill bacteria and protect the beer from infection, and were introduced to British brewing in the 14th or 15th century chiefly as a preservative. But they are vital for flavour, too: their acid may give beer its bitterness, but they also contain oils and resins that produce much of its taste and aroma. Some hops are more acid than others; some more aromatic. And the aroma characteristics vary hugely from strain to strain: Goldings, for example, produce a citric tang, while Bramling Cross are said to give an aroma of blackcurrants. Again, you will need a thorough knowledge of hop varieties if you are to become a master of your craft.

Yeast

A microscopic fungus, yeast digests the maltose in the wort and excretes alcohol and the CO_2 that puts the fizz into the beer. Every brewery has its own strain, and every strain is different both in its handling characteristics and in the flavours it produces. Yeast is tricky stuff to handle and is very prone to infection; at the University of East Anglia in Norwich is the National Yeast

Bank, where brewers send samples of their yeast from which to propagate fresh supplies if problems occur at the brewery. Brewers are very proud of their yeast strains, saying they give their beers their house character; so the strain you choose at the outset will define your brews for years to come.

Other Ingredients

More and more these days, you will come across other ingredients, especially fruit. Fruit has been used for centuries by brewers, especially in Belgium, where some beers are fermented by naturally occurring wild yeasts rather than cultured brewing strains. Wild yeasts and the other microfauna and flora that accompany them often produce sour flavours which are not to everyone's taste: adding pulped cherries or blackcurrants to the mash of sour brown ales and lambic beers is a traditional method of tempering their sourness. In the last 20 years or so these Belgian fruit beers have become more widely available in Britain, and many British brewers have been inspired to experiment with fruit as well. Grapefruit beer from the St Peter's Brewery of Suffolk is one unlikely but surprisingly palatable example

Almost as important as the raw materials to the character of the beer are the processes by which it is made. The grist must be mashed at a specific temperature for the starch to be fully converted and the sugars to be fully dissolved. The boil can be long or short – a long boil caramelises some of the sugars in the wort and produces a richer, darker beer – and hops are added in different quantities and at different points in the process. The hopped wort has to be cooled before the yeast is pitched, and there are various methods of fermentation which each produce different results. All of this you must learn thoroughly.

Vessels

The vessels can be critical, too, especially the shape and size of your fermenters and conditioning tanks. We'll come to the number and type of vessels you'll need in a later chapter. But as an example, take fermentation. It's a biochemical process which, like all biochemical processes, generates a certain amount of heat. This can dictate the speed of fermentation and help or hinder the creation of by-products such as phenols and esters, all of which will affect the finished product; and the thermodynamics of different-shaped fermenters will give different results. Modern cylindro-conical lager fermenters produce more heat and work more quickly than old-fashioned horizontal ones, so a lager conditioned in a cylindro-conical will be detectably sweeter and less clean than one aged in a horizontal. There are plenty of other similar examples; so even before you build your brewery, you will have to have made critical decisions about what sort of beers you want to brew. And it's important to make these decisions from a position of knowledge, which you can get right now – assuming, that is, that your local is open. Because the best way to learn about beer is to drink it, but to drink it intelligently. That means sampling as many different examples of as many different styles as you can get hold of. And sampling is not the same as swigging!

Tasting Beer

The first time I was invited to an organised beer-tasting, on a press trip to Bruges nearly 20 years ago, I thought someone was taking the mickey. Arriving at a bar called 't Brugs Beertje, the party was shown into the function room in which was a huge table garnished with an astonishing array of glasses (you shouldn't use the same one too often), and bottles of mineral water and dishes of dry crackers to cleanse our palates between samples. Once seated, we first held up each sample to the light to check its colour, clarity and head. There followed a thorough swirling and nosing à la Jilly Goolden, with tasters detecting aromas of leather, tobacco, new-mown hay et al. A meagre mouthful was then ritualistically swilled; air was sucked; and mouthfeel (ie residual sugars, if any, coating the tongue) and flavours were pronounced upon. Finally, we swallowed (you don't spit out beer as you do wine, since the bitterness receptors are at the very back of the tongue). A long hush ensued, with expressions of intense concentration while the length and bitterness of the finish (or aftertaste) were thoroughly cogitated. Finally, there followed a brief but intense discussion of each sample – was it true to style? Were there any off-flavours? How complex was it? – and each beer was marked.

Well, it seemed daft to me at the time. But after many years of attending such tastings, I have discovered the value of really concentrating on what you're drinking; and at tastings you have to strain your tastebuds in exactly the same way you have to strain your ears to hear a distant melody. Conveying your experiences is difficult, because you have to describe the flavours you detect in terms of others that are commonly recognisable; hence the descent into vocabulary such as "green fruit", "treacle toffee", "marmalade" and other comparables. It all sounds incredibly pretentious, yet the language of tastings is expressly not intended to exclude the uninitiated. In fact the very opposite is true: it's meant to allow a group of individuals (normally brewery staff) to describe their personal experiences of a range of sensations in a format that can be shared. But the difficulty of translating tastes and smells into words even affects skilled and experienced brewers. You might expect, perhaps, that professionals who live and breathe diacetyls, esters, phenols and sulphites would describe their beers in those terms. They do, but only to a limited extent. The flavour wheel used by brewers all around the world since the 1970s to delineate the aromas and tastes of their products includes those terms, but also uses expressions such as liquorice, chocolate, butterscotch, toffee, pineapple, catty, papery, leathery, grassy – even Horlicks!

It struck me quite early on in my beer-tasting career that there's a metaphysical dimension to it, especially to the attempt to explain your findings. You're trying to do two things, both of which are impossible: to objectify the subjective, and to describe one set of sensory experiences in terms of another. You might as well try to paint Beethoven's Fifth, or describe red. Nevertheless, you have to do it. You have to explore all the different possibilities of beer with your intellect as much as with your tastebuds, and for two good reasons. First, having chosen what you want to brew you have to be able to recreate your choice exactly, every time you brew it. And second, you need to upgrade from mere organolept – that is, a dilettante who just likes beer – into a ruthlessly efficient sensory analyst whose finely honed *papillae* (Latin for "tastebuds") can instantly and accurately detect and identify imperfections and variations from brew to brew.

From a practical point of view, though, wide-ranging tastings of a good selection of beers aren't that easy to arrange. To be meaningful, tastings need to be comparative: you need to be able taste and decide between a range of at least half-a-dozen bitters or best bitters or old ales or stouts or whatever. Very few pubs stock more than one example of any one beer style other than British-brewed lager, of which they might have two or three. Even the handful of real ale Meccas that carry 10 or 12 cask beers at a time will try to stock as wide a spread as possible. The same is true, if to a lesser extent, of supermarkets. They may carry a bewildering variety of pilsner-style beers, from cheap "slab-packs" of canned French or Belgian lager brewed mainly from corn syrup to top-notch Czech beers such as Budweiser Budvar, but of bottled ales they will have only one or two examples of each style. But by shopping around you can assemble wide enough selections of styles to hold meaningful tastings of your own, possibly inviting friends round to make an event of it. And don't exclude women! It's long been known in the industry, and recently confirmed by medical research, that by and large they have more accurate sense-memories than men. So a serious beer-tasting is not merely an excuse for a night in with the lads.

You should also join the **Campaign for Real Ale (CAMRA)**. Each CAMRA branch is supposed to field an official tasting panel to help select entries for the *Good Beer Guide* and to judge the branch's annual beer competition. Members of these panels receive free expert training, which will be invaluable to you later on. But for some reason, branches are often short of volunteers to serve on their tasting panels, so if you put yourself forward you will undoubtedly be a very welcome member of the team.

Further Reading

Membership of CAMRA will also give you access to lots of useful reading matter. Its monthly newspaper, *What's Brewing*, is sent free to all members and carries interesting features on other breweries as well as beer-related news from around the country. The organisation is also a book publisher and seller. There is a host of good and informative books about beer styles and traditions by authoritative writers such as Roger Protz and Michael Jackson on the market; you may not find them in bookshops, but CAMRA stocks most of them for sale by mail order at a discount to members. There's also a commercial bookseller called Beer Inn-Print which, despite its title, has a good selection of out-of-print titles. Finally, a subscription to *Beers of the World* magazine is also a good idea: it's highly informative and carries material from all the country's leading beer writers.

You should also visit as many breweries as you can. Ten or fifteen years ago it used to be almost impossible to tour a working brewery unless you were in the licensed trade. Visitors were generally considered a nuisance who only got in the way, and most old-established breweries were such a jumble of pipework, narrow spaces, uneven floors, and steps and stairs, mostly awash with water, that tour parties were a health and safety nightmare. Today, it's all different: most of the older regional breweries run conducted group tours, and some even have visitors' centres with shops, bars and museums or, at least, displays of antique brewing equipment and brewery ephemera. This change of attitude has been driven mainly by marketing considerations. Smaller breweries with little to spend on advertising have come to see the benefit of drawing the public in. As a result, most brewery visitor centres are aimed more at the tourist than the would-be brewer; even so, they will acquaint you with the sights, sounds and, indeed, the smells that will surround you every day once you have opened a brewery of your own.

For more informal tours, often conducted by the brewer himself, which gives you a chance to ask questions and get full and informed answers, your CAMRA membership will come in handy yet again. All local branches organise regular trips to breweries large and small in their areas and sometimes further afield. You may even get the chance to do a bit of real hands-on brewing: most branches have a special beer made by a local brewer for their annual beer festivals, and sometimes branch members are allowed to do the actual mashing. This could be you! And if you get friendly enough with a local brewer, he may even allow you to help out occasionally (don't expect to be paid, though!).

Brewing at Home

Would-be brewers are luckier in one enormous respect than people considering new careers in other industries. For brewing is one of the few trades, along with baking and one or two others, in which you can coach yourself almost up to professional level in your own home, without giving up your job, and without investing too much of your savings.

Many of today's local brewers started off as home-brewing enthusiasts who finally tipped over and turned their hobby into their living. But even if you're not a frequent and regular home brewer yet, you should become one: it's the single most important step in your preparations for your new career. If you are already a home brewer, you'll understand the advantages: for instance, that it's possible to start slowly, with a kit that requires little more than the addition of hot water to make a passable beer. From the all-in-one kit you can graduate step-by-step through the various phases of difficulty until you're quite at home with all-malt, whole-hop brews. Home-brewing kit can also be upgraded piece by piece from a bucket in the airing cupboard to a miniature tower brewery complete with mash tun, copper, hop back, wort cooler, fermenter and conditioning tank, all of gleaming steel and copper, perfect in every detail. One is always reading of enthusiasts whose garden sheds or garages are home to lovingly constructed brewing plants that need only an excise licence to start operating commercially – indeed, there are one or two cases where this has actually happened.

Brewery Visitor Centres

This is just a selection of brewery visitors centres of different ages and sizes around the country. Most of them are walk-in centres; a few require booking in advance. However, in almost all cases, guided tours require advance booking, so it's essential to check the website and/or ring ahead. Details of other breweries that conduct tours are published in CAMRA's *Good Beer Guide*.

Badger Brewery, Hall & Woodhouse Ltd, Blandford St Mary, Dorset DT11 9LS; Tel 01258 452141, **www.hall-woodhouse.co.uk**

Batemans Brewery, Salem Bridge, Wainfleet, Lincs PE24 4JE; Tel 01754 880317, **www.bateman.co.uk**

Black Sheep Brewery, Wellgarth, Masham, N. Yorks HG4 4EN; Tel 01765 689227, **www.blacksheepbrewery.com**

Bridge of Allan Brewery, The Brewhouse, Queens Lane, Bridge of Allen, Stirling FK9 4NY; Tel 01786 834555, **www.bridgeofallan.co.uk**

Coors Museum of Brewing, Horninglow St, Burton-on-Trent, Staffs DE14 1YQ; Tel 08456 000598, **www.coorsvisitorcentre.com**

Greene King, Westgate Brewery, Bury St Edmunds, Suffolk IP33 1QT; Tel 01284 763222, **www.greeneking.co.uk**

High House Farm Brewery, Matfen, Newcastle upon Tyne NE20 0RG; Tel 01661 886192, **www.highhousefarmbrewery.co.uk**

Hilden Brewing, Hilden House, Hilden, Lisburn, Co. Antrim BT27 4TY; Tel 02892 660800, **www.hildenbrewery.co.uk**

Hook Norton Brewery, Hook Norton, Banbury OX15 5NY; Tel 01608 737210, **www.hooky.co.uk**

Marston's Brewery, Shobnall Rd, Burton-on-Trent, Staffs DE14 2BW; Tel 01283 531131, **www.wdb.co.uk**

St Austell Brewery, Trevarthian Rd, St Austell, Cornwall PL25 4BY; Tel 01726 74444, **www.staustellbrewery.co.uk**

Saltaire Brewery, Dockfield Rd, Shipley, W. Yorks BD17 7AR; Tel 01274 594595., **www.saltairebrewery.co.uk**

Shepherd Neame, Court St, Faversham, Kent ME13 7AX; Tel 01795 532206, www.shepherdneame.co.uk

Theakstons, The Brewery, Masham, N. Yorks HG4 4YD; Tel 01765 680000, **www.theakstons.co.uk**

Woodforde's Norfolk Ales, Broadland Brewery, Woodbastwick, Norwich NR13 6SW; Tel 01603 720353, **www.woodfordes.co.uk**

Brewing at home will familiarise you with brewing materials and techniques, with faults and their cures, and with different beer styles. It will also give you the chance to experiment with recipes; and I have heard of local brewers who perfected their entire ranges during their amateur days and were able to turn professional with enviable smoothness. But there's more to it than that. Home brewing will help you in practical terms, yes, but also in psychological terms. Have you really got what it takes to be a brewer? Are you a true enthusiast, or merely a dabbler? If you find your interest in brewing as a hobby palls after a few months, you can be sure it's not going to be a wise move to try and make a living at it. By the same token, if you find the bug is really biting, you can be more certain than many others in your position that the step you're about to take is the right one.

Since Boots stopped stocking home-brewing and wine-making equipment and materials some years ago, they are regrettably hard to come by. However, the Craft Brewing Association (CBA), founded in 1995, can fill the gap. Its website, **www.craftbrewing.org.uk**, lists local home-brew supplies shops and, for those who don't have one in their area, mail-order suppliers too. It's a mine of information in other regards, as well: anyone with even a passing interest in beer could browse its technical pages for hours. In addition to that, the CBA offers training for beer tasters, runs competitions, helps with recipe designs, has beer style guidelines of its own, and has a quarterly newsletter, *Brewer's Contact*. It's divided into local groups covering most of the country; if there isn't one near you, use the link on the site to the **National Association of Wine and Beer Makers**, which is more wine-oriented but still lists many home brewers among its membership.

Formal Training

So you've drunk intelligently; you've read up on the subject; you've toured breweries; you've brewed your own beer. Now you're ready for your formal training. But where are you going to get it?

Fundamentals of Minibrewing

The obvious answer is that you'll get all the information you need from the person or company who (assuming you're not going to do it all yourself) designs and installs your brewery. And in fact the man recognised as one of the country's leading microbrewery designers started out 17 years ago as a trainer. David Smith of York had spent over 20 years brewing at the legendary

Sam Smith's in Tadcaster before branching out as a consultant on his own in 1989, just as the microbrewing boom was about to go into overdrive. Teaching people how to brew was his next venture; but it soon became clear that obtaining small-scale brewing equipment was one of the new entrant's biggest problems, so David branched out into sourcing and fitting the kit as well as imparting the knowledge needed to operate it. Since then he has designed and installed nearly 100 small breweries, but he has never lost sight of the fact that the equipment isn't much use without the know-how. So, twice a year, he teaches his four-day fully residential Fundamentals of Minibrewing course, using the conference suite at York Brewery as his classroom and York Brewery itself for the practical side of the course.

Fundamentals of Minibrewing, which costs £625, is firmly rooted in the practical experience that David and his guest lecturers from other areas of the brewing industry – including maltsters and hop merchants – have gained in their working lives. The purpose of the course is to instill the basics of good brewing practice and a greater insight into the art and science of brewing.

It combines lectures and workshops, run by a number of specialists from the industry, with visits to a maltings, other microbreweries and retail outlets. For those who may not have any practical experience there is the opportunity to help with a complete brew at York Brewery before the course gets under way.

Heriot Watt University

At the other end of the scale is the Bachelor of Sciences course Brewing and Distilling at Heriot Watt University in Edinburgh, one of the world's leading brewing schools since 1903. The BSc course has an annual intake of 10–14 undergraduates who in their four years (this is a Scottish university, not an English one!) at Heriot Watt will learn not only how to make beer but how to turn it into whisky as well. But perhaps it's a little more than most would-be microbrewers really need.

Heriot Watt is also world-renowned for its Master's degree in brewing and distilling – so world-renowned, in fact, that usually only one or two of the annual intake of 16–20 are British. If you fancy the letters MSc after your name, you need a first degree in chemistry, chemical engineering, biochemistry, microbiology or something similar, and £3,500 for the fees. Again, perhaps not an option for the average microbrewer.

Heriot Watt's Postgraduate Diploma distance learning programme, though, is a different matter altogether. Consisting of 12 modules at £570 each plus

Case Study: Home Brewer Turned Professional– Hoggley's, Kislingbury, Northants

It was a burning desire to find out what people really thought of his beer that started Roy Crutchley on the path to full-scale commercial brewing. And the path was, quite literally, his garden path.

Youth worker Roy had been brewing his own since his student days in the 1970s, but only using kits and malt extract. Then he got hold of one of the many CAMRA-published books by home-brew guru Graham Wheeler, which explained the mysteries of full-mash brewing – and from then on he dreamed only of turning pro.

Partner Julie Hogg gave him another powerful push in the right direction when she evicted him from the kitchen of the couple's cottage in the Northamptonshire village of Kislingbury. For full-mash brewing is a very different proposition from boiling up a dollop of extract in the old Burco.

"Mashes will occasionally boil over however careful you are, and wort is the stickiest substance known to man," says Roy. "The whole process was incredibly messy, and eventually Julie chucked me out of the kitchen.

"Fortunately there's a patch of ground at the bottom of our garden just big enough for a shed – so I built one."

It wasn't quite that simple, though: as Kislingbury is a conservation area, and the shed Roy had in mind had to be 10-foot tall to accommodate a three-stage gravity-fed or "tower" brewery, he needed full planning permission. And he was sure he wasn't going to get it – until, that is, he got a visit from a sympathetic environmental health officer.

"His dad had been a full-mash brewer, and he seemed to be the only council officer with a grasp of what I was proposing," says Roy. "I can't say for sure it was down to him, but after his visit the whole thing seemed to go a lot more smoothly."

The equipment itself was home-assembled and had a capacity of 100 litres, and Roy put it together with a lot of help from the Craft Brewers' Association.

"The advice of the CBA is essential for anyone like me who is evolving rather than jumping in at the deep end," he says. "They were incredibly helpful."

Roy always planned to go commercial, as much to massage his ego as anything else. "I'd brewed for family and friends but you can never be sure how good you are when you give people free beer, because they're always going to say nice things about it," he says. "What I wanted was to see a pumpclip with my name on it on a beer handle in a pub, with people I didn't know buying a pint of my beer – and then coming back for another."

There were other issues as well – Roy often felt frustrated that as a youth worker he couldn't see the results of his efforts until years later; and anyway, he felt he had reached a career plateau. But chiefly, he says: "Running your own brewery is every middle-aged man's dream."

Actually turning pro, Roy and Julie found (the brewery is called Hoggley's, although Crutchley & Hogg might have had a certain traditional ring to it), wasn't that difficult: change of use permission went through on the nod, and Customs couldn't have been more helpful. Roy did forget at first that he needed to talk to the water company as well, but that was soon put right.

Anyway, in March 2003 the first pint of Hoggley's Northamptonshire Bitter went on sale at the Alexandra Arms in Kettering, and Roy's dream of seeing people actually buying his beer came true. A year later, it was formally confirmed that people he didn't know liked his beer when Hoggley's Mill Lane Mild was named joint Beer of the Festival award winner at Milton Keynes.

All this was achieved without Roy giving up his day job or moving out of the 10-foot tower brewery at the bottom of his garden. But in 2006 he was made redundant, and the money went into equipping a new eight-barrel brewery on an industrial estate in nearby Litchborough. And he's a happy man.

"If any home brewer is thinking of going all the way, I would say: DO IT!" is his advice.

www.hoggleys.co.uk

a research project, it's tailored for busy working people and you can take up to seven years to complete it. But you don't actually have to complete it at all: you can instead choose only the modules that seem most useful to you, getting a separate certificate for each module you complete. The modules are taught entirely electronically via email, electronic tutors and e-study groups. The annual intake of 135 attracts brewers from all over the world including, rather oddly, a high proportion of American theology graduates. For more details, go to **www.postgraduate.hw.ac.uk/course/118**

Brewlab

David Smith's Fundamentals course may not be quite enough to satisfy your thirst for brewing knowledge, but then a full-blown undergraduate course at Heriot Watt is probably a little too much (although there are plenty of Heriot Watt graduates who have gone on to found breweries of their own). Somewhere between them you will find the most popular source of formal training for small brewers: Brewlab, the centre for brewing studies and microbiological services at the University of Sunderland.

Brewlab teaches courses such as Start Up Brewing and British Brewing Technology and also provides specialist training in taste evaluation, microbiology and small-scale bottling. Its courses range from one-day introductory workshops in bottling and microbiology to three-week and even three-month programmes in brewing theory and practice. It also runs a range of what you might call after-sales services to assist brewers with quality control, Tax & Excise compliance, yeast storage and culturing, and the due diligence service that helps brewers maintain quality and comply with industry codes of practice.

And actually, it was services like these that came first. Brewlab was founded at the City of London Polytechnic in 1986 to provide laboratory analysis for brewers large and small, and the training side of the operation was only developed later to enable staff in the microbrewery sector to understand and act on analysis results.

In 1992 Brewlab moved to the University of Sunderland to take advantage of its fermentation facilities and biotechnology strengths, and is now part of the university's School of Health, Natural & Social Sciences. Its laboratories provide up-to-date facilities for practical work alongside dedicated equipment for detailed studies. There is a fully operational 100-litre (18-gallon) pilot training brewery with bottling facilities, allowing practical experience and the opportunity for students to brew beers for sale in local outlets. Brewlab students also have access to other laboratory and research facilities, libraries, internet services, catering facilities and the Students' Union shop, copy service and sports centre.

Brewlab's sister company, **Darwin Brewery**, was set up in 1997 and is a fully commercial 12-barrel plant which can provide an industrial setting for student placements and allow them to experience full-scale production. Darwin Brewery is located in the heart of Sunderland and as a commercial brewing business provides cask ales to over 80 pubs.

Managing the teaching programme and laboratory activities are Dr Keith Thomas and Dr St John Usher, who also teach university courses such as microbiology and food science. Dr Thomas's specialist research areas are yeast physiology, beer composition and bioremedioration. He was a judge at the Great British Beer Festival 1986–2001 and the Great American Beer Festival 1987–2003 and is a beer festival organiser for SIBA. Dr Usher is a member of the Institute & Guild of Brewing, and a visiting lecturer at the University of Sunderland specialising in microbiology and brewing studies. His specialist research area is microbiological contamination. Additional staff provide specialist support for both teaching and laboratory work, while students also benefit from the expertise of visiting lecturers who work in the brewing industry.

Students on the Practical Brewing and British Brewing Technology courses are now eligible to enrol at the university and receive certificates and diplomas on successful completion of their courses. This follows the university's official assessment of Brewlab's course structure and teaching quality, which found them to be of higher education standard and therefore suitable for inclusion on its list of programmes. Brewlab students may also study for external qualifications through the Institute of Brewing & Distilling and can focus on developing practical skills using the brewing facilities available on site.

The British Brewing Technology course's five modules are Brewing Technology, Microbiology, Taste Training, Practical Brewing and Placement Brewing. Each module carries higher education credits which may be used in a longer programme of degree level study, either full or part time. Students may also progress to full degree study.

Brewlab Training Courses

- Brewing Skills Development for Production Personnel
- Start Up Brewing
- University Certificate in Practical Brewing
- University Diploma in British Brewing Technology
- Microbiology Workshop
- Small Scale Bottling
- Advanced Craft Brewing Workshop
- British Brewing History

The courses range from one-day workshops for craft brewers who want to develop their skills and knowledge to residential three-day, three-week and three-month courses for those who wish to make a career in brewing, either to manage their own brewery, to seek employment in the industry, or to further career prospects.

For many courses, groups are limited to 12 students to enable staff to spend more time with individuals. Although some knowledge of maths and chemistry would be beneficial on the more detailed courses, Brewlab provides full student support and additional tuition.

There is a range of professional and personal development courses for those who already working in the brewing industry wanting to improve their technical and analysis skills.

Since 2006, the Practical Brewing and British Brewing Technology courses have been accredited by the University of Sunderland. Students successfully completing a course assessment will receive a University Certificate in Practical Brewing (comparable with NVQ level 2) or a University Diploma in British Brewing Technology (comparable with NVQ level 3), relative to the course of study undertaken.

Brewing Skills Development for Production Personnel

(NB: all course dates and fees are published on Brewlab's website)

Brewlab has created this new course following requests from clients for training to enhance the knowledge of existing staff. The course is aimed specifically at staff involved in the brewing production processes and those wanting to improve their understanding of:

- The key factors on which quality ale production depends
- The brewing process – from raw materials to final product

- Production problems, enabling them to be addressed on site, leading to more consistent quality products.

The course starts with targeted sessions on the four main raw materials – brewing liquor, malt, hops and yeast. Each session discusses the raw material, its specifications and commonly encountered problems with its usage. The fundamental brewing processes are covered in brewers' terms, along with current industry specifications.

The processes covered include malting, mashing, sparging, boiling, cooling, fermentation, conditioning, maturation, finings, racking, casking, cleaning, hygiene, quality control and tasting.

Course Programme
- Day 1: Brewing liquor, malt and mashing, sparging
- Day 2: Hops, boiling and cooling, yeast and fermentation
- Day 3: Beer maturation, racking, casking and fining, quality control and due diligence
- Day 4: Cleaning and sterilisation, infection and microbiological assessment
- Day 5: Beer flavour profiling, taste defects relating to production problems, tasting panels

It is not necessary to attend for the full five days and participants can pick and choose which days they want to study. Please read the course pdf for full programme details.

Start Up Brewing

Start Up Brewing is a comprehensive three-day course providing a realistic introduction to the brewing process and the requirements of commercial brewing. It is suitable for potential or recently engaged brewers and those looking at brewing as a possible career change or business opportunity.

No background knowledge of brewing is required for the course and we aim to provide you with a sound overview of the industry and an understanding of the requirements of operating a commercial brewing venture. We offer opportunities to view the stages of a commercial brew, to study the basic steps of brewing and to discuss start up issues with working brewers and specialists.

University Certificate in Practical Brewing

A detailed three-week course in the theory and practice of brewing. The new University Certificate in Practical Brewing has an emphasis on traditional procedures and provides up-to-date knowledge, with a strong practical element through laboratory work and placement brewing opportunities. Course work is extended with a series of site visits. Subsidiary components cover:

- Basic microbiology
- Taste training, cellarcraft
- Brewery history
- Marketing & sales, and business start up

We have introduced a third week to provide opportunities to gain more practical experience, with an extra brew day, placement and workshops in microbiology and bottling.

British Brewing Technology Semester Programme

This course has been restructured to provide more practical experience and skills, including microbiology and bottling. The first three weeks run alongside the new University Certificate in Practical Brewing course. Various modules and placements are timetabled throughout the 12 weeks and additional time is dedicated to self-study and research where relevant. The final week of the course is an intensive study week for those students wanting to take the Institute of Brewing & Distilling examinations, the General Certificate in Brewing and the General Certificate in Packaging.

The course is also accredited by the University of Sunderland. Students successfully completing a course assessment will receive a University Diploma of Achievement, comparable with NVQ level 3.

The main undergraduate module supporting the course, Brewing Technology, has no formal prerequisites for study but students are advised to anticipate the basic biology and chemistry where possible and to have some background experience of brewing on a home-brew or commercial basis.

One-day Microbiology Workshops

Brewlab's dedicated Microbiology Workshop offers a comprehensive introduction to the use of microscopy and microbiology techniques. The

Case Study: Brewlab Graduate – Potbelly, Kettering, Northants

For Northamptonshire businessmen Toni Hooper and Glenn Morris, starting thier own brewery was a sternly practical exercise.

Toni and Glenn run a factory in Kettering where they employ 40 people making leather fashion accessories. But increasingly cut-throat competition from cheap imports prompted them to consider diversifying, and setting up brewpubs seemed a likely venture. A one-day seminar on the pub trade soon changed their minds, though. "We went along to have our choice confirmed or to be put off and when we came away we'd decided we didn't want to run pubs after all," says Toni.

They hadn't given up on the idea of brewing, though, and Toni booked them in for Brewlab's three-day Start-Up Brewing course in early 2004.

"We went on the course for the same reason we attended the seminar – to confirm our choice or to put us off," says Toni. "It confirmed our choice."

Following the course the two men set about installing a 10-barrel plant at the back of their factory, and Toni immediately booked himself in for the two-week Practical Brewing course that July.

"It covered much the same ground as the Start-Up course, but in much greater detail and with hands-on training that included a placement at York Brewery," says Toni. "I was never a home brewer and we decided to go into brewing for purely commercial reasons. Our intention was always to go to market with products of consistent high quality, and Brewlab helped us achieve that."

The proof of the pudding is in the sales ledger – and in the trophy cabinet. Within a year of going into full production, Toni and Glenn's Potbelly Brewery had won the Society of Independent Brewers' 2006 National Beer Awards with Beijing Black. Potbelly is now brewing twice a week and Toni has had to co-opt one of the factory staff, Ben Bulcock, to do the brewing while he hits the road to drum up more sales. Ben, too, was trained on Brewlab's Practical Brewing course.

If Toni has one criticism about the training he's received, it's that it doesn't tackle the nuts-and-bolts engineering side of the business.

www.potbelly-brewery.co.uk

course can be used to develop practical skills in laboratory analysis as well as to instigate a quality assurance programme for due diligence purposes.

Small Scale Bottling

Brewlab's Small Scale Bottling Workshop provides a technical insight for the small scale brewer looking to bottle beer on a limited scale either on site or via a contract bottler. The course provides an overview of the process and of beer preparation. It demonstrates the process on typical equipment used by successful bottlers and introduces the quality control requirements to guarantee a sound product satisfying legislative requirements.

The course is taught by practising brewers with experience of bottling and by laboratory staff regularly engaged in the analysis of bottled beers. A session on marketing considers how these beers fit into the industry at present and how best to promote bottled beers and a cost analysis looks at how best to obtain a saleable product.

Opportunity is provided for participants to cover all parts of the bottling process in detail and to receive feedback on specific products and systems they may consider. The course outlines the theoretical background of each operation clearly and with reference notes. Direct access to equipment is provided for illustration and hands-on demonstrations.

The relevance of retail and wholesale services to the small scale brewer is illustrated through discussions on marketing opportunities.

Advanced Craft Brewing Workshop

Advanced Brewing Workshops provide opportunities for brewers with amateur or small-scale commercial applications to investigate their brewing operations in technical detail. The sessions run over an intensive weekend, based at the University of Sunderland.

Full laboratory support is provided including technical staff, brewing facilities and a dedicated analytical laboratory. Participants are provided with opportunities to develop analytical skills including microscopy, basic chemical procedures and flavour evaluation. Some experimental work conducted during the sessions and participants have access to past research conducted by Brewlab on relevant brewing issues. The sessions are intensive but rewarding and excellent value in helping to improve your products or to provide quality assurance.

British Brewing History

Brewlab's course British Brewing History provides instruction in the history and operation of the British brewing industry with a focus on technical developments, beer styles and the techniques of historical investigation.

Analytical Services

Brewlab provides extensive analytical and investigative services to the brewing industry ranging from routine microbiological and chemical testing to detailed fault finding and product evaluation.

Microbiological services

- Quality control and fault finding
- Analysis services
- Due diligence analysis package

Yeast

- Yeast supply
- Yeast storage
- Yeast analysis and characterisation

Chemical and Physical Analysis
Product Development
Antimicrobial Assessment

Brewlab's facilities include high-quality microbiology laboratories with a variety of fermentation options, as well as access to the following types of analytical equipment:

- Gas and HPLC chromatography
- Mass spectroscopy
- X-ray analysis and transmission and scanning electron microscopy

Sensory analysis services include dedicated tasting laboratory facilities and a panel of fully trained and experienced beer tasters. Where appropriate we will advise you on how to conduct analyses on site and are pleased to work with breweries to develop quality assurance schemes involving both analysis and preparation.

Metal-bashing

Learning to make beer is not the end of the skills you'll need as a full-time brewer. Big breweries have their own engineering services departments; you'll have to be your own engineer, because brewing on a small scale is a very hands-on business. Assuming that you can't afford just to hire contractors and sit back and watch them work, you'll need both building and project management skills to prepare your premises even before the brewery equipment arrives.

Knowing one end of an oxyacetylene torch from another, unfortunately, doesn't form part of any known brewing course; so some experience of practical fabrication will be a must when the plant is being installed and assembled. Your consultant, if you use one, will oversee the project; but you'll need to play an active part because once the contractors have left it will be up to you to run and service the plant. And as there's a lot of pipework in a brewery, there's no better way of gaining the intimate knowledge of your plant that you'll need to keep it running smoothly than actually rolling up your sleeves and helping install it. And once it's installed, you'll need the skills and experience to make alterations and to carry out running repairs. Some people delight in metal-bashing and take to it naturally; others don't. Which category you fall into is something you'll only discover when a crucial valve springs a leak in the middle of the night...

Chapter Two
Where to Brew

ONE of the first, most important, and in some ways most difficult tasks you are going to face is finding a home for your brewery. In some cases it won't be such a problem because the premises will have come first. You might be a publican installing a brewery in an outbuilding, for instance, or you might even have been inspired to start brewing commercially because the ideal site has come up. But whichever direction you decide on, finding a home is the first major practical step.

And once you've found the premises, there's a long road ahead before the first brew is loaded on to the dray. Not only does the building have to be converted and equipped, but there are more regulations to satisfy and procedures to go through than you can shake a stick at. More of these later, though; for now, let's stick with finding the right place to make your brewing dream a reality.

The first new brewery in post-war Britain, as we have seen, was founded in a Scottish baronial pile, Traquair House, when the laird restored the 18th-century brewhouse that had originally kept the castle's many inhabitants and visitors supplied with ale. By a strange coincidence, the first new brewery in Northern Ireland was also founded in the outbuildings of a grand country house. Hilden Brewery was set up by Anne and Seamus Scullion in 1981 in the stables at Hilden House, which was built in 1837 by the owners of Barbour Threads in nearby Lisburn, one of the biggest thread mills in the world. The immediate advantage was the instant availability of a suitable building; but Hilden House also had plenty of room for a bar and restaurant and for an annual beer and music festival, which becomes more popular every year.

Few would-be local brewers have a Traquair or a Hilden House to base themselves in, and the vast majority find homes on industrial estates. But there's an important question to answer here, because your first brewery may have to last you for years. Do you see brewing as purely an industrial activity, something you just want to get on with as efficiently as possible? Or is there more to it than that? Is the brewery itself part of the retail strategy with tours, a shop, a bar, maybe a restaurant?

Both strategies have their pros and cons. Making the brewing process as efficient as possible, without the distraction of tour parties and retailing, will hold your costs down and give you more time to spend out on the road selling your beer. On the other hand, welcoming people into the brewery generates cash and can also be a useful marketing device. But whichever model you choose, you will be bound by it for some time. If the former, you will opt for a unit on an industrial estate which no tourist will ever see. If the latter, you need to find a site that is attractive in itself thanks to its location, or to its architectural and historical value, or even both.

Historic Properties

The local brewing revolutions in mainland Britain and Northern Ireland started in grand country houses, as we have seen, and historic properties have proved popular sites for small breweries ever since. But by historic properties, I don't only mean grand country houses like Traquair and Hilden, but also units in regenerated industrial areas – 18th-century canal wharves, 19th-century cotton mills – and one-off conversion opportunities such as watermills, railway sheds, smithies, bakeries and so on. What these have in common is that they make the brewery itself a focus of interest, with the potential to generate considerable income from shoppers and tourists. This category could also be extended, therefore, to cover breweries in caravan parks, garden centres and other locations that attract paying customers.

Country Houses

Let's deal with country houses first. Ironically, perhaps the most ideally sited country house brewery remains resolutely off the tourist trail. Stanway House, near Winchombe in the Cotswolds, is a fabulous confection of late Elizabethan and Jacobean stone with a baroque water garden that boasts the world's highest gravity-fed fountain and, for good measure, a 14th-century tithe barn. But the house is no museum, and the family that still lives in it after nearly 500 years only opens it to the public on Tuesday and Thursday afternoons in June, July and August. The brewery founded by Alex Pennycook in 1993 in Stanway's original brewhouse doesn't even unbend that far: if you want to see it and its two ancient wood-fired coppers, you have to content yourself with a virtual tour on Alex's website.

Another country house brewery; another wood-fired boiler. With the help of Keith Bott of Titanic Brewery of Burslem, Staffordshire, the National Trust has restored the old brewhouse at Shugborough Hall near Cannock. Keith oversees the brewing there, and says he has a lot of fun with that boiler. For getting the temperatures right can be a nightmare: on calm days it's a struggle to get it to boil at all, he says, while on windy ones it's a struggle to get it to stop!

Then there's North Yorkshire Brewery which, like Hilden, makes good use of its very stately home. Pinchinthorpe Hall near Guisborough is also a bistro, restaurant and hotel. Mention might also be made here of St Peter's Brewery, tucked away deep in the Suffolk countryside. It's not quite a stately home, but a Tudor moated manorhouse that was built using medieval gothic stone doorcases and huge ecclesiastical windows salvaged from the nearest dissolved monastery. The brewery is housed in former farm buildings in the grounds; St Peter's Hall itself, decorated with the owner's collection of French medieval ecclesiastical artwork and other antiquities, is surely the most unusual and beautiful restaurant and functions room in the country.

Another country-house-based brewery is Elvedon, set up in the old stableyard at Lord Iveagh's stately home near Thetford as part of a larger development of visitor attractions. And although these are exceptional cases it might still be worth your while knocking on the doors of country houses in your district and asking if all their old stables, coach-houses, kennels and so forth are in use. After all, the worst they can say is "'Fraid so, old boy".

Restored Industrial Areas

A better bet, if you have decided on a visitor-based "heritage" dimension to your business, is a unit in a restored industrial quarter. Rents in these kind of developments are likely to be high, but they attract shoppers and tourists, they ought to be well suited to the purpose, and planning permission should be fairly straightforward – either they're designated as light industrial land will already have all the utilities and access you need, or they're unsuitable, in which case you'll be told at the outset.

The list of local breweries that have found themselves a home in some gem of industrial archaeology is a long one. Grainstore is in a Victorian railway granary in Oakham. Stonehenge is in the turbine-house of a hydroelectric power station that originally supplied the Royal Flying Corps aerodrome in Netheravon, Wiltshire. Big Lamp occupies a former steam-powered pumping station in Newburn, Tyneside. Archers, Atlas, Beckstones, Empire, Howard Town, Millstone, Old Mill, Saltaire, Shardlow, Slaughterhouse, Stirling, Strathaven – the list goes on.

Surprisingly often, the old industrial buildings in question were once breweries, maltings or hop kilns themselves. Exmoor of Wiveliscombe, Somerset, Wickwar Brewery of Wickwar, Gloucestershire, Wychwood of Witney, Oxfordshire, Tower Brewery of Burton on Trent, Uley Brewery of Uley, Gloucestershire, and Shaw's of Dukinfield, Greater Manchester, all occupy former breweries. Frog Island of Northampton and Black Sheep of Masham, North Yorkshire, are both housed in former maltings, and Marches and Mayfields of Herefordshire are in old hop kilns. This kind of location adds general interest to any brewery lucky enough to find one, and sometimes makes a quirky and attractive shop, brewery tap and/or visitors' centre too.

As well as stately homes and historic industrial buildings, local breweries are to be found in a wide range of often bizarre locations. Plassey and Haywood Bad Ram are on caravan parks whose bars sell their beers. Bell's is in a garden centre. Nelson is in the historic dockyards at Chatham, Kent. Country Life is in the Big Sheep visitor attraction near Bideford, Devon. Brew Wharf is attached to the Vinopolis permanent wine exhibition in Southwark. Barearts is part of an art gallery in Todmorden, West Yorkshire, which is devoted to the human nude. Locations like this are one-offs, and finding one depends on your local knowledge. If your business model involves retailing from the brewery, though, finding a site that already has a substantial footfall of people who come prepared to part with cash could be well worth the effort.

Farm Buildings

Farm buildings have always been popular locations for new breweries, and in fact more than 100 of today's 600-odd local breweries are sited on farms. (Another half-dozen or so are on vineyards, which is pretty much the same thing.)

Usually, these are straightforward commercial arrangements where new brewers looking for sites have found farmers trying to get a rent out of older buildings that don't suit modern agricultural needs. In many cases, farmers with surplus buildings and homeless would-be brewers have been brought together by good fortune, sound local knowledge and a wide network of contacts. In others, old farm or estate buildings have been converted into straightforward industrial units for rent just like any other. This accounts for the location of Oldershaw's on the Harrowby Hall estate near Grantham, and Wentworth Brewery in a former generating room on the Wentworth estate near Rotherham.

Often there's a conservation aspect to these arrangements. Old brick or stone dairies, cowsheds, hay barns, granaries and the like may be picturesque, and may even be listed; but if they're to be preserved they need a commercial raison d'être, and brewing is in many cases the ideal use. Two such breweries are sited in redundant farm buildings owned by the National Trust. Branscombe Vale was founded in 1992 in two former cowsheds on the quaintly named Great Seaside Farm at Branscombe, Devon, while Westerham was founded in barns at Grange Farm, Great Cockham, Kent, in 2004. An increasing number of new brewers are finding derelict farm buildings to renovate, and in some cases the farmers themselves are converting their disused buildings into breweries on their own account. For many, though, it's more than just a sideline aimed at making some additional profit out of disused buildings; it's actually a way of giving some life and purpose to an economic activity that has become almost marginal.

Farm-based Breweries

Making the leap from growing the ingredients to brewing the beer is nothing new. Paine's of St Neots and Ridley's of Chelmsford, two old-established regional brewers that have disappeared within the last two decades, started as farmers; a branch of the Paine family is still in the flour-milling business. Following their lead, Larkins Brewery was set up by the Dockerty family on

Case Study: Brewery in a Former Agricultural Building – Peak Ales, Pilsley, Derbyshire.

Rob and Debra Evans were teachers living in Worcester and working in the Black Country. But Rob knew what he really wanted to be – a brewer. And he knew where he wanted to brew – the Peak District National Park, near his native Chesterfield. So Rob and Debra sold the family home and moved with children Lucy and Matthew to a rented house in Bakewell so they could pursue the dream.

It took a good six months to find the right place to base their brewery – and much, much longer than that before Peak Ales beers began to flow. At first, with York-based brewing consultant David Smith as their guide, the Evanses trawled the usual round of industrial estates. One promising unit fell through, and David urged them to reject a second because if they'd ever wanted to move out they would have had to surrender it as they'd found it. That would have meant removing such necessary works as sloping floors, so moving out would have been as expensive as moving in.

Rob had already decided that the project needed a more characterful setting than an industrial estate, anyway. If the brewery was going to establish a connection with the Peaks, he felt it needed a more traditional building. He had decided to start asking farmers about surplus buildings when the landlord of the Devonshire Arms at Beeley, where Rob and David were having a meeting, suggested they approach the Chatsworth House estate office. Rob wrote a letter on the spot and dropped it round to the office, where he happened to meet the estate's deputy manager. And yes, the estate had the perfect building, quite nearby, the right size, a good sound roof; it just needed a bit of restoration.

Well, that roof (recently retiled) and four stone walls were just about all the barn had. It didn't have luxuries like floors or water or electricity.

It also had a yard that was several feet deep in the litter of generations of cows. But the estate had already decided to restore it and had in fact tried to get permission to turn it into housing or a shop. No way, said the Peak Park Authority. It could only be agricultural or light industrial. So Rob came along at just the right moment.

The restoration was a partnership. Rob applied and – after much form-filling – got a Rural Enterprise Grant from DEFRA (which is what the Ministry of Agriculture is called these days). The Chatsworth estate matched the grant and recommended a specialist firm of builders to do the work. It also appointed a project manager.

"It was very much a two-way street," says Rob. "I got my business in a beautiful location; the estate got a good building with offices and storage and a tenant paying a commercial rent."

Despite the estate's co-operative attitude, though, it wasn't all plain sailing. The work included building internal walls and floors, digging drains, laying cable and laying on a water supply – and it wasn't a help when a brood of baby barn owls was discovered in the building. Barn owls are protected, and work had to stop for three months while they grew up. And all that was before the brand-new Ten-barrel brewery from German manufacturer Moeschle was installed.

Finally, though, in February 2005 Peak Ales was open for business.

"It was a bit tricky and there were plenty of headaches," admits Rob. "It was two years behind schedule and all our contingency funds had disappeared, and I'm not sure I'd recommend it to anyone else.

"But in the longer term the Chatsworth connection will be invaluable. It's an idyllic setting and one that epitomises everything craft brewing is supposed to be about."

There's a short-term advantage to the Chatsworth connection, too. Both the pubs owned by the estate – the Devonshire Arms at Beeley, where it all began, and the Devonshire Arms at Pilsley – stock draught Peak Ales beers, as does the estate workers' social club. And both the Chatsworth gift shops stock the bottled versions. In crudely commercial terms, identification with Britain's premier stately home has instantly given Peak Ales sales volume and brand recognition that goes right off the scale.

And it's quite a nice place to work, too.

www.peakales.co.uk

their hop farm at Edenbridge in Kent in 1986; while Rother Valley Brewery was set up on a Sussex hop farm in 1993.

More recently, though, this tendency has gained new impetus. Many growers are not only fed up at the rock-bottom prices paid for top-quality produce – premium malting barley, for instance, has sold at little more than feed prices in recent years – they are also keen to join the environmental movement. So we have farm-based breweries such as Atlantic in Cornwall, High House in Tyne & Wear, Wagtail in Norfolk, and Wold Top in East Yorkshire growing organic barley and having it specially malted for them to reduce food miles; disposing of waste water in natural reedbeds; generating the electricity to power their breweries with wind turbines; feeding livestock with their spent grains; and using spent hops as mulch. If you see yourself and your brewery as part of this movement, you could do a lot worse than seek out a like-minded farmer to team up with. In purely commercial terms, environmental awareness is no longer a mere fad but an important and growing aspect of the market; and of course there is also great satisfaction to be derived from the knowledge that you are doing your bit.

The attractions of life on the farm are many and compelling. But, realistically, for most would-be local brewers there are two alternatives: an industrial estate or a pub.

Pub Breweries

Once upon a time almost all pubs brewed their own ale, and in many parts of the country pub-breweries were still relatively common until the late 19th century. By the early 1970s, though, there were just four left: the **Three Tuns** at Bishop's Castle and the **All Nations** at Madeley, both in Shropshire; **the Old Swan** at Netherton, West Midlands, universally known as Ma Pardoe's; and the **Blue Anchor** at Helston, Cornwall. (All four are still brewing, although Ma Pardoe's did actually close for quite a long while and has recently started brewing again.)

Reviving the tradition of pub brewing has been one of the driving forces of the real ale revolution, and not for romantic reasons alone. With most of the pub trade firmly closed to the new brewers, ownership of the means of retail has seemed a sine qua non to many, and buying a brewery tap has been an important goal. There have even been some cases where the brewer has bought a pub expressly as a base for the brewery: Wensleydale Brewery in North Yorkshire, for example, won awards for its Rowley Mild when it was Lidstone's, based in Cambridgeshire. The owner then decided to move north, and spent a long time looking for a suitable pub to base production in before settling on the Foresters Arms in the Yorkshire Dales National Park. It was a bold move that paid off, and within a year the brewery was forced to relocate for a second time to a farm near Bellerby.

Buying a pub expressly as a home for a brewery is probably a bit extreme for most start-ups, though, especially if you have no experience in the licensed trade; but before moving on, mention should be made of the most extreme variant of this type of venture: the boutique brewery.

Boutique Breweries

Boutique breweries are much more common in America and on the Continent than in Britain, but there are examples. Essentially, the boutique brewery is a bar or beer café where the brewing equipment itself occupies centre stage, normally behind a huge sheet of glass. Big vessels and pipework of gleaming brass make a spectacular backdrop for an evening's drinking; not surprisingly, the few boutique breweries in Britain are all urban and often very chic. In London there's the **Porterhouse** and the **Bünker Bar** in Covent Garden, **Mash** in Great Portland Street, and **Zerodegrees** in Blackheath (branches also in Bristol and Reading); in Glasgow there's **Clockwork Beer Co**; and in Peterborough there's **Oakham Ales' Brewery Tap** in a converted 1930s dole office opposite the railway station. They were all founded by people with seriously deep pockets, which is perhaps why there are so few.

More commonly, breweries have been installed in cellars or barns by publicans who feel that the wholesale price of beer is simply too high, and to whom brewing on their own account looks like cutting out the middleman and pocketing the extra profit. It also adds a unique selling point to the pub and attracts real ale fans from all over the country, and there's more money to be made by selling ale to beer festivals and other pubs. The success of the best-known figure in the history of microbrewing in Britain, David Bruce, who chose pubs as the sites for his Firkin breweries, merely proves the point. He put his first brewery into the cellars of the Duke of York in Southwark in 1979. Renamed the Goose & Firkin, it was the first in a chain of brewpubs that eventually (and under different ownership) covered the country.

Actually, it's something of an illusion that you need to own a pub or pubs in order to make a go of a microbrewery. Many of the best-known survivors from the earliest days – Chiltern, Larkins, Cotleigh, Exmoor and others – have done perfectly well without trying their hand at retail. Conversely, many of the casualties – Trough, Hull and very nearly Banks & Taylor, which went into receivership but was bought by a white knight and is thankfully still with us – only got into difficulties through ownership of pubs. For the truth is that running pubs demands a completely different set of skills from running a brewery; and possessing the latter doesn't necessarily mean you possess the former.

Brewing on the Premises

Be that as it may, surplus space at a pub is an obvious location for a brewery; and more than 130 micros, or about a quarter of the total, give their address as a pub (or in one case a workingmen's club, and in a couple more a restaurant). Many more of today's crop of local brewers started out in pubs but have since had to move to larger premises. There are dozens of highly successful publicans turned brewers, some of whom have gone on to sell their pubs to concentrate on wholesale brewing. Many small pub-breweries, on the other hand, brew pretty much exclusively for their own use: Front Street Brewery at the Chequers at Binham, Norfolk, is one example; Leith Hills Brewery at the Plough at Coldharbour, Surrey, is another. Often their breweries are squeezed into the tiniest of spaces – at Front Street and at Gwynant Brewery at the Tynllidiart Arms in Capel Bangor, Ceredigion, the brewing equipment is housed in the old outdoor loos. They might let the odd firkin out for beer festivals, but given the price of casks and the difficulty of getting their empties back, they have decided to supply their own pubs but not the wider free trade. Some of these pub breweries have achieved cult status, perhaps thanks to the very fact that their beers are so hard to find. The Railway Tavern at Brightlingsea, Essex, is a fine example: its Crab & Winkle Mild regularly wins awards at beer festivals, and although one or two favoured stockists might have it, to be absolutely sure of getting any you have to go to Brightlingsea. As indeed many beer-lovers do.

Partnerships

Less common are partnerships between publicans with spare space to let and would-be brewers looking for homes. This is a very good option for the brewery, since the host pub invariably stocks some or all of its products. Perhaps the best-known example is Hesket Newmarket in the Cumbrian village of the same name, where the brewery and its host pub, the Old Crown, are owned by two entirely separate co-operatives of villagers (many of whom, though, are members of both). The miniature tower brewery at the famous Three Tuns at Bishops Castle, Shropshire, is also now under separate ownership from the pub across the yard, and there would be a national outcry if the pub didn't stock the brewery's beers. Other similar examples include the Alexandra Arms in Rugby, whose plant is shared between two local CAMRA members going under the name Atomic Brewery and the landlord, who brews his own ales under the pub's name. If you're looking for a home for your brewery, sounding out local free trade licensees (although not the tenants of tied houses, of course!) is a very good first step.

Industrial Estates

If your hopes of brewing in the stables of a stately home, or in a converted woollen mill, or a former dairy or cowshed, or in the yard of a friendly pub come to nothing, there is always the industrial estate; and the fact that maybe half of all new brewers operate from units on industrial estates speaks volumes.

The advantages are many and obvious. They're often fairly cheap to rent; there's little conversion work to do; and they're comparatively easy to find. Considerations such as adequate access for delivery vehicles, industrial-grade flooring, three-phase electricity and proper drainage can pretty much be taken for granted (in theory, at least), while all the necessary planning permissions ought to come with the lease. Often, too, a base on an industrial estate offers the option of quick and easy expansion into neighbouring units – **Hop Back Brewery** of Salisbury, for instance, now occupies almost the entire industrial estate onto which it moved 25-odd years ago. (It was actually founded in a pub.)

But although they are usually both well equipped and cost-effective, industrial estates do have their disadvantages. They are never going to figure on the local tourist trail, for instance; and an integral brewery shop or tap is pretty much out of the question too. So choosing a home on an industrial estate is not just a question of cost and convenience but has longer-term implications for how you plan to run your business. Unless you decide to relocate, you will inevitably remain first and foremost a manufacturer.

Case Study: Renting Buildings From a Pub – Farmer's Ales, Maldon, Essex

Brewing may not be rocket science – but it's pretty close to it when you're talking about Farmer's Ales of Maldon, Essex. For founder Nigel Farmer used to be an engineer in the nuclear power industry, and worked at Bradwell power station until the opportunity of redundancy came up.

Nigel had been home brewing since his teenage years and had progressed as far as installing a full-mash brewery in his shed. There, his friends told him, he turned out beers that were better than some of East Anglia's leading brands. So with the prospect of spending more time with his mash tun looming, he decided to look for somewhere to set up a more serious operation.

Keen to find a home with a bit of character to give his beers a unique selling point, his first choice was an old shop at the dusty end of Maldon's high street. But a local Businesslink adviser soon put him right.

"He was asking questions I simply hadn't entertained, questions about footfall, about parking, about access, about services, and by doing that helped me avoid a costly disaster," says Nigel. "With his help I put together a checklist of criteria, and set about looking for somewhere that satisfied each one.

My advice to anyone would be not to jump at the first place you see. I nearly made that mistake and I'm lucky I didn't."

The disused outbuildings of a pub always seemed like a good prospect to Nigel, not least because the host pub would be bound to stock his beers. Several landlords were interested at first, but problems always cropped up that stopped the project going through. Then a friend suggested the Blue Boar, an imposing 18th-century coaching inn at the top of Maldon's high street, with a run-down stable-block that – with love and attention would be ideal. Nigel approached the owners, Old English Inns, which to his delight the company was very interested indeed.

"I think they saw it as adding interest to the hotel, and the deal was that I would restore and repair the stables to an agreed standard in return for a lower rent," says Nigel. They shook on it, and Nigel applied for planning permission to restore the Grade II listed building – the hotel's glory hole, he calls it, full of broken furniture and ancient VAT records – and change its use.

Getting all the necessary consents wasn't at all straightforward – although along the way Nigel found he was due a 40% English Heritage grant towards restoring the exterior, provided he used authentic materials such as cast-iron guttering – and it took nine months for the council to give him the go-ahead. A few days later, Old English Inns sold out, and the Blue Boar's new owner, Greene King, wasn't interested in Nigel's proposal.

"I went from elation to dejection in the space of a week," says Nigel. "Greene King just didn't want to know. I wrote, I rang, I got shunted from department to department – it was all very dispiriting."

A few months later, though, the Blue Boar appeared on the list of former Old English Inns that Greene King didn't want to keep, and was sold to local landowner John Wilsdon. Nigel approached him with the idea; he liked it; the planning permission was still in force; and in 2002 the first beers flowed out of the hotel's old stables.

That heart-stopping moment when Greene King took the hotel over illustrates the downside of basing your brewery in someone else's back yard: you're not really in control. But for Nigel, the advantages still outweigh the drawbacks.

"It made moving in easier because all the mains services were already in place, and I actually buy my electricity and water off the hotel which means I don't pay any standing charges," he says.

"The biggest advantage to me, I suppose, is that I have a brewery tap, and the biggest advantage to the hotel is that having a beer of its own has hugely increased its bar trade. There used to be four casks on stillage behind the bar – now there are 12.

"Another advantage to the hotel is that I manage its cellar, and when I first started trying to sell beer to other pubs I had someone to talk to who knew the licensed trade and could tell me where I was going wrong."

"The hotel manager sometimes calls it 'his' brewery, but I don't mind," says Nigel. "I'm not sure a working relationship like this would suit everybody – but it's certainly worked for me."

www.maldonbrewing.co.uk

Size and Services

The choice of premises will not only be one of the first decisions you make, but also the hardest to go back on; and in large part the style and scope of your future operations will be determined by what you find now. So having made the choice between an industrial estate and something more characterful and picturesque, start your hunt for premises with a clear idea of where you'd like to be in five or ten years' time.

Size, especially, is going to matter. You can brew in a broom cupboard if you have to, but it's difficult and uncomfortable and leaves no room for expansion when your beers become a cult hit, as they undoubtedly will. Many's the brewery that has chugged along quite happily in a cramped and crowded basement until a major award came along, and with it a deluge of orders. Three such breweries, Mordue, Kelham Island and Coniston, found that winning the Champion Beer of Britain competition – held every August at the **Great British Beer Festival** – brought as many headaches as it did joys. They all had to farm out part of their production, and two of them then moved into bigger premises.

And although the brewing itself can be made ergonomically efficient almost to the point of absurdity – Rob Jones of Sussex's Dark Star Brewery, for instance, sells a prefabricated plant dubbed the Russian Doll, whose vessels fit inside one another – other activities, notably cask storage and washing, can't. So although you may be impressed, on your brewery visits, by miracles of compact engineering such as Front Street or Green Jack in Lowestoft, do get as much space as your budget allows. Even if the building itself is small, a good-sized yard can always be partly covered over to shelter a cask-washer – and additional fermenters, when you need them.

If you're looking at older premises for conversion, be sure to keep a project manager's eye out for practical pitfalls. Brewing in a largely residential area is possible; but some people object to the smell, and getting your plans past them can be difficult. While the fabric of the building itself may be sound or, at least, not unfeasibly unsound, you also have to think about things like flooring, drainage and water treatment (essential – you can't just pour waste water down the drain), and ventilation (equally essential: you're going to be filling the place up with CO_2 which, believe me, you don't want to breathe in). Can your building be adapted, within your budget, to meet all these needs?

Planning Permission

Having found the perfect building – picturesque, perhaps; on a well-trodden tourist trail; in reasonable condition; suitable for adaptation; with space for future expansion, yet still miraculously within your budget – you have to discover whether you're actually going to be allowed to brew there.

Getting planning permission can be drawn-out, time-consuming, complicated and expensive. But it's not half as drawn-out, time-consuming, complicated and expensive as not getting it. Councils vary in their attitude to enforcement, some being absolutely rigorous and others more flexible, but the last thing you want is to have to undo work you've already done. And if you don't have planning permission, or if you do have it but then breach the terms and conditions set by the council, enforcement is a very real danger.

Class B2 Planning

If you've gone for the industrial estate option, getting permission to brew in your unit should be relatively straightforward. The site will already have permission for general industrial use – or use class B2, in planning jargon. However, there will still be some issues to settle with the local council – city, borough or district – before you start grinding your grist. If B2 use exists – and your solicitor should check this with the vendor or landlord of the site before you exchange – then the exact details of what you propose to do will be classed as "reserved matters" (another useful piece of planning jargon!), which you will need to agree with the council's Development Control department.

Other necessary compliances involving building regulations, health and safety matters, and waste water disposal will be dealt with in Chapter Four, Installation. However, you may find that the council won't give you the final go-ahead unless these compliances, especially health and safety and waste water disposal, are fully dealt with in your application.

Change of Use Permission

If you propose to brew in a historic property of some sort – or a farm or pub, that isn't already classed as B2, you will need change of use permission. You may very well need another, more difficult, permission, too: older buildings are frequently protected by statutory listing and need listed building consent before any alterations, however minor, can be made. Strictly speaking, this is not part of your change of use application as it's covered by different laws;

but in practice the two applications can be submitted at the same time. They remain separate applications, though, and the outcome of one doesn't affect the outcome of the other. You can be granted listed building consent on the grounds that your proposals don't affect the building's character, but still be refused change of use permission on the grounds that, say, vehicle access is inadequate. Refusal of either application can be challenged; so if you're knocked back on the one but get through on the other, the game's not necessarily up.

Planning Applications

Getting your planning application under way will involve you in two processes: evaluating your building itself, and evaluating its surroundings. Obviously, it's wise to carry out this exercise as thoroughly as possible before signing a lease or making a purchase – you don't want to be stuck with premises you can't brew in, or face a long hard battle to get your application through before you can start trading.

As far as the building is concerned, there's quite a long list of questions to answer:

- If it's an older property, is it listed? (The local council will give you this information.)
- Can it jump all the relevant health and safety hoops?
- How good is the vehicle access?
- Is there room on the site for all employees, visitors and deliveries to park off-street and for vehicles to manoeuvre, i.e. for articulated lorries to reverse?

As for its surroundings, is it in an area where general industrial use is permitted by the Local Development Framework (LDF)? And while you're at the town or city hall or on the council's website checking the LDF ask yourself the following questions:

- Will you in future be likely to require a shop (use class A1) or a bar (use class A3)?
- Are permissions for these uses likely to be granted, or does the LDF frown on the volume of traffic a shop and bar are likely to generate?
- Is the premises in a conservation area, an Area of Outstanding Natural Beauty or a National Park?

- How many traffic movements on and off site do you envisage? Can you control noise and emissions to the satisfaction of local residents, if there are any?

Getting planning permission is – supposedly, at least – somewhat more straightforward these days than it used to be; and thanks to the web, it's also much easier to get the information you need than it was. At **www.planningportal.gov.uk** you'll find a pretty exhaustive guide to planning matters; it even enables you to apply online and includes a fee calculator to help you work out roughly how much the council will charge you. It also has links to other sites detailing, for instance, national policy on converting surplus agricultural buildings to other employment-related uses (Public Planning Guidance note or PPG 7). Since 2002 there has been a presumption that councils should approve "well-conceived farm diversification proposals, particularly involving the re-use of existing buildings for business purposes". Another useful link is to the **Royal Town Planning Institute's** site, which includes a list of planning and development consultants. Hopefully you won't need one, but if your application is any less than perfectly straightforward, you very well might!

In law, councils have to determine your application within eight weeks of receiving it; but they have the power to extend the permitted period under certain circumstances. If they do, you can appeal to the Secretary of State, but it's rather self-defeating as the appeal will almost certainly take longer than the council would. So if you want your application to be determined as quickly as possible – and if you want to be sure of getting the right result – then everything hinges on thorough preparation and good communication. What this means, in effect, is that the whole planning process will take longer – a lot longer – than eight weeks – eight months, more like! – but the vast bulk of the work will be done before your application actually goes in.

Preparing the Planning Application

The important thing is not to be afraid. Some people are: they think the council is there to frustrate them, or tie them up in red tape, and the only sure way to get an application through is to sneak it under the town hall's radar somehow. And while it's true that councils can be awkward if they want to, and that there are more formalities to go through than at the State Opening of Parliament, in essence the council is there to help you and even has an obligation to make suitable provision for industrial developments such as yours. The grounds on which applications can be refused or substantially varied are finite; and if you discover in advance what they are, you shouldn't find it too hard to put together an application that is more or less bound to succeed.

First, check the relevant sections of the LDF thoroughly. This is available from the city, borough or district council, or on its website. Unfortunately it's not a single document, but a collection of them: however, the site should be fairly easy to navigate. In the case of my local district council, South Cambridgeshire, the home page has a link to "planning", which has a further link to "district planning policy". Finally, there's a link to "Local Plan 2004" (as this book goes to press, old-style local plans are being replaced by new-fangled LDFs, but in most cases the old plan is still in force). The Local Plan is divided into two sections: general policy across the whole district, and more specific policies location by location. Armed with this information, you should at least be able to tell whether the building you have your eye on is likely to be acceptable for B2 use. Other council websites I have checked are less clear than South Cambridgeshire's, but still far from impenetrable; and by and large I have found that, once all the documents are located, LDFs are fairly straightforward and easy to understand.

However, the Planning Portal site and LDFs are very general documents and paint rather a rosy picture of the planning process. Things can and do go wrong. It took Oakham Ales two frustrating and interminable years to get permission to move from its original home in Rutland and convert the former DSS office in Peterborough it inhabited until only recently. It later transpired that discussions aimed at razing the whole area to extend the neighbouring shopping mall had been opened, but the project hadn't made it as far as the Local Plan when Oakham put in its application. Two years later the Brewery Tap had a compulsory purchase order slapped on it, and has lived under the shadow of demolition ever since. (At the time of writing it's still trading, and indeed still brewing, although the company has found a new and much bigger production base on an industrial estate.)

Other breweries could doubtless tell planning horror-stories just as hair-raising, but in the main, where applicants have run into really serious planning delays the premises have been in urban centres where there is strong competition for development sites. (And often, councils can't reveal details of negotiations such as those in Peterborough because of commercial confidentiality.) On other occasions, applicants have tried to get their putative breweries approved as B1, which covers light industrial use in residential areas and imposes stricter conditions than B2 on noise, fumes and traffic movements. Then again, attempts to install breweries in quirky or unusual premises have often run into problems with planning officers who argue that the use is unsuited to the building. And another big stumbling block that has faced pub-breweries in the past has been the thorny question of mixed used. A lot of local planners have simply been unable to get their heads round the concept that a single business premises might want A4 use for part of the site and B1 or B2 for another. This was part of the problem that caused so much delay for Oakham, but with the huge increase in the number of pub-breweries round the country, local planners seem to be getting less resistant to the idea than previously. If mixed use does seem to be presenting a problem, you can usually overcome it by arming yourself with a good number of precedents, preferably fairly local.

The Planning Officer

There is no way of guaranteeing that these kind of problems won't arise; but one way of reducing the risk is to open a good channel of communications with the planning officer working on your proposal. You will have to pay an administration fee to cover the costs of your application anyway, but some councils will charge extra for an initial consultation with your planning officer.

However, as it's this very officer who will recommend acceptance or rejection of your plan to the council's Development Control Committee, the extra charge is probably money well spent. Involving this officer in the evolution of your brewery makes it almost as much his or her baby as yours; in fact one planning officer I spoke to while researching this chapter told me: "We always like getting a brewery to work on – it's a lot more interesting than most of the cases we get!" So by the time the application is ready to be formally considered, the two of you should have made it almost watertight. Of course, this process may itself have its ups and downs; but remember, if your planning officer flatly vetoes an idea of yours, it's not out of bloody-mindedness (probably not, anyway) but out of a deep knowledge of local policies and a very shrewd understanding of what will or won't get through.

The planning officer's main concern, after the suitability of the building itself, will be the impact of your business on its neighbours, especially if there are any residents in the immediate area. This concern is partly met by the LDF's approved uses for the locality. But the officer will also be interested in noise, smells and other emissions, waste discharge and any changes you propose to the appearance of the building, particularly if you will need equipment such as extractors, flues and tanks.

Consultation

A large part of the process involves consultation, and not just with the neighbours. Of course, you will have to advertise your application both in the local press (another expense!) and on the application premises, to give them the chance to object if they fear your plans will threaten the "amenity" of the area. But the grounds on which they can object are limited by statute, and the planning authority is specifically instructed (see the Planning Portals website again) that the mere number of objections is irrelevant.

But the main consultation will be with other statutory bodies:

- The local council's own environmental health department
- The county council as highways authority
- The parish council
- The Environment Agency
- The Health and Safety Executive

This is the part of the process that really takes the time, and it's these agencies that are likeliest to have objections. If your application conforms to the LDF and is made out thoroughly and in proper form, you should hopefully clear this last hurdle and start brewing. But what if you fall at this stage?

Appeals

The obvious thing is to appeal, and you have six months from the rejection of your application to do so. Once again, the Planning Portal contains all the details you need – you can even appeal online!

Appeals are handled by the Planning Inspectorate, which appoints an independent inspector to whom you can state your case and comment on the planning authority's statement of case. The Inspectorate also appoints a case officer who will help by telling you what documentation to present and when, although when dealing with unfamiliar, complex and jargon-ridden rules and regulations you may well feel you need the (expensive) advice of an experienced surveyor or planning consultant.

An appeal is the only way to overcome refusal of listed building consent;

but if you are refused change of use permission, a quicker and cheaper option is to find out what the council didn't like about your application, amend it accordingly, and resubmit. If you do this within 12 months there will be no fee and as objections to the original application are considered to have been dealt with already they can't be submitted again. This is the way large corporations wear down local objectors – they simply present slightly altered applications again and again until their opponents either run out of new objections or are simply too worn down to continue. That's perhaps not quite what you have in mind but if you have been refused on minor or technical grounds this is the simplest solution.

Once you have been granted planning permission, you have three years to act on it before it expires.

Chapter Three
Planning Your Finances

S O you've done your training and you've found your premises. Your next step is to move in and install your brewery. But not just yet. First, you've got to make sure you have enough money not just to set yourself up but also to keep yourself afloat until the business starts paying its way. This is not the place to tell you how or where to raise the money you'll need. You've doubtless got some capital already: the proceeds of the sale of your house, perhaps, or a redundancy cheque, or your life savings, or a bequest. You'll probably need more, though, and the obvious place to go is the bank. But before it parts with any money, the bank is going to ask some searching questions and will expect to see a detailed business plan.

The Business Plan

A business plan, as you undoubtedly already know, is far more than just a rosily optimistic cash-flow projection cobbled together to lull the bank into underwriting a daydream. If carried out thoroughly, it will confront you with the mathematics of your project coldly and in stark detail. And if it doesn't make you run away screaming, it will help ensure that your newborn business will be a sturdy infant capable of making it through to adulthood.

Your business plan will force you to answer hard questions about practical issues such as your premises, your products, your personnel, your market, and indeed your very purpose in starting up your brewery. But the final and most important section will be a cash-flow projection that should tell you, just as it will the potential lender, how long it's going to take to get into the black, and whether your brewery really has a financial future. Now, a business plan is a very specific document – a highly detailed and indeed compendious questionnaire that leaves nothing out. But to put a proper business plan together you don't have to reinvent the wheel and set yourself, as it were, your own exam. Rather, use a specimen business plan supplied either by your bank or by a **Local Enterprise Agency** (LEA); visit the National Federation of Enterprise Agencies (NFEA) at **www.nfea.com** to find your nearest.

LEAs are just one source of invaluable start-up help and advice available to all businesses. In fact there's a staggering amount of information on the web from a surprisingly wide variety of agencies. Plunder them all.

Online Advice

An especially useful link on the NFEA site is to the **Small Business Advice Service (SBAS)**, which has more than 200 trained and accredited business advisers all of whom can be consulted free online on topics ranging from starting a business while on benefits to international copyright protection. The SBAS site also has a start-up guide you will, I guarantee, find indispensable.

As well as the NFEA and the SBAS there's **Businesslink**, the official government body that supports and advises start-ups and small-to-medium enterprises, or SMEs, at local level. Visit **www.businesslink.gov.uk** for a guide to everything from starting up your business to selling it on, and also for a directory of grants and other forms of assistance. There's a surprising amount of grant schemes, soft loans, training programmes and other practical and financial help out there if you know where to look; the Businesslink site includes an online directory, and your local Businesslink will give you practical assistance in the tedious and time-consuming business of applying. And don't imagine that because you're not restoring a historic building, or creating jobs in a deprived area, or planning to export, you don't qualify for help. The chances are that you do, and while your bank may be able to help you source grants (and there are commercial agencies that will do so for a fee), with Businesslink you have a better chance of getting access to any and all relevant sources of assistance – and all for free.

Businesslink and LEAs are not only useful as sources of business advice and factual information. They also hold regular seminars and other events covering all sorts of topics from environmental considerations to employment law that are not only useful in themselves but are also opportunities to meet other local businesspeople. It's called networking, and it's not to be sneered at!

But every type of business has peculiarities that will affect its financial prospects, and this chapter aims to identify some of the peculiarities of the brewing business.

Capital Expenditure (Capex)

Your financial planning should fall under two headings: capital expenditure and running costs. Let's start with the capital you'll need.

By the time you get round to writing your business plan, you will know the exact purchase price (or premium, if leased) of your **premises**. But making your new home ready to receive your brewing equipment will, as we saw in the last chapter, entail costs that other businesses might not have to bear. Breweries use water, lots of it, not just to brew with but to heat up and cool down the various vats and vessels and, of course, to keep everything squeaky clean. In terms of capital, using so much water means you must have adequate drainage including sloping floors (which you may have to lay at your own cost even in a brand-new unit on an industrial estate) and washable surfaces. It may also mean you will have to treat effluent before disposal, another capital item to consider. The cost of non-slip flooring, essential on safety grounds, should also be built into your capital estimates; and, again on safety grounds, so should adequate ventilation. Carbon dioxide, one of the products of fermentation, is deadly not only to the microbes that would otherwise colonise your beer, but also to you and your staff. Your council's environmental health department will insist on the prevention of concentrations of CO_2; so – and especially if you plan to use traditional open fermenters – you will have to factor in the cost of whatever ventilation and/ or extraction measures (as well as monitoring equipment) it stipulates.

Casks

After your premises, your **equipment** will be your largest item of capital expenditure, and it can be anything from £7,500 (plus installation costs) to – well, the sky's the limit. One item of capex that is frequently and sometimes disastrously underestimated in brewery start-ups, though, is the stock (or population, to lapse into jargon) of casks that you will need. The most common size in use today is the nine-gallon firkin, and orthodoxy has it that a free trade brewer whose beers are distributed widely and whose empties trickle home with agonising slowness needs around 30 firkins for every bulk barrel, or 36 gallons, of production capacity. A five-barrel brewery should therefore own a stock of at least 150 firkins, which cost around £80 each new; so put down at least £12,000 in your capital estimates for casks. The temptation to skimp on casks is almost irresistible, especially if you're on a tight budget and other costs are running above your estimates. But you really will need that many: it's easy to be caught short by even a modest surge in demand, and disappointed customers tend not to come back. And do buy new: there are cheap second-hand casks around, but ask yourself why they're being sold. Unless they are the stock of a brewery that has closed, the answer, very probably, is that they're "leakers", and therefore worth only their scrap value. No publican or wholesaler likes to have to deal with a leaker, nor has any affection for the brewery that sends them one.

A vital note regarding casks is that they're extremely vulnerable to theft. After use they tend to be stacked at the pub's back door until the owner comes to collect them; so if you're talking about an irregular account that only orders every month or two, your expensive firkin could be sitting out in the open for weeks. The temptation to swipe it soon becomes irresistible to the more light-fingered of the local inhabitants (casks do have a scrap value), or alternatively it might be "uplifted" by another brewer collecting his own empties. For this reason the **British Beer & Pub Association** allocates a unique colour band to any brewer, whether a **BBPA** or **SIBA** member or not the joining kind, who cares to apply for one. The banding consists of three hoops chosen from 10 colours, normally painted round the middle of the cask between the rolling rings. For more details of the scheme visit **www.beerandpub.com** and follow links to its colour band register or email Andy Tighe on **atighe@beerandpub.com**.

The BBPA register is free to join and is an entirely voluntary scheme, so brewers are at liberty to pick their own colours if they prefer. However, if you're unregistered and your banding duplicates that of a registered brewer, you may find that helpful people keep sending your casks back to the wrong place. So you can either register, or choose a colour scheme of your own that's so unusual it's bound to be unique. And your unique identifying mark doesn't have to be in the form of bands, either. Some brewers I know paint both ends of their casks; one paints the entire vessel pale pink! It's also a good idea to stamp your name indelibly on the cask end.

The Delivery Van

Another vital piece of equipment that's easy to get wrong is the delivery van. A full firkin of beer doesn't take up much space but weighs about 50kg, so unless you don't mind being done for overloading your van from time to time, you need to choose with an eye to axle-weight rather than capacity. You also need to think about what sort of licence and tax-disc you will need. An ordinary Transit-style van should carry 20–30 full firkins without straying into the "Larger Goods Vehicle" vehicle excise licence category (TC55), and you will be able to drive it on your ordinary driving licence. This should be perfectly adequate for local deliveries; if you're planning anything more ambitious you may need a vehicle whose total laden weight or maximum authorised mass exceeds 3.5 tonnes. Visit **www.direct.gov.uk** and follow the links to "motoring" for more details.

Finally, managing the start-up will not be cost-free. For instance, there are the administration fees referred to in the previous chapter, payable to the local council merely for the privilege of applying for planning permission. Your consultant will also want paying: factor his fees into your financial plan. Find out in advance when these payments, as well as those due to builders and fabricators, will fall due. Knowing when you need to have funds available gives you two benefits: you won't be caught short when tradesmen demand payment; and you can organise one of those loans which you only draw on (and start paying interest on) when necessary.

Running Costs

Your brewery will have to bear many of the same general running costs as other businesses: utilities; insurance; business rate; rent or mortgage repayments; repayments on other borrowings; wages (if any) and associated costs; marketing and advertising; and deliveries. The information you will need to compute all these should be available from your bank or accountant, from one of the agencies listed above, or even from the websites of the relevant government departments.

However, as with any business sector, brewing has its peculiarities. One, in particular, might just help you with your business rate.

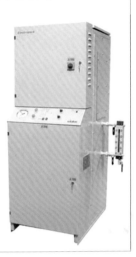

Your business rate, which is the property tax levied by your local council, is perhaps the easiest of your regular outgoings to calculate. It is based on a valuation carried out in 2003 (and due to be updated soon) aimed at establishing the rent your premises would command on the open market – exactly the same system, in fact, that used to be used to calculate domestic rates. This notional rent is known as the property's **rateable value** or **RV**, and what you actually pay is calculated as a percentage of it. The difference between modern business rates and old-fashioned domestic rates is that the council doesn't decide what percentage of your RV it may levy. Instead, the government sets it each year: for 2006–7 the standard percentage, or "multiplier", is 43.4p in the pound, rising to 44.4p for 2007–8. There's a small concession, though, for businesses with an RV of £15,000 or less (£21,500 or less in Greater London): 42.6p for 2006–7, and 44.1p for 2007–8. So make it a priority to find out the RV of your premises before you move in – if you find a site with a lower RV, it could save you quite a bit. Another relief that may help you with your business rates is that any part of your premises that is empty and unused can be rated separately, with a 50 per cent reduction.

Finally there's a third, rather complicated, relief aimed at protecting threatened village amenities, and which you might just be able to benefit from. The only pub in a village of 3,000 inhabitants or less is entitled to a business rate rebate of at least 50 per cent (or up to 100 per cent at the council's discretion) provided its RV is less than £14,000. If you base your brewery at a qualifying pub, and it doesn't push the RV over the £14,000 ceiling, you'll still get the full rebate. Even if it does, you might be able to have the brewery and the pub rated separately; in which case the pub will still qualify for its 50 per cent relief, while the brewery might qualify for the small business multiplier.

Excise Duty

When you pay your excise duty, and how much you'll pay, are explained in detail in the appendix. To give you some idea, though, duty is calculated as hl% per percentage point of alcohol by volume per hundred litres or hectolitre. (A 36-gallon barrel is 163hl). The current (2009-10) rate is £16.47 per hectolitre per degree alcohol; so the full rate of duty on a barrel of a 3.8 per cent ABV session bitter would be £102.01. However, if you're a small brewer producing up to 3,000 barrels a year you're entitled to 50 per cent relief and would only pay £51. There is also a sliding scale of relief for brewers producing more than 3,000 barrels a year; the complicated equations by which this is calculated are set out in the appendix, see page 194. Duty must be paid by direct debit on the 25th of the following month – again, details are in the appendix on page 198.

That leaves your ingredients – malt and hops – which are not going to be the biggest items on your list of outgoings. In fact, and to many people's amazement, they could well amount to less than £11 per firkin of standard-strength bitter.

Hops

The amount of hops you will need depends on your recipes, but a very rough guide for budgeting purposes is a maximum of 500g of aroma and a slightly lesser quantity of bittering varieties per barrel of a pretty hoppy beer. A five-barrel brewlength would therefore require about 2–2.5kg of each or 4–5kg all told. The price, of course, varies from harvest to harvest and according to the type of hops you use but is usually in the range of £5–10 per kilo: at the time of writing, the Worcestershire hop merchant Charles Faram was charging £7.35 per kilo for Goldings; £7.65 for Fuggles. Your hop bill is therefore likely to be in the region of £20–50 per five-barrel brew; £5–10 per barrel; or £1.25–2.50 per nine-gallon firkin.

You will need to be more precise than this when making the cash-flow projections for your business plan, but Faram's produces a brochure for start-up brewers that will give fuller details. Faram's will also accept payment over the phone by credit, which – assuming you pay your credit card bill in full every month – is the equivalent of 30 days' free credit.

Malt

Calculating the amount of malt you will use is more complicated, but a rough rule of thumb (again, very rough) is that a tonne will make 40 barrels of 4 per cent ABV bitter. A tonne of pale ale malt, at time of writing, is upwards of £500 – again, depending on what type of malt you are using. So that's about 125kg costing £62.50 per five-barrel brew; 25kg costing £12.50 per barrel; or 6.25kg costing £3.12 per firkin. So your ingredients, excepting the liquor, will have cost only £4.77– 5.62 for 72 pints of best bitter. The duty, with the 50 per cent small brewery relief, will be £13.37 for a 4 per cent ABV beer – a total, then, of about £25 a firkin. Throw in the cost of your utilities, and you should be able to produce a five-barrel brewlength for about £550; which is £110 a barrel or £27.50 a firkin.

You may have to pay a delivery charge, but even that is only about £45 for a one-tonne pallet – enough for eight five-barrel brews – carried by Palletline, Palletways, or a similar group haulier. (Most merchants will make up a mixed pallet for you, so you don't have to buy the crystal and other specialist malts you will only use in small quantities in one-tonne lots: they come in 25kg bags. Many malt suppliers will also deliver packs of hops on the same pallet.)

These are, as I have said, very rough costings intended only to give you an overall picture of what you are likely to spend. Your brewing consultant will go into more detail with you, but before you reach that stage I strongly recommend you to visit a **www.murphyandson.co.uk**. Murphy & Son is a very old-established firm of brewers' suppliers based in Nottingham, which stocks all the consumables and process additives that you will ever need, from liquor treatment to finings. More than that, though, its site is an absolute treasure-trove of highly detailed technical and other information including extraction tables for all varieties of malt. In fact Chris Garrett of Warminster Maltings in Wiltshire recommends the Murphy's site not only to start-up brewers planning their first year's outgoings, but also to more established brewers working out hop and malt grists for new recipes.

Pricing

So much for your outgoings. Now we come to the more pleasant side of the equation – namely, your likely income.

The most important thing you'll want to know is the price you can expect to charge per firkin – the nine-gallon barrel in which most cask beer is delivered these days. Many years ago, the Society of Independent Brewers worked out a formula to enable members who swapped beer among themselves to set a price. The idea was to enable brewers to swap different-strength beers with the minimum of fuss: instead of invoicing and paying each other in full every time, the brewer of the weaker of the beers being swapped simply paid the other brewer the strength-difference. The Bristol formula, as it is known, bases the standard price on the average production cost of beer; at the time of writing the price is the beer's ABV times £25 plus £70 per barrel; so a 4 per cent ABV beer would swap at £170 a barrel, or £42.50 per firkin.

Note, though, that the Bristol formula yields a swap price, not a wholesale price. The brewers who use it almost always add a margin of their own when selling the beer into trade – although wholesale prices have actually been declining recently thanks to the number of new breweries opening, and there are brewers who will indeed sell at the formula price or even lower. A great deal depends on how efficient your brewery is, and how much of your beer you retail yourself. If you produced 2,999 barrels a year at an average of 4 per cent ABV and got the Bristol formula for all of it, your annual turnover would be £570,000. Your ingredients and duty would account for £300,000 or thereabouts; only you know, having totted up your rent, rates, repayments, utilities, wages, marketing costs and so on whether there would be enough change out of the remaining £270,000 for you to live on. Probably not; so you'll doubtless be looking to charge your own margin on top of the formula price.

SIBA's Direct Delivery Scheme (DDS)

A good idea of how big a margin you can reasonably expect is provided by the prices agreed with pubcos and supermarkets by SIBA's Direct Delivery Scheme (DDS). Like the Bristol formula, these prices are based on alcoholic strength rather than the cost of ingredients, which you might perhaps see as an incentive to pad out your malt with as much rice and corn syrup as you can get away with. But don't give in to temptation. As a craft brewer, the quality of your beer is your greatest strength, and if it's no good no one will buy a second bottle or pint. Anyway, the DDS-agreed prices aren't always that bad: with one company SIBA has agreed a price of £48.53 per firkin at 4 per cent ABV. That's £24 a barrel extra margin over the Bristol formula price, or an additional £72,000 a year.

The problem is, though, that thanks to the recent proliferation of brewers and the introduction of new tiers of middleman in the form of wholesalers and non-brewing pubcos, the brewer's slice of the cake is actually dwindling. A pub in south-eastern England will charge, at time of writing, around £2.50 including VAT per pint of session-strength bitter – call it £2.10 net. Publicans typically add 100 per cent to the wholesale price to cover their own not inconsiderable overheads, which suggests that they're paying at least £75 a firkin for a beer of less than 4 per cent ABV. That price comes, typically, from a pubco or a wholesaler; you can bet the brewer isn't getting much more than 60 per cent of it. Unless, that is, the brewer in question happens to be one of the shrinking band of established regionals with tied estates whose tenants have to pay whatever they're asked.

In fact tied tenants are famously the only people in the pub trade who pay list-price for their beer: anyone with any bargaining power at all gets a discount. Often, small brewers deliberately ramp up their price-lists so they can appear to be generous with discounts; I have often heard of free trade publicans who negotiated discounted prices from microbrewers that were actually higher than the pre-discount prices offered by competing regionals. What's important in all your price negotiations, though, is that you should keep a firm idea in your head of what your lowest economical prices are, and should never give in to the temptation to take less for the sake of volume.

The thought of all that extra margin has lured many small brewers down the path of pub ownership. Whether you should think of owning a pub or pubs yourself will be explored in Chapter Eight, see page 152

Cashflow

No matter whether you have agreed comparatively low prices for bulk orders, or are charging a premium for single-firkin orders of ales that have just won major awards (always a good opportunity for a temporary price uplift), actually getting paid can be a nightmare. I have even heard stories of small, and generally new, breweries that went under because their credit with their suppliers had run out, their overdraft facilities had been exhausted, and they were missing loan repayments – and all the while, they were owed enough to cover the problem and more but simply couldn't get their money.

Whether these stories are true or not I don't know, but poor cash-flow is a perennial problem for local brewers whether it's large customers whose accounts departments aren't as sharp as they might be – later on in the book you will meet one brewer whose regular pubco cheques kept going to a competitor with a vaguely similar name – or small one-off accounts who had ordered a couple of firkins as a guest ale and never got round to paying for it.

The smaller debts used to be the bigger headache – you could be sending out invoices and reminders for months and then get an unsigned or undated cheque and have to start the whole procedure again. These kind of accounts need not be a problem any more, though: if it's a small enough account you can demand payment in advance by credit card either via your website, by email, or simply over the phone. If customers proves awkward, remind them that provided they clear the card in full every month, this amounts to 30 days' interest-free credit. Your bank will advise you on "customer not present" card payments, but there are other providers who you may find are cheaper.

Paypal (**www.paypal.com**), for instance, charges no start-up or one-off fees and takes a 20p fee plus 3.4 per cent commission on all transactions up to £1,500 per month. You can take payment on your website or, if you don't have one, by email or even by phone. The commission goes down in stages to 1.4 per cent, so you might even arrange for your bigger customers to pay you in this way. If they pay the whole month's bill in one go at the very end of the month, they can actually get two months' free credit while you pay just a single transaction fee. And if the month's bill is more than £1,500, the commission you pay goes down as well. Play the system – charge really trusted regular accounts every two months or even quarterly, and as long as your cash-flow will stand the wait, everybody gains.

There are, of course, other providers such as WorldPay, and you can spend many a happy hour trawling the net to find the provider that suits you best. None of them, though, can help you with big customers – supermarkets and pubcos – whose alleged credit periods of 60 or 90 days are honoured more in the breach than the observance. And once a glitch enters the system, it can take months to iron out. One way round this is to join SIBA's Direct Delivery Scheme which ensures, among other things, regular and reliable payment; however, there is a joining fee and some brewers aren't too happy with the prices they get through DDS.

Exit Strategy

At some point in the future, the likelihood is that you'll want to sell up. You might fall ill, you might fall out with your partners (a very common cause of the closure of small breweries), or you might just want to retire. It may, when you're planning to get started, seem a bad omen to be planning your demise as well. But remember, this is not only your living but your pension. The question you'll want to ask, then, is: how much is my brewery worth? And the simple answer is that it's worth what somebody will pay for it.

The actual value, however, is not the same thing as reaching a valuation, which depends very much on what you're selling. If you boil the brewery down to its constituent parts, there's the site, the equipment; and the brands and goodwill. The valuation of the site depends on whether it's freehold or leasehold and is something that only you can determine. A freehold you can have valued by any commercial property broker. A lease may or may not be "heritable" – that is, it may revert to the landlord, or you may be able to sell on its unexpired term. If the latter, the same commercial property broker will determine it for you. Your equipment undoubtedly has a second-hand price, which will depend on its condition and fluctuate according to market conditions; any brewing consultant can assess it for you. The valuation of the brands and goodwill will depend on how well you're trading, but a figure of three times net profit is often mentioned in valuing businesses without assets.

The same could be said of the value of your business as a going concern. It's such a rare occurrence in the small brewing world that there are no reliable guidelines: whether you can sell it as a business at all depends very much on whether there's someone willing to buy, and also on the nature of the sales. One brewery that I know sold recently for 2½ times its gross profit of £60,000. It had a turnover of £200,000 but was in leased premises, and sold relatively easily because it had top-class, fairly new equipment and a good steady trade with plenty of repeat custom. It may not seem a huge sum, but it was still considerably better than the break-up value. However, the deal depended very much on the fact that owner was introduced to a waiting buyer by a brewing consultant; and given that mature small breweries sell relatively rarely, perhaps the best way to get your business valued and sold is through one of the established consultants.

Chapter Four
Brewing Equipment

THERE'S many a good tune, my father used to remark, played on an old fiddle. And although he didn't actually have brewing equipment in mind, he might as well have. For a brewery doesn't have to be brand spanking new, all gleaming steel and copper and costing a small fortune to produce perfectly good beer. It can equally well be second-hand or even – if you really know what you're doing – cobbled up from scrap.

And indeed in the early days of small brewing, it had to be. There were, of course, long-established firms of brewers' engineers, mostly based in Burton-on-Trent, which could design and install a world-class brewery for you at the drop of a blueprint – provided, that is, that you wanted to brew a hundred barrels at a time. But if you only wanted to brew five, you had to forage for your vessels. In fact many small brewing pioneers – especially Peter Austin, founder of Hampshire's Ringwood Brewery – were just as well known for helping other start-ups as they were for their own. And I well remember a visit as late as 1993 to Central Bottling International (CBI) of Doncaster, which originally specialised in selling reconditioned second-hand bottling lines but found a new lease of life once the real ale revolution started. Microbrewers used to swarm all over its huge yard looking for usable vessels and pipework,

Monty's Brewery, Montgomery, Powys

Pam Honeyman was looking for career change having previously been a teacher and then working for a local charity. She had always been interested in real ale. With her husband Russ they run a successful beer wholesale business in Montgomery. They noticed a gap in the market in

that Montgomeryshire did not have a microbrewery of its own.

She signed up for the two week practical brewing course at Brewlab in June 2008 to see if she enjoyed the experience and to find out if she could work as a brewer. After successfully completing the course they then set out to find equipment and somebody to put it together for them. From local brewers they sourced two second hand FV's and after spending a day with Dave Facer at Facer's Brewery in Flint, he recommended contacting Johnson Brewing and Engineering.

The order was placed for a 12 Barrel LPG fired Brewhouse built from new at the start of November 2008 and the first brew was put through the new equipment on 28th January 2009. Vincent from Johnson Brewing & Engineering tells of how most of their business is based on word of mouth and clients recommendations. 'The best advert for us, is our equipment being successfully used to make top quality beer in an efficient manner, we set our breweries up to be easy to use and easy to maintain. We are often surprised in that clients expect pretty low levels of efficiencies in that they have been told 80% extracts are the norm. They are pleasantly surprised that a minimum of 90% is what we expect from the equipment. This adds up to lot of extra beer in the long term.'

Pam is looking to add more beers to her range as she gains experience of the market. From the initial decision to set up to the completion of a working brewery took a little over seven months, which as Pam says felt like an age, but is a lot quicker than most from conception to start up.

www.montysbrewery.co.uk
www.johnsonbrewing.com

and my visit coincided with Scottish & Newcastle's decision to take the old-fashioned cellar tanks out of its big managed houses and workingmen's clubs and replace them with conventional keg dispense. There they all stood in rows, fully insulated freestanding, five-barrel tanks with pipe-stubs at their tops and bottoms and even little viewing panels so you could see what was going on inside – 1,800 of them. They made absolutely perfect fermenters and/or conditioning tanks, and CBI sold the lot in a few weeks of getting them in.

Constructing your own Equipment

You could, if you had to, follow the example of those pioneers and cobble up your brewery from scrap, and not just out of parsimony, either. Tim Dunford of the Green Jack Brewery of Lowestoft did just that as recently as 2003, but only because he had to. Green Jack occupies the back part of a house that was, rather weirdly, left standing when the front was demolished for road-widening, and it's such an odd shape that he couldn't get what he needed off the peg and had to fabricate his own. His tanks were all originally used to make onion flavouring for the crisps and snacks industry, and when he first got them they stank of it. They all had to be altered in various ways, but Tim sought the aid of a local fabricator who instructed him in the finer arts of the angle-grinder and the oxyacetylene torch, and he did a brilliant job – as the rows of award certificates decorating one wall of his pub, the Triangle, demonstrate.

A word of caution here, though. The pioneers of the 1970s were able to make their Heath Robinson breweries work because, almost to a man, they were themselves refugees from the mainstream brewing industry. They'd been working with mash tuns and hop backs and paraflows since their teens and they knew everything there was to know about brewing equipment. Similarly Tim Dunford, although he has never worked for a mainstream brewery, had run another micro for a long time before founding Green Jack. He too knew from workaday experience what vessels he needed, what was going to be expected of them, and how to connect them all up. You, even if you're a veteran home brewer, are probably not quite so intimately familiar with the hardware you're going to need; and you're also not going to be quite as expert in keeping the whole rig running once it's actually set up.

A wise maxim here, then, is that you should spend as much as you can on your equipment, even if it means skimping elsewhere. Once you're up and running you're going to be more than grateful for well-designed and well-built plant that works smoothly and efficiently, using up a minimum of energy and a minimum of labour and never breaking down. Something you can take for granted, really. And that, for most mortals, is going to mean a purpose-built brewery from one of the main consultants – people like ABUK, Mossbrew, David Porter, David Smith and Brewing Design Services.

Brewing Consultants

If your budget isn't big, you may at this point be getting a bit nervous about how much you're likely to have to spend on your all-singing, all-dancing, cutting-edge computer-controlled brewery. Well, it depends on who you talk to. Some consultants can do the job for less than £20,000. Then there are others who would advise you to spend not less than £100,000. That doesn't mean that the former are cheapskates and the latter are con artists, though. All it means is that there's a broad spectrum of people coming into the industry, all with different philosophies, ambitions and levels of resource, and the various consultants specialise in catering for different segments of the market. They will all, by and large, do you proud; just make sure, though, that you talk to three or more of them before deciding which you want to hire. Whichever of the consultants you opt to put your business with, however, you will soon discover one unexpected fact: at bottom, the equipment you will need is surprisingly simple, and the actual pieces of kit are surprisingly few.

Opting for purpose-built brewing equipment rather than improvised kit made from vats with former lives in other industries (and one brewery has vessels originally used to mix lipstick!) doesn't necessarily mean buying new, though. There's a lively trade in second-hand kit too. Something like 20 breweries close every year, some of them tiny, some of them (like Gale's and Ridley's, which both closed in 2006–7) pretty big. Much of the equipment that comes on the market as a result is fairly well worn, but then much of it is brand new.

Well-established family brewers aren't above picking clean the corpses of their fallen rivals; if you're lucky enough to be shown round by the brewer himself when you visit an old family brewery, he will inevitably and often rather gloatingly point out plant and vessels rescued from recently deceased competitors. And if it's good enough for them, it's good enough for you!

But most of the second-hand kit you or your consultant are likely to pick up won't come from closed breweries at all, but from successful breweries that are expanding and replacing outgrown gear.

Let us now pretend that we're walking through a classical tower brewery – that is, one where the malt and water are hoisted or pumped up to the top, and all the subsequent processes are on successively lower floors to allow gravity to do the work. We are in the company of Richard Shardlow of Brewing Design Services of Tring, to whom I am indebted for this virtual tour. As we go, you can tick off what you're going to need piece by piece

Utilities and Services

Water

Beer is mostly water, and you're going to use an awful lot of it. What with cooling (and automatic temperature control at every stage of the process means a more consistent product and a less exhausting life) and cleaning, in

Fulton Boiler Works

Fulton have been associated with supplying steam boiler plant for the brewing industry for more than forty years. As the larger breweries have closed and merged and the move to smaller micro breweries has developed the Fulton range of small vertical steam boilers has proved to be ideal for the application. Compact with a small footprint, the fuel fired and electric boilers are suitable for even the smallest brewery. Reliability,efficiency and longevity are essential considerations for the brewery owner when selecting steam boiler plant and Fulton provide equipment with a national after sales service support to meet these expectations.

The Fulton reputation has been built on providing a "total service" for our customers. Whenever possible, we like to be involved at the initial planning stage with the customer or design team when our expertise in steam boiler application is available at no cost. As a British manufacturer with a factory in Bristol, we can then provide the boiler and ancillary plant as individual components or as an off site pre-fabricated package as a turnkey CE certified assembly which minimizes the site work.

We welcome enquiries to either the company website or to the Bristol office. www.fulton.com Tel 0117 972 3322

Brewing Consultants

Most start-up brewers these days will use the services of the brewing consultancy sector, which has evolved as the small brewing industry has grown over the years. In fact, given today's regulatory complexities it's a brave would-be brewer who doesn't exploit the vast expertise that is available from the various consultants, most of whom have huge experience and access to a network of other support services that you will find indispensable. However, they all have different specialities and ranges of services, so shop around!

Below are listed details of the best known of them.

Abbott & Co: A long-established firm of engineers – founded in 1870 – Abbott & Co of Newark, Nottinghamshire, supplies and installs complete breweries from 5–15 barrels. Recent customers include Potbelly, Surrey Hills, Hesket Newmarket and WF6. Tel 01633 704208 or visit **www.mashtuns.co.uk**.

AB UK: The full name of AB UK, based in Misterton, Nottinghamshire, is Advanced Bottling, and it supplies and installs bottling equipment as well as breweries. Specialises in reconditioned equipment. Tel 01427 890099, email info@abuk.co.uk or visit **www.abuk.co.uk**.

Brewing Design Services: Founded as Inn Brewing by former Whitbread senior brewer David Shardlow in 1982, the company changed its name 10 years later to broaden its appeal beyond the brewpub and is now run by David's son Richard, who also runs Tring Brewery. BDS specialises in larger projects such as Butcombe's brand-new 60-barrel brewery in Somerset. Tel 01442 890721 email info@tringbrewery.com.

Iceni Brewery: Iceni is owned and run by Brendan Moore, founder of the East Anglian Brewers co-operative. Brendan also installs both brewing and bottling equipment and advises on marketing techniques. Tel 01842 878922 or visit **www.icenibrewery.co.uk**.

Johnson Brewing & Engineering Ltd: Vincent Johnson set up Johnson Brewing & Engineering in 2003. Time served as a boilermaker working on M.O.D contracts, the end of the cold war meant redundancy and a career change into brewing. Successful completion of a BSc (Hons) in Brewing & Distilling at Heriot Watt in 1997 followed a year working for S&N as a Project Engineer. Then followed five years working for brewing maverick Brendan Dobbin, installing brewplant all over Europe and the UK. Since 2003 he has concentrated mainly on the UK market and has supplied & installed new many breweries from 4 barrel to 50 Barrel in size. Cask washing and keg washing equipment is also a speciality. With his previous experience in Europe they have help set up lager brewing plant and filtration equipment in Sweden (Jamtlands Bryggerri) and the UK (Taddington Brewery). Tel 01706 715107 or visit **www.johnsonbrewing.com**

Mossbrew: As well as running Mossbrew, Graham Moss owns the Ministry of Ale brewpub in Burnley. A biochemist by training, he also holds master's degrees in Malting & Brewing Technology and Business Adminstration. He founded Mossbrew in 1994 and supplies everything from half-barrel pilot breweries upwards, with full installation, training, and consultancy services thrown in. Tel 01282 830909 or visit **www.mossbrew.co.uk**.

David Porter: Founder of Porter Brewing based at the Griffin Inn at Haslingden, Lancashire, David once owned a chain of five pubs but slimmed down to two to concentrate on his installation and consultancy business. David has installed over 50 breweries in Britain and many overseas, and runs a full service including training and troubleshooting. Tel 01706 214021 or visit www.pbcbreweryinstallation.com.

David Smith: York-based David Smith had brewed at Samuel Smith's in Tadcaster for over 20 years before establishing DH Smith Brewing Services in 1988, primarily to supply microbiological testing and other technical services. In 1989 he branched out into training, and then, as a natural next step, into sourcing and installing breweries as well. He still runs his twice-yearly Fundamentals of Minibrewing course at York Brewery. David has designed an installed over 100 breweries, including Le Brewery at la Ferté-Macé in Normandy. Tel 01904 706778, email david.smith999@ntelworld.com or visit **www.brewingservices.co.uk**.

fact, you're going to use about five times as much water as you will actually brew with. So if you produce 3,000 barrels of beer at 36 gallons per barrel, you're actually going to get through more than 400,000 gallons of water a year. This will put you on your water company's industrial tariff, details of which you will need anyway for your business plan. If you are lucky enough to have your own well or borehole, however, your water will be free. The Environment Agency allows the abstraction of up to 20m³ or about 4,400 gallons of groundwater per day from wells and boreholes without a licence. That's more than 1.6 million gallons a year, or nearly four times what a 3,000-barrel brewer is likely to need. You can even have your own well sunk: numerous commercial borehole diggers can be found by surfing the web.

(The water company doesn't just supply water; it also takes it away. However, to take advantage of this service you will need trade effluent consent, of which more below.)

Electricity

As well as water you will also need energy to move it around, heat it up and cool it down. You can have a gas-fired copper, if you like; but even if you do, you are still going to use electricity on a literally industrial scale. You are therefore recommended to install a three-phase supply, even in a five-barrel plant, both as an economy measure (a single-phase supply, will draw 120–130 amps to generate 36kw of heat, whereas a three-phase supply will draw only 63 amps) and so that you don't keep blowing fuses.

Laboratory Tests

A key heading under services is the laboratory. The number and sophistication of tests and checks required out these days places a fully functional lab beyond the resources or expertise of the smaller brewery. But there are plenty of contractors who will undertake them for you; your consultant will provide some of these services and will be pleased to put you in touch with a specialist such as Brewlab who can do the rest. Before you start brewing, you'll need to have your liquors analysed, and it's a good idea to carry out regular checks in case of changes to the water supply. Your consultant can arrange these. The regulations concerning sampling for alcoholic strength are set out in the appendix; again, a specialist such as Brewlab can carry these out, but nearer to home there are many commercial providers of laboratory services. If your consultant hasn't recommended one, check in Yellow Pages under "chemists

Case study: Expert Help with a Difficult Installation – Le Brewery, La Ferté Macé, Normandy

On the D908 between La Ferté Macé and Joue du Bois is an ancient cider farm that is home to a former teacher from Peterborough, Steve Skews, and his wife Jane. It has also, since 2001, housed Le Brewery, a project the Skewses cooked up with Jane's sister Sue Green and her husband, another Steve, after the winter storms of 1999 destroyed two-thirds of the orchards. It was a blow that the Skewses knew would take years to overcome.

Back in England, the Greens had seen not one but two microbreweries sprout in their home village of Wickwar, near Bristol. And although there were no breweries in Normandy, says Steve Green, there was no shortage of interest in beer. So installing a micro looked like a short-cut to getting the Skewses back on their feet.

"Normandy had a large British population both of residents and tourists," he says. "Local people were also known to have an interest in a good half-litre, and there were bars around the region that sold premium Belgian beers and would surely be interested in a good local product. We discussed the idea over a long evening and decided to investigate the feasibility of setting up a brewery at the farm."

After visiting the nearest brewery – 200km away – the partners decided their idea was worth pursuing and sought the professional services of York-based consultant David Smith, who visited the farm in late 2000.

"His report listed a number of hurdles but showed that a brewery could be installed and operated in some of the buildings," says Steve. "Considerable work would be needed to make them suitable, but it was not impossible."

While the Skewses set about tackling French officialdom – no easy task, since the authorities themselves seemed to have little idea of what was necessary – Steve Green and David Smith started the hunt for suitable second-hand kit. After visiting a number of breweries with plant for sale, they finally settled on the Worldham Brewery, located in an old oasthouse on a farm near Alton, Hampshire, and recently closed by owner Hugo Sharpe, who was calling it a day after 10 years .

"It was of the ideal brewlength and in a good location for transport to France," says Steve. "It was a 10-barrel plant with extras that allowed its use as a five or possibly 15-barrel plant – a flexible future-proof solution for a new company setting up in a new market in a new country."

Getting the brewery to Normandy wasn't so simple, though. In fact, getting it out of its oasthouse wasn't so simple.

"A team of engineers, electricians, and other helpers assembled one cold weekend in mid-January to dismantle the brewery," says Steve Green. "I could come up with many quotes in connection with moving the plant, but they'd all be unprintable! "The brewery had evolved over many years and it was hard to believe the building wasn't built around the pipework rather than the pipes fitted into the building."

The main difficulty was shifting the heaviest items such as the copper over floorboards of insufficient loadbearing capacity.

"We had to lift the vessels down using a site trolley and various pieces of wood, all of which broke during the process," says Steve. "No one was seriously hurt, but we came close. It was also icy during most of the work, which made things more difficult still."

Although the stables at the farm had been in a state of dilapidation, one feature proved ideal for a brewery: they're in a row. This made it possible to house each stage of the process in a separate temperature-controlled compartment, in a series, with the malt store and mill in the old haylofts above.

Test brews were soon completed, and the first batches of Norman Gold, a blonde beer of 4.9 per cent ABV, and the hoppier, darker Conquerant at 5.5 per cent were soon ready for drinking. They caught on, too – not only are they stocked in local supermarkets, but Le Brewery now owns two English-style pubs.

"I don't think we could have done it without David," says Jane. "He found us the ideal brewery and then came over here to inspect the site and work out how it could all be set up in the buildings we had. Then he planned the installation and supervised it, and he wasn't above rolling his sleeves up and mucking in.

"He's still a good friend, and he comes over to see how we're getting on with the brewery every now and then. He's even brought his family over, too."

www.le-brewery.com

– analytical and research" or "laboratory facilities". Local laboratories can also carry out the regular microbiology tests recommended in the Society of Independent Brewers' code of conduct. If you sell beer to large retailers such as supermarkets, you will also be required to check regularly for heavy metals such as lead and arsenic, aflatoxins produced by fungi, and toxins produced by nitrites in the water supply.

Pipework

Finally, not exactly a utility or service, but an essential part of the brewery that won't fit under the heading of any particular vessel, is the pipework. This is something you will become intimately familiar with very quickly, and Richard's advice is not to cut corners by choosing flexible hoses over solid pipes. There are two reasons for this: hoses won't last and will have to be replaced; and there will be an irresistible temptation to tuck them away where you won't see them. Actually, you're better off with highly conspicuous pipes in places where they can easily be inspected, cleaned and, if necessary, repaired or replaced.

Malt Mill and Hot Liquor Tank

The brewing process starts when you fill your mash tun, so up in the very attic of our tower we find our malt mill and hopper and our hot liquor tank. Only Richard's advice is: don't bother with the malt mill. Years ago, maltsters expected their customers to grind their malt to their own specification and were rarely called on to do it themselves; and when they did, the grists they came up with weren't necessarily exactly what the brewers wanted. Nowadays, though, with so many micros not possessing mills of their own, grinding is all part of the service; so why spend good money on kit you don't need? (You'll still need the hopper, though.)

The other constituent of the mash is, of course, hot liquor. A fairly plain insulated stainless steel tank with everyday immersion heater elements will do the trick, says Richard. It needs to heat the liquor to 72°C but can be allowed to do so overnight; an energy-saving thermostat and a timer switch (so you don't have to slip back to the brewery last thing at night to turn it on) might be useful extras.

Also in the attic we're likely to find the cold water tank. This is going to supply the four-fifths of your water requirement that you don't actually brew

On the right, an example of a mash tun

with, and it's got to be both refrigerated and well insulated. This is because the hopped wort hot from the kettle is going to have to be cooled rapidly to 18–19°C before it can be pitched with yeast; given that the cold water tank is right up there in the attic where the sun can beat down on it uninterrupted, it will need refrigerating down to about 12°C before it can do the job.

Mash tun

The mash tun is one of the most important vessels in the brewery, for it's where the malt is made to yield up its fermentable sugars to create the sweet wort that will, eventually, be beer. But it's also one of the simplest – basically, it's just an insulated stainless-steel cylinder with a tight-fitting lid on top and a sieve in its bottom.

To get the best extraction, your mash tun will need to be well enough insulated to hold the mash at 72°C for an hour or an hour and a half. It also needs a sparging arm built into the lid: this is rather like the spray arm in your dishwasher at home, and once the wort has been run off it sprays the grains with hot water to get the last little bits of sugar out of them. The grains lie either on a stainless steel plate drilled with just the right number of right-sized holes to let the wort run through once mashing has been satisfactorily completed, or on a wedgewire mesh that does the same job.

Emptying the mash tun is quite a job: a five-barrel brew of session bitter requires something like 120kg of malt, which will by this stage be sodden and therefore even heavier. It all has to be dug out by hand, which is made more difficult by the fact that a five-barrel mash tun isn't actually all that big, so it's very awkward to get at its contents. There is a tilting mash tun on the market that makes the job easier, although digging out the mash tun is the brewing industry's time-honoured way of keeping apprentices and juniors fit, and it's certainly a good work-out.

Spent Grain

What do you do with all that spent grain? If you're brewing every day it will soon mount up, so the best thing to do is to sell it as animal feed. Since July 2005, though, thanks to swine vesicular disease and foot and mouth, British brewers have had to conform to European feed hygiene legislation (although you can bet that French brewers don't!) as they affect "co-products". In practice this means registering with the **Brewing, Food & Beverage Industry Suppliers Association** (BFBi) Feed Assurance Scheme, going on a one-day training course and paying a one-off fee of up to £350 depending on how big a brewery you are. It may seem just another bit of bureaucratic nonsense, but given the devastation caused by foot and mouth it is perhaps a forgiveable precaution. Anyway, the sale of co-products is so important for your cash-flow (the first payment you ever receive will almost certainly be not for the sale of beer, but for the sale of spent grains), and any other means of disposing of spent grains would be so difficult, that registration is indispensable. Visit **www.bfbi.org.uk** for more details.

The Copper and Hop Back

The next stop for your wort on its journey towards becoming beer is the copper, where it will be boiled up with hops. The wort will already be pretty hot when it is run into the copper, so a couple of thermostatically controlled immersion heater elements should suffice to bring it nicely to the boil and keep it there for as long as need be. But although this is the cheapest and easiest way to do the job, it's by no means the only way. A handful of breweries, notably Caledonian, have coppers fired directly by gas-jets, which is picturesque and produces caramel that gives the beer a highly distinctive taste, but there are health and safety issues. Another more expensive method is a gas immersion coil, which is highly efficient. Then there's steam either in a coil or an external jacket, which is very expensive to install and highly dangerous if not assiduously maintained, but is both cheap to run and very flexible, since the same steam can also be used for cleaning. The copper needs to be vented externally to get rid of the steam it produces, and it can have a sprayball built into its lid to allow thorough cleaning with detergent and rinsing with boiling water after use (although you can just hose it out with boiling water, since it should already be sterile).

Perhaps the hop back should come under the same heading as the copper, although strictly speaking it's the next stage in the process. Essentially it's just a huge sieve, like the steel plate or wedgewire mesh in the mash tun, only in this case it's the "trub" or used hops that it's there to collect so the hopped wort can run clean into the fermenters. Richard, who runs Tring Brewery as well as Brewing Design Services, actually uses the hop back for the last addition of hops. Instead of putting the late hops into the copper itself, he puts them in the hop back, dampens them a little, and then lets the wort sit on them for a while before it drains through them. Adding the late hops directly to the boil, he says, evaporates many of the aromatic resins. Doing it his way gives him more aroma from fewer hops. Be that as it may, the used hop litter or "trub" has to be got rid of. Pelletised hops, says Richard, tend to disintegrate in the boil to the extent where (with the water company's express approval) they can simply be hosed down the drain. Used whole hops have to be dug out by hand (not a very onerous task, since they're not used in any great bulk) and make excellent mulch.

Fermentation

This is where your plentiful supply of refrigerated water comes in, since the hopped wort leaves the copper having just boiled and has to be rapidly cooled to 18–19°C ("collection temperature") before it can be pitched with yeast. The wort therefore needs to be run through a heat exchanger, of which there are a number of types, into the fermenting vessel, whose temperature also needs to be controlled (preferably automatically, so you don't have to alter it manually every two hours day and night) by means of a cooling jacket. Fermentation is an exothermic reaction – that is, it generates its own heat – and the temperature of the fermenting wort will gradually creep up as the process goes on. Too hot a reaction will generate off-flavours, so the fermentation temperature needs to be kept down to about 21°C. Different shapes of fermentation vessel produce different temperatures, too; consult your installer as to which shape – cylindrical, cylindro-conical or square – will suit you best. The cooling jacket also needs to be efficient enough to bring the temperature of the wort down sharply to 8–12°C within 24 hours of fermentation ending.

Open Fermenters

There is some argument as to whether fermenters need lids or not. In some parts of the country, especially in the north of England, open square fermenters made of slate are traditional; and being able to peer into the fermenting vessel as the yeast begins to grow its thick, rocky head is perhaps the most aesthetically pleasing part of the whole operation – visitors love it. But there are drawbacks, says Richard. Open fermenters demand excellent ventilation and extraction equipment, since the CO2 given off during fermentation is lethal even in fairly low doses. CO2 in high concentrations burns the nose and eyes; but it will cause unconsciousness at much lower levels than that, and will then asphyxiate you. Your environmental health officer will probably stipulate what monitoring and ventilation equipment you will need at the planning stage; some EHOs have been known to veto open fermenters altogether.

Closed Fermenters

Closed fermenters are also more hygienic, says Richard – which is vitally important, as this is the most delicate stage in the proceedings. Historically,

Pitching yeast starter into a fermenter

it's infection when fermenting that is the brewer's biggest danger. Improved hygiene and handling mean that spoilt brews due to yeast infection aren't as common these days as they were; nevertheless, you need to be ruthlessly disciplined in your hygiene procedures at this stage. Not only do closed fermenters mean there is no risk of birds, rodents or brewery visitors making unwelcome deposits in them, but they are less vulnerable to passing bacteria and spores and can have "cips" or cleaning in place systems built in. And opting for closed fermenters means that your entire brewery is virtually a closed system from mash tun on. Almost the only time it needs to be opened during the process is for the addition of hops – which are, of course, added to the wort while it is boiling and therefore safe from infection.

Once fermentation is complete – and it can last for anything from a day to a week – there are really only two processes left for most microbrewers: collecting the yeast, and racking the beer into casks. Your yeast will grow by five or six times during fermentation; you can skim excess barm off the top of the wort with a sterile bucket, and there's a trap known as a thimble that fits into the base of the vessel to collect the clumped or "flocculated" yeast cells that sink down to the bottom. Once you've harvested enough yeast for your next brew, the rest will go as highly nutritious pig-feed – provided, of course, that you have signed up to the BFBi's Feed Assurance Scheme.

Casks

As we discovered in the previous chapter, most brewers reckon they need a ratio of seven casks for every one out in trade. The commonest casks these days are nine-barrel firkins at around £80 each, so they're not cheap, and you might also want a handful of 4½-gallon "pins" for very

Cask racking at St Peter's Brewery

strong beers or 18-gallon "kilderkins" for fast-selling beers.

(The full 36-gallon barrel is almost obsolete as an actual cask and is really only used as a unit of account these days. That's not because few pubs or clubs can sell beer quickly enough to warrant such a large container: there are probably thousands whose throughput of lager would justify the use of full-sized barrels. But they are nightmares to handle, weighing 200 kilos or more when full. I do believe there are still a handful of 54-gallon hogsheads in circulation in the north-west, but I have never seen one. And you may also come across metric barrels of 11 and 22 gallons, which were once quite commonly used for lager but are now pretty much obsolete. If you are offered

Case study: A Brewery Put Together from Scrap – Green Jack Brewery, The Triangle, Lowestoft, Suffolk

East Anglian brewers scored a resounding double when Ripper from Lowestoft's Green Jack Brewery won the CAMRA's Winter Beer of Britain award in January 2007. For the overall Champion Beer of Britain title was already held, for the second year running, by Crouch Vale of South Woodham Ferrers, Essex, with Brewers Gold. And as it happened, CAMRA's reigning National Pub of the Year, the Swan at Little Totham, was also in Essex.

Not only was Ripper's victory a historic hat-trick for the region, but Green Jack itself must be one of the smallest breweries ever to win a national title. Its 10-barrel plant isn't unusually small in terms of capacity; but it's squeezed into the tiniest space imaginable, and with only two fermenters it can only turn out three brews a fortnight. "We're part-time brewers looking to go full-time," says boss Tim Dunford, who is permanently on the lookout for bigger premises.

What Tim has got is an odd-shaped outbuilding across a tiny yard at the back of the Triangle, a pub in a Victorian residential quarter on the edge of Lowestoft town centre. But the pub known today as the Triangle actually used to be called the Oddfellows Arms; and the outbuilding that houses the brewery is all that remains of the original Triangle. The back-to-back pubs coexisted perfectly happily for many years until the Triangle was partly demolished – to widen the street it fronted. Somehow its name migrated to the Oddfellows; and it was universally known as the Triangle when Tim embarked on his drinking career – slightly but not dramatically underaged – just over a quarter of a century ago.

The story of Green Jack starts in 1988 when one Charlie Forbes started brewing at Oulton Broad just outside Lowestoft. Tim, a local lad who was first a signmaker and later an antique dealer, was an enthusiastic customer and a pal of Derek Longman's, who actually ran the brewery while Charlie lived in London.

"I thought to myself, if Derek can do this I could probably do it better!" says Tim. "So I got hold of Charlie and started hassling him, and eventually he sold me the brewing equipment and the lease on the premises."

That was in 1993, and – Charlie having taken his surname with him – Green Jack was born, with Tim brewing in partnership with his sister. That arrangement lasted until five years ago, when the partnership broke up and Tim took over the Triangle. The constraints of the new site made buying a standard brewing plant impossible. Instead Tim and local fabricator Richard Payne – a childhood friend – purpose-built the kit themselves.

From a local scrap-yard they bought four small steel tanks that had once held onion flavouring for crisp manufacturers. Once the lingering odours had been scrubbed away, one of them became the mash tun, while Tim and Richard welded a metre and a half of extra capacity to the tops of the others to become the copper and two fermenters. The whole process is digitally temperature-controlled using equipment which had to be sourced from a German firm because the brewery doesn't have three-phase electricity, which Tim says was required for all the domestically-produced equipment he looked at. It was all rigged up by a local refrigeration engineer who is also a friend of Tim's. And cleaning in place was provided by the installation of simple pumps and sprayheads – they cost about £30 each, says Tim – in all the relevant vessels.

The extempore nature of the kit hasn't affected the quality and consistency of the beers it produces, either. Almost as soon as it flowed from the fermenter, Ripper was winning awards: it was champion barley wine at Peterborough Beer Festival in 1996, '97, '98 and '99. The summer seasonal beer, Summer Dream, has won a few trophies too, and Orange Wheat – "a bastardisation of Hoegaarden", Tim admits – was champion specialist beer at Peterborough and Norwich in 2006 and overall winner at both Norwich and Leicester in 2005. But it was Ripper, a dangerously drinkable, hoppy, pale ale of 8.5 per cent alcohol, that notched up Green Jack's first national title, much to Tim's delight.

A word of caution, though. You might opt for a brand-new brewhouse, or prefer to put one together yourself from second-hand vessels of respectable provenance. Tim was able to create an award-winning brewery from used vessels employing local tradesmen with no prior experience of brewery equipment because he already knew his brewing inside out. Do you?

www.bikeways.freeserve.co.uk/greenjack.htm

any, check them scrupulously: they are not only second-hand but probably very old and likely to leak.)

Alternative Barrels and Casks

The price of new barrels may tempt you to investigate second-hand ones; but do be careful, especially if there are any visible mends, for a "leaker" will cost you dear. Not only does it have to be replaced, but if it fails all over a publican's cellar, it may well cost you his business. Similarly, plastic casks have attracted considerable criticism. On paper, they're the answer to the small brewer's prayer – lightweight, rigid, durable and cheap. But some say they're prone to sudden and dramatic failure, that they don't stand up to the stresses of frequent rough handling, and that the plastic is degraded by washing at high temperatures. And whether the criticisms are justified or not, there are many licensees (including beer festival organisers) who simply won't accept them, not because they've had bad experiences themselves, but because they've heard of others who have. Still, plastic casks have their uses. If you're a brewpub or have a retail outlet on site, you can use plastic casks and reduce the risk of failure by handling them carefully. And if one does fail, the only person you've antagonised is yourself. You can also keep a stock in reserve for emergencies and for special events such as brewery open days that might make too much demand on your population of steel casks.

Whatever casks you use, cleaning them to sterility is absolutely essential. Rinse them out thoroughly with a power-washer; use a sprayball with detergent; and then steam them. (In fact ease of cleaning is one reason why the industry has resolutely refused to countenance cubic containers. Barrels are traditionally barrel-shaped so they can be rolled round the brewery yard and up and down the ramps in pub cellars quickly and easily. Cubic containers would be more efficient, stacking into a smaller space, and could easily be moved around on tail-lifts and similar devices. But the corners would be havens for bacteria, which single disadvantage outweighs a multitude of advantages.) Let discipline in your cask-washing procedure slip even once and you risk sending out spoilt or infected beer, for which the retailer on the receiving end may never forgive you. Let it slip more than once and you risk being labelled as a dirty brewery, a reputation that is hard to shake off and that could kill your business (and I do know of one brewery near my home where this actually happened; other brewers will doubtless have other examples).

Bottling and Kegging

Not all your beer, of course, will go into casks. Depending on your business model, you might well sell as much in bottle as on draught. Bottled sales will almost certainly be very important to you, and the ramifications of bottling your beer will be dealt with in a later chapter. But there's a small but growing band of brewers interested mainly in foreign beer styles whose draught volume is not cask-conditioned but keg.

Keg Ales

Keg ale – filtered, pasteurised and dispensed under CO_2 or nitrogen – is the traditional enemy of the microbrewer. Indeed, the march of keg ales in the 1960s and 70s was the single most important driver both of CAMRA and of the microbrewing movement. But perhaps the real enemy isn't kegging technology per se, but the way it was exploited by the emerging national brewers at the time to foist on the public beers so weak and bland (the preservative qualities of kegging having rendered both alcohol and hops largely redundant) that children could legally drink them. But beyond these shores, serving draught beer under CO_2 pressure (if, in many cases, unpasteurised) is too natural to be thought worthy of comment. Indeed, most European vocabularies can't even distinguish between cask-conditioned beer and "brewery-conditioned" (techie speak for keg) beer: in French, for instance, all draught beer is "sous pression"; its logical opposite, "sans pression", is meaningless. And this is not necessarily a bar to serving good beer: I have frequently been served good sound beers such as De Koninck from Belgium and Sierra Nevada from the USA via keg dispense, and they are delicious.

Nevertheless, British microbrewers are indissolubly linked with cask-conditioned beer; and only a brave handful have strayed into the world of keg. Not least because, according to Richard Shardlow, the equipment you would need in order to refrigerate the beer adequately, to filter it through kieselguhr sheets, and finally to carbonate it to the high pressures necessary, would add something like 70 per cent to the cost of the brewery.

Brewing foreign beer styles, especially lager, involves another expense – if you're going to do it properly, that is. The "lagering" process is, essentially, a long, slow, secondary fermentation at low temperature, which can and should take between 60 and 90 days. So not only does making lager properly impact on your cash-flow; it also involves the purchase of temperature-controlled lagering tanks, which have to be kept refrigerated for anything up to three months. No wonder big brewers invariably slash their lagering times as much as possible and then claim it doesn't make any difference!.

Water Disposal

The last step in the brewing process is getting rid of the four-fifths of water you used but didn't brew with safely and hygienically. This water is going to be full of all sorts of pollutants, some of them organic – bits of hop-litter, protein, suspended solids – and some of them chemical, in particular, industrial-strength detergents. It may also have a low ph value.

You can't simply flush it down the drain – not, at any rate, without trade effluent consent from your water and sewerage provider. This comes with a detailed questionnaire about what sort of and how much effluent you propose to discharge; the advice is to be scrupulously honest, since if you breach the terms of your consent the sewerage provider not only can but probably will revoke it altogether (it can fine you, too). And since sewerage providers continually monitor discharges, you won't get away unnoticed with craftily tipping it away, either. Especially as it's going to be in the region of 450,000 gallons a year!

If you don't have mains drainage, you might consider planting a reed bed, for which you will need discharge consent from the Environment Agency. It is becoming increasingly popular to dispose of pollutants by creating a reed bed certain reeds can actually digest most if not all of the nasties a brewery generates, and the site itself will be a haven for wildlife and is therefore environmentally friendly. But there are drawbacks: you may not have enough space, and establishing a reed bed is a slow and expensive process. Most brewers who have done so seem satisfied with the result, though, and I have heard of only one instance where the reed bed's performance has been ruled inadequate by the Environment Agency. Two sites where you'll find more information about reed beds are **www.oceans-esu.com** and **www.sheepdrove.com**, and for more details on effluent discharge regulations visit the ever-helpful **www.businesslink.gov.uk** and follow the "health, safety, premises" link to "managing health, safety, environment". The Environment Agency also has a helpline: Tel 08708 806506.

Chapter Five
What to Brew

Wine snobs like to be dismissive of beer. Wine, they say, has infinite variety: red, white, rosé, still, sparkling, dry, sweet, New World, Old World, grown on chalk, grown on flint, grown in a hot climate, grown in a cool climate, grown on a south-facing slope, grown on a west-facing slope – and as for grape varieties, why, the permutations are endless! But as for beer... well, it's just beer, isn't it?

And if the big multinational brewers had their way, the wine snobs' scorn would be justified; 90 per cent of the world's beer is a pale (both in colour and in character) imitation of Czech or German pilsner, brewed (as one disgruntled ale brewer of my acquaintance once put it) from broken biscuits and old bus tickets, and served cold to mask the nasty tinny flavour that comes from too short a lagering period (which is the only flavour most of it has). It's made as cheaply as possible, using the lowest-grade ingredients available, taking every short cut in the brewing chemist's book, and intended to be the same wherever you go, whatever the label. However, some 90 per cent of the world's wine is pretty ropy, too, if you think about it, but as a craft brewer you stand shoulder to shoulder with the makers of the best 10 per cent. That's the bracket you want to be in; it's only a pity that the best of beers can't command the same price premium as the best of wines!

Don't, whatever you do, let the winemakers command the high ground, or get you down, or dent your self-esteem. Beer has just as many variations as wine – more, in fact – and you are setting out to master all of them. And in so doing, you have picked a harder row to hoe than any winemaker, for most of their work is done for them. All their ingredients come in one juicy little package, the grape, the sweetest fruit of them all, with liquor, fermentable material and aromàtics all contained in one skin. All they have to do is grow it – and in many cases they needn't even choose which variety to grow, so protected are they by regulation – press it and ferment it. If things go wrong, they can always blame the weather. Even the choices they do have to make – how to prune, whether and how long to macerate, what temperature to ferment at – are largely dictated by tradition and regulation. They don't have to make anything like the number of choices you will – how to treat your liquor; what grains to blend in your grist, and in what proportions; what hops to use for bitterness and aroma, and in what quantities, and at what stage of the boil to add them; what strain of yeast to propagate; even what styles of beer to brew. For you, the choices are infinite, and you are going to have to make them yourself.

Don't be daunted, though. For as a brewer you are free to make whatever you want.

- Pale
- Cloud
- Lemony
- Belgian-style wheat beer
- Baltic-style porter
- Bitter
- Mild
- IPA
- Brown ale
- Stout
- Barley wine
- Pilsner
- Bock
- Kölsch
- Alt
- Bière de garde

And as for ingredients! There's pale malt, brown malt, amber malt, black malt, crystal malt, chocolate malt, unmalted roasted barley, malted wheat, unmalted wheat, torrefied wheat, oats, rye, rice (if you're American), sorghum (if you're African), buckwheat (if you're gluten intolerant), invert sugar, candy sugar, honey... and we haven't even started on the hops yet!

As a home brewer, you may have played around with all of the above, and you might also have experimented with flavourings such as ginger and other spices, various fruits, exotic sugars and even spirits. Some of your experiments may have been, frankly, mistakes; others may have been triumphant successes. But as someone whose livelihood now depends not so much on what you can brew as on what you can sell, you're going to have to think hard about the range of beers you can realistically put out there in the market place.

Being thoughtful and realistic, though, needn't mean being too cautious. Yes, it's a foolhardy brewery that doesn't have a session bitter, a best bitter and perhaps a special bitter in its range. But in order to compete effectively – with the established regionals in the early days and more recently with each other – small brewers have always had to offer something different. And part of the glory of being a micro is that you can create something completely off the wall that will break even at only two or three barrels a week, whereas for someone like Greene King or Marston's it would have to sell two or three hundred barrels a week to be worthwhile.

The ability to brew interesting beers in small quantities has always been one of the small brewing sector's key advantages over the older and larger brewers. By the time the small brewing revolution came along, regional and national breweries had been rationalising their ranges for years. It was the downside of economy of scale: any beer style they couldn't brew in economic quantities was doomed, even though there might still be some demand for it. The tied house system and the closed mentality that it engendered meant there was no chance of two or three brewers combining to continue to offer, say, a single old ale between them: if they couldn't sustain a brand of their own, they wouldn't buy in from another brewer. The exception to this rule was Guinness, which as it was Irish and had no tied estate wasn't regarded as dangerous. So old-established breweries that hadn't had a dry stout of their own for generations would happily stock Guinness; and Guinness got a very healthy trade out of it, commanding five per cent of the entire British beer market. Why the brewers couldn't extend this logic to other beer styles remains a mystery; only recently have some family brewers that no longer produce a dark mild allowed those of their tenants who still have a demand for it to stock Bateman's DM.

Even in the early 1970s, though, most regionals produced quite a wide selection of draught beer. Mostly there was a light mild, a dark mild, a session bitter, a best bitter, a special bitter and sometimes a strong Christmas special. On the bottled side, most brewers, even quite small ones, still had a light or pale and a brown ale of their own (often just the bitter and the mild pasteurised and bottled), a sweet stout and a barley wine. But these were dying out, and regional brewers were increasingly concentrating on their core ranges. It was years before they noticed that the micros were succeeding by experimenting and diversifying; ever since then they too have been experimenting and diversifying, but you can safely say, in terms of beer styles at least, that where the micros have led the regionals have tended to follow.

For having the motive, means and opportunity to experiment has always suited the temperament of microbrewers in general. Few of them turned to brewing for the money; and the love that drives most of them has always been evident not only in the quality of what they brew, but also in their enthusiasm for different styles and genres. There's also, sometimes, a strong sense of fun in evidence. Yes, these people are trying to make a living. But for many of them the conventional ways of making a living have been crushing disappointments, and they're out to enjoy their working hours as much as their leisure time. This is a wholly laudable urge (which you must share, or you wouldn't have picked this book up), and it has produced some wholly laudable, if somewhat eccentric, beers.

For instance, there was the Kitchen Brewery of West Yorkshire, now defunct, whose beers were all brewed with various vegetables. Then there was a hotly contested but strictly unofficial competition in the early 1990s between Parish of Leicestershire and Sheffield's Frog & Parrot brewpub to see who could brew the stronger version of their respective barley wines, Baz's Bonce Blower and Roger & Out. I can't remember who managed to keep their yeast alive and fermenting for longest, but the eventual victor was, as I recall, over 20 per cent alcohol. I never got to try either contender. I did, however, try the ginger wheat beer produced by Salopian, always an experimental brewery. It was a delight, and I wish it were still being produced.

I could mention Hanby's Cherry Bomb; I could mention Nethergate Umbel Ale. I could go on and on, indeed; but in a way it would be misleading. For where the microbrewing industry as a whole has really led the way has not been in the production of eccentric one-offs, fascinating though they are, but in the setting of trends that the rest of the industry has followed.

Themed Ranges and Unusual Ingredients

The creative drive that has allowed smaller brewers to get away with experimenting is based on the inversion of the law of economy of scale described above: micros can make an acceptable margin on volumes that would be loss-making even for the smallest of regionals. This has proved very useful in preserving beer styles, especially the darker styles such as mild, barley wine and old ale that would otherwise have vanished completely or, indeed, that already had. The first micro-brewed beer to win CAMRA's Champion Beer of Britain Competition back in 1987 was Pitfield Brewery's Dark Star, a strong dark ale of a type not listed by a regional or national brewery within even the longest of living memories.

Since Dark Star's triumph, Pitfield has gone on to recreate a whole raft of historic styles using recipes that are mostly more than 150 years and in one case over 200 years old. Its XXXX Stock Ale at 10 per cent alcohol is a comparative stripling, being made to a recipe dating from 1896. The London Porter recipe comes from 1850, the IPA from 1837, the Amber Ale from 1830, and the Imperial Stout from 1792. There are many frustrations in trying to re-create old recipes. The brewers of yore were often frustratingly inexact in recording quantities, boil times, and so on; and the varieties, characteristics, and methods of processing malt and hops have changed so much over the generations that we really can't know what sugars and acids the ingredients of a century ago contained, and what flavours they would yield. Nevertheless, Pitfield is only one small brewer that has looked to the past to inspire the present. The Teignworthy Brewery at Tucker's Maltings in Newton Abbot, Devon, produces a similar range under the Edwin Tucker brand. And although its recipes are undated, beers such as Empress Russian Stout, East India Pale Ale and Old Walnut Brown root it firmly in the glory days of British brewing history. And mention must also go to Williams Brothers of Alloa, Scotland, which for many years and under several names has specialised in researching and re-creating historic Scottish beer styles remarkable for being flavoured with locally available alternatives to hops. Fraoch was the first and best-known and claims to re-create Pictish heather ale. Almost nothing is known about Pictish heather ale, as you might guess; it may even be that the heather was not actually used as a flavouring agent at all, but that its microfauna included wild yeasts and that sprigs of it were therefore used to ferment the beer. Be that as it may, Fraoch (pronounced "frook") is an excellent beer that has won friends around the world and is widely exported. Its stablemates – Alba, flavoured with spruce tips; Grozet, flavoured with gooseberries; and Ebulum, flavoured with elderberries – are not as big sellers as Fraoch but are just as... interesting.

Theming

Theming the range in this way is an enjoyable and effective way of creating a strong identity for the brewery, and of course the theme needn't be retro. In most cases it's only the beers' names that are themed, while the recipes themselves are unconnected. An outstanding example of this is Triple fff of Alton, Hampshire, whose beers are all named after classic rock singles and album tracks – hence a range that includes Witch's Promise, a 6 per cent Christmas special; Moondance, a 4.2 per cent best bitter; and Pressed Rat & Warthog, a 3.8 per cent dark mild. (Bryncelyn of Swansea, another pop-pickin' micro, has a range themed entirely on Buddy Holly.) Abbeydale of Sheffield has a huge range of beers all on a monastic theme – Absolution, Matins and so forth, although what any God-fearing abbot or prior would make of a beer called Black Mass I leave to your imagination. More common are beers named after local landmarks or local events, or even the locals themselves (not necessarily living ones, though: Wood's Local Heroes range commemorated South Shropshire worthies going all the way back to King Caractacus).

There are brewers for whom theming means more than just a common source of brand names: try any beer from Rooster's of Harrogate, for instance, and you know you're in for something hoppy. For owner Sean Franklin is a hop enthusiast, who pioneered the use of exotic American and other New World varieties. Other brewers have also looked abroad to find a common identity for their ranges. In some ways this is counterintuitive, for the genesis of the new wave brewers lies in the consumer revolt of the 1970s against keg dispense and dreadful British-brewed lagers (which in those days were often no more than very pale ales served ice-cold). In the cynical and exploitative hands of the big bad brewers of 30–40 years ago, both the "k" word and the "l" word became instantly recognisable signifiers of weak beer, brewed as cheaply as possible, and as bland as the brewer's chemists could make it. But in time, more widely travelled beer lovers – both drinkers and brewers – came to realise three important truths: that not all foreign beer is "lager"; that not all foreign beer is bad; and that if beer is brewed well, it won't be ruined by being dispensed under CO_2 pressure.

Continental Styles

These realisations have prompted many British microbrewers to experiment with continental styles, with varying degrees of authenticity and commercial success. The two don't always go hand in hand, mind: Pilgrim Brewery's excellent and extremely authentic Bavarian-style wheat beer, Springbock, is no longer brewed; while Harviestoun Brewery's lager, Schiehallion, also excellent but not nearly so authentic, wins prize after prize and goes from strength to strength. Many other microbreweries brew lagers and other German-style products with varying degrees of success, and thanks to the German influence, wheat, malted or not, has become a commonplace ingredient in British brewing. (Many regionals also brew foreign-style beers, either under their own names or under licence from foreign proprietors. Holsten, Kingfisher, Asahi, Red Stripe, Ayingerbrau – you may think they're imported, but in reality they come from exotic locations like Faversham, Tadcaster and Bedford.)

Only a handful of breweries have gone beyond producing one or two examples of foreign styles, though, and most of those that have are boutique breweries where the emphasis is as much on the style of retailing as on the beer itself. Freedom Brewery in Putney, west London, brews three lagers that conform with the German purity law, the Reinheitsgebot, that forbids the use of anything other than malt, hops, water and yeast in brewing. Cotswold Brewery in Foscot, Oxfordshire, only produces lager. Mash in Great Portland Street, central London, is a US-style boutique brewery with a wheat beer, a Pils, and a fruit beer on its list alongside a porter and an IPA. Meantime in Greenwich, run by German-trained brewer Alastair Hook, produces authentic Kölsch and Altbier for Sainsbury's and a US-inspired range of specialities including chocolate and coffee-flavoured beers. West Brewing in Glasgow lists a hefeweisse or cloudy wheat beer; a Helles or everyday pale beer; a Dunkles or dark lager; and a Dunkel Hefeweisse, or dark wheat beer with yeast sediment. Finally there's Zerodregrees with branches in London, Bristol and Reading brewing German-style wheat beer, Pilsner and dark lager.

Interestingly, although many British brewers are prepared to try their hands at German beer styles, nobody I know of has dared have a go at anything Belgian yet – except, that is, fruit-flavoured concoctions whose base beer is nothing a genuine Belgian would recognise. Are Belgian beers simply too idiosyncratic and too formidable to imitate? Is the prize so far out of reach that to make a grab for it and miss is to risk a nasty fall? Whatever the reason, the field is open for a British-brewed abbey ale, strong blonde beer or oud bruin. Are you up to it?

Golden Ales

Earlier, I spoke about new brewers setting trends that regionals have followed. Would Fuller's, I wonder, have released its superb London Porter, or Marston's its authentic and stunning Old Empire IPA, if micros such as Pitfield had not delved into the brewing books of yesteryear in search of forgotten flavours? Would Badger (as Hall & Woodhouse likes to be known) have brought out its extraordinary peach-blossom beer if micros had not experimented with fruit flavours first? Would we have Young's Waggle Dance or Fuller's Organic Honeydew if Enville Ales had not pioneered the use of honey in brewing?

Regionals, though, are still pretty conservative in their attitude towards speciality beers. Mostly, given the downside of economy of scale already mentioned, their regular ranges only encompass the more popular styles; and when they do try something outrageous, it's normally as a seasonal special. But there are two trends established by microbrewers that regionals have followed enthusiastically: pretty much everybody now brews a "golden ale" of one sort or another; and regionals by and large are pursuing the green agenda as energetically as they can.

The emergence of golden ales over the past 20-odd years has been perhaps the climax of the shift away from dark beers in modern ale brewing. Porters died out in the First World War , thanks to malt rationing; and stout would have gone the same way if the government hadn't been too nervous to ration Irish brewers as well as mainland ones. Dark mild, once country's leading beer style, was a casualty – although its death has been hideously long drawn-out – of post- Second World War prosperity. Bitter or pale ale, as it used to be more widely called, was the toff's drink, expensive and aspirational, and started outselling mild in the 1950s. Lager pretty much finished it off in the 1970s, and today it is a minority style, brewed in significant volume only in Leeds and Manchester.

Golden ales as a definable beer style first emerged some 20 years ago, when Somerset's Exmoor Brewery produced Exmoor Gold and Hop Back of Salisbury came out with Summer Lightning. There had been very pale beers before then:

Boddington's from Manchester was perhaps the best-known, but Wem Pale from north Shropshire was just as light-coloured, and so was the main beer from the famous Three Tuns brewpub in south Shropshire. Green's of Luton, Burt's on the Isle of Wight, and Holdens of Dudley were among the many brewers that had produced beer brands with the words "gold" or "golden" in their names in the preceding 30-odd years. But from the early 1990s onwards, ale brewers increasingly looked to much lighter-coloured and lighter-bodied beers, often with a hop aroma so pronounced as to be almost unbalanced, to challenge lager's strengthening grip on the market. (I'm proud to say that I was the first to identify golden ale as a separate beer style in print, in a 1994 issue of *Brewers Guardian* with a précis in the *Journal of the Institute of Brewing* May–June 1995.) The turning point for golden ales, though, came in 1996 when an extraordinarily hot summer plunged ale-brewing into crisis. It wasn't just that ale-drinkers turned to chilled lager as the temperature soared; it was also that the weather ruthlessly exposed weaknesses in the supply chain. Ale that had been virtually cooked in warehouses and drays arrived at the pub as an undrinkable soup; there were even tales of casks bursting in the heat.

Before then, micros had been more interested in re-creating the stronger, darker styles of the past, and the listing sections of successive *Good Beer Guides* are packed with stouts, porters, barley wines and old ales. The 1996 *Guide*, compiled in spring that year, has only 22 microbrewers producing ales with the words "gold" or "golden" in their names, and just three regionals, Belhaven, Gale's and Timothy Taylor (although Elgood's, Fuller's, and Wadworth had also brought out golden ales under different names: Barleymead, IPA and Summersault). After 1996, though, the balance began to change. Two years after that summer, the *Guide* listed 55 gold or golden beers from micros and 11 from regionals; the 2007 edition lists 134 and 16 respectively. Golden ales have won the Champion Beer of Britain title every year since 2001, prompting CAMRA to recognise the style with a category of its own in 2005 (since when Crouch Vale Brewers Gold has won twice in a row). So golden ale is a style pretty much invented by microbrewers that has come to a position of huge importance in the ale market.

Case Study: Brewery with a Huge Range – Bartram's, Bury St Edmunds, Suffolk

When you look at the list of beers Marc Bartram produces on his five-barrel plant on the Rougham Estate in Suffolk, all you can say is: "Wow!"

The *Good Beer Guide* lists 22 regular brews ranging from Marld at 3.4 per cent alcohol to Comrade Bill Bartram's Egalitarian Anti-Imperialist Soviet Stout (Marc's take on the classic Russian Imperial stouts) at 6.9 per cent. Added to that is his Zodiac range, all 12 of which use the same malt grist but have different hopping regimes, and five seasonal specials.

It's not just the number of different beers that Marc brews that's impressive, though: it's the huge variations in style. His big sellers are Little Green Man, a 3.8 per cent golden bitter; The Bee's Knees, a honey-flavoured best bitter at 4.2 per cent; Cherry Stout, which is self-explanatory, at 4.8 per cent; and the aforementioned Comrade Bill's. But his other styles include the ginger and lemon-flavoured Cat's Whiskers; the gooseberry-flavoured Grozet; Catherine Bartram's, a hoppy IPA; Jester Quick One, using American hops; the straightforward Captain Bill Bartram's Best Bitter; Coal Porter; Damson Stout – need I go on?

Marc's then, is a very different approach from the strategy adopted by more cautious – and, Marc admits, more versed in marketing – brewers with industry backgrounds such as Butcombe and Black Sheep, who started by focusing on a single brand and only then establishing a wider range.

"It all comes down to your attitude to marketing," says Marc, whose career before starting Bartram's has included stints in psychiatric nursing, local government and cleaning toilets. (He also used to design ready meals for Marks & Spencer but, he says, "the tastings weren't as much fun as they are in brewing!".)

Marc first discovered that there was more to beer than just a few pints of whatever happened to be on offer at Hull Beer Festival in 1977. "I used to go out on pub crawls with the lads around Hull, and there'd be pubs owned by three or four different breweries but the beer was very much secondary," he says. But after that 1977 epiphany he started seeking out different beers in local pubs and then, as a keen home brewer, experimenting with different recipes and ingredients.

"I was always searching out different styles and looking up ancient recipes, and diversity has been my thing since then," he says.

Marc's passion for diversity is twinned with an interest in art to create his huge and idiosyncratic range. He likes artists to come up with labels for his beers, which are mostly bottled. The Zodiac range was actually suggested by a local artist, while both the label and the name for The Cat's Whiskers came from a student of commercial art. Marc told him that the recipe included ginger and lemons, and the student came up with a painting of a ginger cat reclining on a bed of lemons. "The people who buy it often do so simply because they love cats," says Marc. "They might not know anything about beer, but the label attracts them; and if they like the beer they come back for more."

But Marc acknowledges that he could never sustain a range of anything like the size if his beers weren't mostly sold in bottle-conditioned form. He has a nucleus of eight or nine publicans who stock his beers, but most of his business is with farm shops and farmers' markets.

"For instance, I only brew a mild every two or three months, and I'll sell a few firkins to my regular accounts and bottle the rest," he says. "It's the shelf-life, you see. I couldn't sell anything like my five-barrel minimum run in cask-conditioned form before it went off; but as most of my sales are in bottle, I don't have to."

www.bartramsbrewery.co.uk

The Range of Beers

So far we have concentrated on the huge diversity of beer styles available to you, and there are many microbrewers who have taken the fullest possible advantage of it. Bartram's of Bury St Edmunds, Suffolk, for instance, has 22 regular brews in its portfolio ranging from a 3.4 per cent alcohol dark mild to a 6.9 per cent stout and including a porter, a honey beer and a gooseberry beer. It also produces five seasonal specials and an entirely separate range under the Zodiac brand. At the other end of the alphabet, Warcop of Wentlooge, Gwent, brews an astonishing 31 regulars and six seasonals. This is rather reminiscent of some Belgian brewers who produce literally dozens of different brews, although in many cases these are actually the same beers rebadged for individual customers. Rebadging is not a practice that has caught on to any great extent in Britain, partly because there are fewer local wholesalers. But some UK brewers will either rebadge a beer as a favoured customer's house bitter, or even make a special blend of one or more of its regular beers for the same purpose. This may be a bit of a performance, but if it means guaranteeing a regular reorder it may well be worth the slight additional effort.

There is, of course, the opposite approach of brewing one superb beer and focusing all your efforts on building it up as the leading brand in its region. Black Sheep of Masham, North Yorkshire, Butcombe of Bristol, and Abbey Ales of Bath are all outstanding examples of breweries that have adopted this strategy, only starting to extend their ranges one their main brands have become firmly established. A common factor linking these three is that their founders – Paul Theakston of Black Sheep, Simon Whitmore of Butcombe, and Alan Morgan of Abbey Ales – were all extremely well-known and senior personalities in the brewing industries in their districts before they struck out on their own. They knew the free trade and the free trade knew them – and trusted them. They knew what the free trade needed, and how to tackle it. They didn't need gimmicks or novelties to help them stand out from the rest of the pack: pinning all their faith on a single beer marked them out as serious players with a serious product. They generated a confidence in themselves and their single brands that has turned out to be entirely justified. I can think of a handful of similar cases, but you have to be a very special person to succeed with the single-brand strategy; and anyway, for most small brewers the diversity is all part of the fun.

Few go the extremes that Bartram's and Warcop do, but many approach double figures in their regular ranges and produce a long list of seasonals and one-offs as well. Seasonal beers in particular have a long and respectable history – or at least, winter warmers and Christmas specials do. Generations of Londoners have eagerly awaited the arrival of winter, whose fogs and chills and long dark evenings are God's way of telling them that Young's Winter Warmer has arrived. Other regionals have also traditionally brewed strong ales for the season. Morrell's Varsity was legendary; McMullen's Stronghart was the first be lauded as "liquid Christmas pudding", although many others have hijacked the description since; and Greene King Strong Suffolk, occasionally allowed out on draught at the right time of year, is a fascinating and unique survival of the centuries-old practice of blending strong old ale with fresh pale.

Seasonal Specials

And it was the regional brewers who first extended the idea of a seasonal special to cover spring, summer and autumn as well as winter. Harvey's of Lewes claims to have been the first to launch a seasonal special – Tom Paine, a summer ale named after Lewes's most famous son, appeared in 1991. The idea quickly spread. Seasonal ales not only gave the brewers' own tenants and direct-delivered free trade accounts some variety in response to the diversity offered by the micros, it also gave the brewers a palette of novelty beers to offer the wholesale trade, which was then a new opportunity for them. Some regionals, Bateman's, for example, extended the idea beyond the merely seasonal and offered monthly specials, too. The frenzy has somewhat abated in recent years: some two-thirds of the regionals and just over half of all microbrewers still produce seasonal ranges; but in many case the "range" is a single beer, normally for Christmas.

Part of the problem is that without a definite tradition of different seasonal beers such as exists in many continental markets, brewers don't really have a clear idea of which style best suits which season. Winter ales have always tended to be strong and dark, although Young's Winter Warmer was originally the brewer's stab at a Burton-style pale ale and is only 5 per cent alcohol. The reigning champion Winter Beer of Britain at time of writing is another pale ale, although at 8.5 per cent alcohol Oakham Ales' Attila from Peterborough can at least claim to be strong. And most brewers have substantially reduced both the strength and darkness of their winter beers in recent years: they may be delicious, they may keep out the cold, but most people can only manage one pint, and where's the profit in that? Summer beers are another no-brainer that turns out on inspection to be more problematical: originally, they were in the main straightforward competitors to lager, very pale, quite aromatic and best served cold. But they failed to woo lager drinkers (by and large an incurious lot, not much given to experiment), and as golden ales became a mainstream style, they lost any claim to seasonality. As for spring and autumn, they have no seasonal styles; so with no traditional template as a guide, brewers simply produce whatever seems most suitable to them. One of the best spring beers is Harvey's Knots of May, a light mild which coincides handily with CAMRA's Mild Month campaign every May; and Shepherd Neame's Late Red is a splendid consolation for the shortening days of autumn. But no ancient tradition makes the one a spring beer and the other an autumn beer. If you are going to produce a seasonal range, therefore, you have *carte blanche* as to what to brew when, and no limits but your own imagination.

One-offs, especially in aid of good causes, are an altogether more straightforward business and well worth investigating. However, they tend in the main to be bottled and will therefore be considered in the relevant chapter. One exception to this is the CAMRA Festival Special. CAMRA branches like to have one, two or in odd cases even more exclusive ales brewed for the annual beer festivals. Often the chairman and other branch committee worthies will descend on the brewery or breweries lucky enough to be chosen as the provider, and "help" with the mashing. Often, too, by a mysterious and undoubtedly psychic process, the specials will emerge as medal-winners in the Beer of the Festival competition. On the whole, therefore, and despite any irritation that might be occasioned by the branch's "help", it's well worth accepting an invitation to brew a festival special. Whatever you send to the festival will sell out, and any surplus you brew is likely to be accepted by the local free trade – especially if it wins a medal.

Pursuing the Green Agenda

Not surprisingly, microbrewers have also been keen to pursue the green agenda with all its various headings: vegetarian, low-impact, organic – they're all values that can be applied to brewing.

Finding beers, particularly cask ales, that are suitable for vegans and vegetarians is surprisingly difficult. This is because the most effective substance for clearing or fining beer is isinglass, a collagen derived from various species of fish. Isinglass is a gel that, when added to the finished beer, flocculates the live yeast into a spongy mass that sinks; the beer can be strained off it. Of course, little or none of it remains in the beer – that's the whole point, after all. But vegetarians still object, correctly, that a living creature has had to die merely in order to clarify a beer. Ironically, isinglass is more rarely used in keg or bottled beer, which is filtered and therefore shouldn't need fining; and a yeasty sediment is an expected feature of bottle-conditioned beer, so that shouldn't really need fining either. But cask ale does; and while there are alternatives, they're not as effective. Filtration agents such as kieselguhr and bentonite, widely used in the wine industry, operate in a different way and can affect the character of the beer; while carragheenan or Irish moss effectively removes protein that would cause a haze but isn't so effective at dealing with yeast. Still, they are used with some success by many brewers, so if you want to appeal to vegans and vegetarians, give them a try.

Keeping it Local

There are many ways in which you can reduce the overall environmental impact of your brewery. Brewing uses a lot of energy, both to move liquids around and to heat them up and cool them down. In your brewery design you can incorporate the same sort of energy-reduction measures that might be used in any other processing plant: good insulation, short pipe-runs, solar panels and wind turbines, which will reduce your electricity bill as well as your carbon footprint. But cutting your food miles will be much harder.

One way of reducing food miles is to concentrate your sales effort on as small an area as possible. But given the structure of the trade this isn't always easy: you have to sell where you can, and if that means long road trips, either on your own truck or on the wholesaler's, there's not a lot you can do about it. Sourcing your materials locally is another possibility, but equally problematic. There's a growing trend among brewers to buy their barley from local growers – and it's not just microbrewers who are doing it, either. Shepherd Neame in Kent, Black Sheep in North Yorkshire, and St Austell Brewery in Cornwall are all keenly developing local sources of supply. But wherever you buy your barley, it all has to go to the maltster to be processed; and as there are only four traditional floor maltings left – Tucker's in Devon, Warminster in Wiltshire, Crisp's in Norfolk, and Fawcett's in North Yorkshire – the trip there and back can be a pretty long one.

Hops, too, can have a long journey. It's all very well for brewers in Kent or Hereford & Worcester to boast about their use of local hops, but they have Britain's last hop-growers right on their doorsteps, and everybody else has to buy further afield. Having said that, hops were once grown in almost every county in Britain, including Scotland, and there's no practical reason why they shouldn't be again. The first commercial hop garden in East Anglia for many generations has just been re-established in Suffolk, and small brewers in other parts of the country, such as the Atlantic Brewery in Newquay, Cornwall, are setting about planting their own. An added advantage of planting new hop gardens is that they're likely to be pest-free, so it's certainly worth considering – especially if you know a farmer or market gardener who is keen to diversify.

Going Organic

Another part of the green agenda that you can pursue is the use of organic ingredients. Organic beers are becoming more and more popular and widespread: many brewers, even quite big ones such as Fuller's, now have at least one organic beer in their range; others have gone over to organic ingredients entirely.

The first British organic beer that I know of was brewed by the now-defunct Ross Brew House of Bristol in the late 1980s; Golden Promise, launched in 1991 by Edinburgh's Caledonian Brewery, was the first to gain national distribution. Sourcing organic ingredients was not easy: the malt was made from a strain of barley also named Golden Promise and developed for the whisky industry, while the hops had to be imported from New Zealand. The dearth of suitable ingredients meant that others were slow to follow Caledonian's example but more than 25 years on organic barley is easily available, although supplies of British-grown organic hops have not kept pace with demand, they can always be eked out with imports. There are still only seven all-organic breweries in Britain, and three or four more that are nearly there, but other brewers between them produce a couple of dozen brands at least, and several more are imported.

The demand for organic ingredients has imposed a new discipline on hop merchants and maltsters, who previously would process raw materials from different growers all mixed together. Now they have learnt to keep organic hops and barley separate from non-organic produce, a good habit that has had an equally valuable but perhaps unforeseen side-effect. For they have

CAMRA & SIBA Awards

Both CAMRA and SIBA run awards schemes. The SIBA scheme is the more straightforward. It's run on a regional basis, and member-brewers may enter any of their beers in the appropriate class. Regional winners go through to a national final held as part of SIBA's annual general meeting each spring.

CAMRA's scheme is less transparent. Local branches make Beer of the Festival awards at local events, but brewers don't enter their beers. Instead, competitors are chosen by CAMRA members by varied and mysterious means. Beer of the Festival awards are decided by equally varied methods from blind tasting to polls of festival visitors, and go through to either of the two national competitions, both of which are judged by tasting panels. Individual CAMRA members also have a chance to get a place in the competitions for their favourite beers via voting forms published in the Campaign's newspaper, *What's Brewing*. Branch tasting panels have a role too: their selections, whittled down through regional competitions, also go forward to the national competitions. This confusing system does not please the brewers a great deal, but it's CAMRA's business and there's not much they can do about it.

The Champion Winter Beer of Britain (WBoB) is chosen at the National Winter Ales Festival in January, while the Champion Beer of Britain (CBoB) is chosen at the Great British Beer Festival (GBBF) in August. Confusingly, the winners of the WBoB competition are also eligible to win the CBoB title; but the winners of the Bottled Beer competition held at GBBF aren't.

CAMRA's categories are detailed below and note that anything unusual you brew, will be lumped in with the catch-all "speciality" category, which are increasing both in number and diversity. A gold, silver, and bronze are awarded in each, and the medallists in each category go forward to the final judging panel to win overall gold, silver, and bronze.

Judged at the Great British Beer Festival: Mild; Bitter (3.4-3.9% alcohol); Best Bitter (4-5%); Strong Bitter (5%-plus); Golden Ale (3.5-5.3%); Specialities; Bottle-Conditioned Beer. Judged at the National Winter Ales Festival: Old Ale/Strong Mild; Stout/Porter; Barley Wine.

www.camra.co.uk
www.siba.co.uk

also learnt to process the produce of individual growers separately, so that full traceability is not only possible but commonplace these days. This means that if you only want to use malt and hops from growers in your locality, you can. Of course, they will still have had to travel to the oasts (or kilns in Hereford and Worcester) or maltings and then to your brewery, so the actual road miles involved will not have been reduced in the slightest. But discerning consumers these days put a considerable premium on traceability, and it may well be worth your while taking advantage of the fact. For although it's not easy being green, people will love you for it.

Since 1993, Britain has conformed to European Regulation 2092/91 regarding certification of organic producers. If you are brewing an all-organic beer as part of a wider range, it is not strictly necessary to be certified organic: you can get away – and many do – with simply stating on your labels that all your ingredients are from certified organic producers. However, to take full advantage of the possibilities offered by "going organic", it's probably best to get yourself certified. To contact any of the 10 certifying bodies (it's not a Soil Association monopoly!) approved by the Department for the Environment, Food, & Rural Affairs (DEFRA), visit **www.defra.gov.uk/farm/organic/standards/certbodies/approved.htm**.

Ingredients: Malt

The malt is, of course, the heart of the beer, providing all the fermentable materials that create the alcohol (unless you're using brewing sugars as well), the residual sugars that create the mouthfeel, and many of the flavour components.

In Britain we have always tended to think of malt as coming entirely from barley, except for the handful of oats used to give some stouts a smooth, silky texture. Until recently, that is. Wheat is now a widely used grain in British brewing, so widely used, in fact, that British wheat beer ranks as a fourth category in its own right alongside Belgian, Bavarian and Berliner. Typically, the British style doesn't use nearly as much wheat as its continental cousins because the desired effect is a lighter body rather than the clove, vanilla, banana and bubblegum flavours that tend to come with higher proportions.

Malt is made, as we have discovered, by tricking barley into beginning to germinate and thereby starting the process of converting the starch in the grain into fermentable sugar. The process involves a lot of soaking and drying, and traditionally the drying was done by heaping the damp grain in rows on a floor for two or three weeks before drying it over a fire. The rows of grain would be turned by a man plodding up and down pulling a device like a cross between a wheelbarrow and a rake; and as is the way of things, this method of "floor-malting" has been mechanised almost out of existence. Most small brewers, though, like to get their malt from the country's four surviving floor maltings, not because the quality of the beer made from traditionally malted barley is necessarily better than beer brewed from machine-made malt, but because they say it's easier to work with. What's true is that all four floor maltings are comparatively small concerns and therefore buy in smaller batches, which they can ipso facto inspect more thoroughly, and that the man plodding up and down turning the malt is simultaneously conducting a continuous quality check. Some Scottish brewers, at the time of writing, were even approaching the few distilleries that still floor-malt their own barley to see whether they'd care to try producing ale malts alongside their whisky malts. Unfortunately most of these distilleries are owned by global corporations which still tend to seek to concentrate production on a handful of huge sites; perhaps the modest extra profits generated by making and selling ale malt on the side might keep some of these traditional little whisky maltings open for a few years more?

Types of Malt

Pale malts of various types, principally lager malt, pale ale malt and wheat malt, kilned at low temperature to preserve the golden colour of the grain, are the base on which nearly all modern beers are founded. The grists of even the blackest of beers generally have pale malts as their main constituents, the colour being supplied by surprisingly small doses of dark malt.

These are the malts that, in the late 18th and early 19th century, changed the world of beer forever. Previously, malt had been dried over peat, straw, dried furze or broom, wood or charcoal and tended to be dark, smoked, and, thanks to the difficulty of controlling the temperature of such fires, uneven in colour, flavour and moisture content. When in the middle of the 17th century the maltsters of Derbyshire started exhausting local sources of timber, they found that the locally mined hard coal produced a low-sulphur smokeless coke ideal for malting. By the end of the century malt was being dried over coke in neighbouring counties and also in parts of Scotland (although peat remained the preferred fuel there). Coke gave an even and controllable heat

Case Study: Going Organic – Pitfield Brewery, North Weald, Essex

It's a long way from the mean streets of London N1 to the rural tranquillity and rolling countryside of North Essex. But that's the journey veteran microbrewer Martin Kemp and trusty henchman Andy Skene made in 2006 when, 24 years after Pitfield started brewing in a former leather goods (!) warehouse in Hoxton, they upped sticks and moved to – well, to the sticks.

The brewery's first move was to Great Horkesley and an enormous but near-derelict market garden that once produced tomatoes by the bushel but was scheduled to be demolished to make way for a brand-new eco-friendly heritage centre of which Pitfield – which makes organic country wines as well as organic beers – was to have been the showpiece. Alas, the project became mired in planning red tape, and in 2008 Pitfield moved again, to a 25-acre organic farm in North Weald.

The move was a symbolic one for Pitfield, whose main outlet had always been the legendary Beer Shop in Pitfield Street. Hoxton, though, had famously become trendy and had consequently been regenerated, a process which included making parking anywhere the shop impossible. At the same time the brewery – which made history as the first micro to win CAMRA's Champion Beer of Britain competition, with Dark Star in 1987 – had gradually gone organic. Added to the virtual destruction of the shop's viability, its new green credentials made a move to the country a logical necessity.

It was in 1999 that Martin decided to try his hand at a totally natural beer, brewed without additives of any kind. At the time, organic ingredients were hard to come by but a maltster in Berwick was producing a whisky malt made from the organic Golden Promise barley. Most of it was earmarked either for distillers or for Edinburgh's Caledonian Brewery for its pioneering pale ale of the same name. But Martin managed to secure a single tonne – which he had to go to Berwick himself to collect – and, with imported New Zealand Hallertau hops from Charles Faram of Worcester, he set about producing Eco Warrior.

At the same time Geetie Singh and Esther Boulton were starting their all-organic Singhboulton pub company, and they contacted Martin to see if he could produce a house bitter for them. Geetie suggested that Pitfield should go for full organic certification; and as Martin had happened to meet a representative of one of the government-approved certifying bodies, Organic Farmers & Growers (OF&G), at an organic show in Brighton, he approached it. It wasn't an easy process.

"Ours was a pretty straightforward case but it still took time and money," he says. "OF&G inspected the brewery and conducted a paper audit, looking through all our invoices and so on to check that all our suppliers were certified organic. That took a day. Then DEFRA, the Department of Agriculture, had to inspect the inspection, which took another day. There's also an annual fee, which depends on how much you produce – we're a five-barrel brewery, brewing two or three times a week, and our annual fee is about £600, so it's not cheap."

Pitfield also pays a premium for its supplies. Organic pale malt costs £120 a tonne more than non-organic and the coloured malts, which are used in much smaller quantities, are £2–300 a tonne more expensive. Organic hops cost about £14 kilo compared to £5–10 for non-organic, but in the pub trade there's no organic premium on the wholesale price. That was another reason for Pitfield's move away from London. Martin still supplies the London pubs that took his beers in cask before the move, but every week he now sets up his stall at three farmers' markets where his overheads are much lower and he can charge up to £2.50 a bottle for his beers. That his bottled beers are all bottle-conditioned and made without fish-derived finings, and therefore vegan-friendly, both help establish Pitfield's green credentials. A new home in the country somehow adds to the proposition.

The switch into organic production has not been without its problems – although now he's a regular he can at least depend on supplies of ingredients – but Martin reckons it's been worth it.

"There are negatives, not least the increased costs, but on the positive side we have established ourselves in a good niche and we now have a name as an organic and vegan-friendly producer," he says. "But part of our success depends on the fact that we are small and intend to stay small. We only brew five barrels at a time, so we can get enough regular supplies to ensure production; and we can sell all we can brew."

www.pitfieldbeershop.co.uk

and worked at lower temperatures than wood or charcoal, making it possible to kiln malts that were pale, clean-tasting and uniform, and produced crystal-clear golden or amber beers. Daniel Defoe was an early supporter of strong Derby pale ales; and Burton brewers were exporting pale ales to the Baltic before the Napoleonic War and to the East Indies after it. In the early 1840s the brewers of Pilsen in what is now the Czech Republic also discovered the potential of pale malt kilned over coke; lager as we know it was born.

Low-temperature kilning preserves the saccharifying enzymes in the malt, as well as its original colour. This means that the malt can be used with other unmalted grains such as wheat, corn and rice.

You will probably learn all you need to know about all the different types of malt and how to handle them during your training. Here, though, is a brief reminder of the wonderful variety of malts available to you, listed for convenience only by degrees lovibond, the scale used to measure the malt's colour.

- **Lager malt** (2°L): the malt that produces the world's most popular beer-style – pale gold, mid-flavoured, Pilsner derivatives – can also be used as the base malt for other beers, even dark ales. Its diastatic capability makes it ideal for use with low-enzyme speciality malts or unmalted grains.
- **Wheat malt** (2°L): has a high protein content, causing wheat beer's characteristic haze. It also has good head-retention qualities: torrefied wheat is often used in small quantities for the purpose. Low in polyphenols, it is often used in modest quantities by British brewers to lighten the body of their golden ales. It has to be mashed with grains that supply a husk bed (lager malt is ideal).
- **Pale ale malt** (3°L): the malt most commonly associated with British ale is kilned at a slightly higher temperature than lager malt for a fuller flavour and darker colour. It also tends to have fewer enzymes than lager malt, although still sufficient to allow the use of adjuncts in the mash.
- **Rye malt** (3°L): can be used in small quantities for its spicy flavour.
- **Vienna malt** (3–7°L): produces the full-bodied amber or reddish beers that were once popular in Austria but survive mainly in Mexico, Dos Equis and Negra Modelo being noted modern examples.
- **Mild ale malt** (4°L): although most surviving milds are dark, the base

malt isn't, creating an amber or copper-coloured wort and producing a dry, full-flavoured beer, with brown, chocolate and/or black malts used sparingly to give the characteristic colour. Mild ale malt is also a good base for stronger ales, whether coloured or not.

- **Carapils malt** (7°L): kilned at low temperature, it adds sweetness, smoothness, and body to pale ales and lagers without affecting the colour or adding caramel notes. Also aids head retention.
- **Munich malt** (10–20°L): an aromatic lager malt that yields a dark reddish-orange wort and a slightly sweet caramel flavour. Munich malt comes in two grades, light and dark.
- **Crystal malt** (10–20°L): produced in such a way that most of the starch is not saccharified and is then caramelised during kilning, crystal malts are very widely used in small additions in ales and lagers to give extra sweetness and flavour ranging in character from delicate light honey to rich toffee flavours. Crystal malts also thicken the mouthfeel, and create an attractive bronze colour.
- **Biscuit malt** (25°L): a base malt toasted and roasted to give the beer a biscuity flavour and a deep amber colour.
- **Victory malt** (25°L): a roasted malt similar to biscuit malt but with a nuttier taste. Also adds orange highlights to the colour.
- **Amber malt** (30°L): similar to mild ale or Vienna malt, but with more colour and a biscuity flavour. Used mainly in old and brown ales.
- **Brown malt** (65°L): traditionally kilned over a wood fire for a smoky flavour; used very sparingly in stouts and porters.
- **Special Belgian malt** (220°L): a rare malt with a nutty, roasted sweetness that in small quantities enriches brown ales and porters, and in larger proportions adds a plummy, vinous quality to barley wines and strong winter beers.
- **Chocolate malt** (350–400°L): its smooth roasted flavour and brownish-black colour with ruby highlights make chocolate malt irreplaceable in dark ales such as milds, stouts and porters; it can also be used in dark lagers.
- **Black malt** (500–600°L): even darker than chocolate malt, with a sharp, burnt, acidic flavour that can take the sweet edge off some stronger beers.

Unmalted Grains

Malting is the process of artificially stimulating the enzymes that in nature convert the grain's starch content into soluble sugar that the yeast can get at. Not all brewing grains need to be malted, though. Up to 50 per cent of the grist of most Belgian *witbier* is unmalted wheat, but the malted barley that makes up the other half has enough enzymes to convert the whole mash. Unmalted oats are added to some beers, especially stout, not for their negligible fermentable material but for their husky roughness, which "scrubs" microscopic particles out of the wort for a silky smooth finish. Maize and rice are almost flavourless, but are high in convertible starch. They have no enzymes of their own, but as with Belgian wheat beer, the barley malts they are mashed with have enough surplus enzymes for the whole mash. They are also very cheap, which is why they are so common in beers from the poorer Latin American countries (and in many mainstream US lagers, but that's another story). Finally, there's roasted barley, which is virtually burnt to an inky black 550°L and has an acrid charred-wood flavour. It's the signature flavour of Guinness and, to a lesser extent, Murphy's and Beamish as well.

Brewing Sugars

The use of sugar in brewing has been legal in Britain since 1847 and is now widespread throughout the world. Some brewers oppose the practice completely, because they say sugar is only used as a cheap source of fermentable material to pad out the more expensive malt; and in some cases this is true. American beers in particular use large amounts of rice or corn-based syrups, and are characteristically light-bodied (or indeed bland) as a result.

However, there are other more legitimate and indeed time-honoured uses for various types of sugar in judicious quantities. Corn-derived sugars are often used to boost the strength of the final product without significantly affecting its flavour, or to adjust from mash to mash to achieve consistent alcoholic strength. In northern Europe a derivative of beet sugar was traditionally used for the same purpose, but beet sugar created an undesirable flavour that could be avoided by "inverting" it – boiling it slowly with a little water and citric acid to produce a highly concentrated syrup, which was then crystallised to form sugar "diamonds". This sort of sugar is still used in Belgium, where it is called "candi".

Corn-derived sugars are also used in small quantities to "prime" beer before it is bottled or put into cask. Priming sugars prompt a slight secondary fermentation to give the beer a bit of fizz and create a head.

Finally, sugars of various sorts are used for their particular flavour characteristics. A dry beer can be sweetened by the use of non-fermentable lactose. Maltodextrin is a soluble starch that creates a heavier body and richer mouthfeel. Honey is an increasingly popular adjunct and retains its distinctive taste throughout the brewing process. And black treacle or molasses is sometimes added to dark beers for its density and depth of flavour.

Maltsters

- **Bairds Malt Ltd**, Station Maltings, Witham, Essex, CM8 2DU; Tel 01376 513566.
- **Thomas Fawcett & Sons Ltd**, Eastfield Lane, Castleford, W Yorks WF10 4LE; Tel 01977 552460.
- **Crisp Malting Group Ltd**, Great Ryburgh, Fakenham, Norfolk NR21 7AS; Tel 01328 829391.
- **French and Jupps Ltd**, Stanstead Abbotts, Ware, Herts SG12 8HG; Tel 01920 870015.
- **Muntons plc**, Cedars Maltings, Stowmarket, Suffolk IP14 2AG; Tel 01449 618300.
- **Greencore Malt**, Eastern Way, Bury St Edmunds, Suffolk IP32 7AD; Tel 01284 772000.
- **Edwin Tucker & Sons Ltd**, The Maltings, Teign Road, Newton Abbot TQ12 4AA; Tel 01626 334002.
- **JP Simpson & Co (Alnwick) Ltd**, Tweed Valley Maltings, Tweedside Trading Estate, Berwick upon Tweed TD15 2UZ; Tel 01289 330033.
- **Warminster Maltings Ltd**, 39 Pound Street, Warminster, Wilts BA12 8NN; Tel 01985 212014.

Ingredients: Hops

Hops, whether used as whole flowers (or "cones"), dried pellets or extracts, contain the acids that will protect your beer from bacterial infection and provide its bitterness as well as the oils and resins that will produce much of its aroma and flavour.

A cousin of both cannabis and the common nettle, hops were used throughout the medieval period as a dyestuff and a herbal remedy for a variety of ailments (they are still used to treat insomnia). The young shoots are a spring delicacy rather like asparagus, still much eaten in Belgium, and the leaves are a good salad vegetable, while the stems yield a strong fibre suitable for both clothing and ropemaking.

Hops are first recorded as being used in brewing in Germany in the 9th century, and until recently it was thought that they didn't come to Britain until the end of the middle ages – as some versions of the rhyme have it, "turkey and carp, pickerel and beer (hopped ale) came into England all in one year" (1492). Modern research, however, suggests that even if they weren't commonly used by British brewers until the later middle ages, they were far from unknown. They may have been used by monastic brewers in Kent even before the Conquest; although if that is indeed the case it was as a purely local version of the herb grist used in different regions. Hopped beer seems to have started arriving in significant quantities in the 14th century as imports to satisfy the thirst of growing communities of Flemish, Dutch, Danish and German merchants and craftsmen for a taste of home. The first English hop garden now seems to have been planted not in Kent in the early 16th century, as used to be thought, but in Suffolk two centuries earlier. Certainly, London brewers were commonly using hops in the early 15th century and over the next 200 years their use became pretty much universal (although unhopped ale held out in the more remote parts of the Pennines until the 18th century).

Hops are now only grown on any scale in two regions, Kent and Sussex and Herefordshire and Worcestershire, although in the 19th century there were commercial hop gardens or yards in almost every county in Great Britain. And indeed there is no inherent reason why they can't be grown just about anywhere. The hedges around my home in Cambridgeshire abound with wild hops, descendants of plants that escaped from the county's hop gardens over 100 years ago; and a new commercial hop garden has just been opened in Suffolk. You might even persuade a farmer near you, wherever you live, to set aside a patch of ground for hops; the big disincentive in the past was that hops, being climbers, needed expensive poles and wirework and all the specialist skilled labour that went with them. The recent development of "dwarf" or "hedgerow" varieties such as First Gold, however, means this is no longer the case: anybody can grow hops anywhere.

One achievement of small independent brewers as a body in the last 35-odd years has been to reawaken interest in different hop varieties. Before that, hops had been prized chiefly for their bittering quality, and most of the efforts of researchers and growers had been devoted to developing high-alpha strains and finding new ways of extracting the prized bittering agents. Pioneers like Sean Franklin of Rooster's Brewery of Knaresborough and Brendan Dobbin (who briefly had his own brewery in Manchester but is best known in the industry as an installer and consultant) began working with imported varieties, mainly from the USA and New Zealand, in the 1980s. Before then, hop grists were almost universally blended from different types, with consistent performance in mind rather than the flavour and aroma characteristics of individual varieties. Today, thanks to these innovators and the many brewers who have taken their lead, single-varietal beers are, if not exactly commonplace, certainly not remarkable, and something you will doubtless want to experiment with.

Native Hop Varieties

Thanks to them, too, hop merchants like Charles Faram of Worcestershire now import weird and wonderful hop varieties from all over the world. They are too many to list here; what follows is a summary of the main native types including the hedgerow strains.

- **Admiral**: bred to complement the Target variety, Admiral produces small compact cones and has shown itself to be a good replacement for both high-alpha and dual-purpose varieties when used as a kettle hop.
- **Bramling Cross**: bred in 1927 by crossing Bramling with a male seedling from a Canadian wild hop. Provides fruity blackcurrant and lemon notes and is increasingly popular in speciality beers. If used as a late hop or dry hop, the effect on the final flavour can be very interesting.
- **Challenger**: bred in 1972 from Northern Brewer crossed with a downy mildew-resistant male; a cousin of Target. Gives a fruity, almost scented aroma, with some spicy overtones. A versatile kettle hop for all types of beer, it blends well with other English varieties and is sometimes used as a late hop and a dry hop.
- **First Gold**: dwarf hop with a very attractive aroma, which some liken to Goldings, but with a higher alpha content than traditional aroma hops. Suitable as a general kettle hop and also for late and dry

hopping in all types of beer. First Gold has excellent aroma qualities, producing a well-balanced bitterness and a fruity, slightly spicy note in ales.

- **Fuggle**: propagated by Richard Fuggle of Brenchley, Kent, in 1875, having first been noticed in about 1861 growing wild. It became the most widely grown hop in England, making up 78 per cent of all acreage in 1949, until wilt made it almost impossible to grow in Kent and Sussex. It now represents only about 9 per cent of the English crop, being grown chiefly in the West Midlands, but is also grown in the USA, mainly in Oregon, and in Slovenia, where is has changed its character and is known as Styrian Golding. Fuggle has a typical English flavour, often blended with Goldings to improve "drinkability" and add roundness and fullness to the palate. Contributes all the essential characteristics of flavour, aroma and balanced bitterness to ales, particularly as its relatively low alpha content means a high hopping rate is needed to achieve desired bitterness levels. Sometimes used as a distinctive dry hop.
- **Goldings**: not one variety but a group including Cobbs, Amos's Early Bird, Eastwell Golding, Bramling, Canterbury Golding and Mathons, the strains usually being named after either a grower or the parish where they were first cultivated. Most are grown in east Kent with the exception of Mathons, which, along with some Canterbury Goldings and Early Birds, are commonly grown in Herefordshire and Worcestershire. Recognised as having the most typical English aroma, with the best flavour historically coming from east Kent, this hop is in demand for copper hopping and dry hopping of traditional ales. Goldings are also useful for late hopping lagers, when a delicate aroma is required.
- **Herald**: a sister of Pioneer, and the first high-alpha dwarf hop with acceptable flavour properties. Yields large, heavy cones. In brewing trials, the flavour and bittering balance has been found very acceptable. Useful both as a bittering hop and as a dual-purpose variety in all types of beer.
- **Phoenix**: developed at the same time as Admiral, this variety is a seedling of Yeoman. In brewing trials, the flavour and bittering balance has been found very acceptable. Useful as a bittering hop and as a dual-purpose variety in all types of beer.

- **Progress**: developed in 1951 as a wilt-tolerant alternative to the Fuggle. Somewhat similar to Fuggle but slightly sweeter, and providing a softer bitterness in beers of all types. With its slightly higher alpha content, it represents good value for bitterness if a recipe demands aroma hops for all the bittering elements.
- **Whitbread Golding**: first cultivated in 1911 and planted extensively in the 1950s for its resistance to wilt. Provides a distinctive sweet fruit flavour similar to, but generally more pronounced and robust than, Goldings. It gives a mild, clean bitterness in traditional ales, and is sometimes used with good effect as a distinctive dry hop.
- **Wye Northdown**: released for commercial production in the early 1970s, it provides cheaper alpha acid than many tradition varieties while having excellent flavour properties. A hop with a very mild, clean, neutral English flavour, it can be used in all types of beer, with no harshness of palate. Particularly with seedless Northdown, the high level of oil makes this a very distinctive dry hop for full-bodied ales.
- **Wye Target**: Target, released for general production in 1972, is a cousin of Challenger and provides high yields of alpha acid with a robust aroma and is Britain's most widely used bittering hop. With strong, typical English flavour and good bittering qualities this hop is used in all types of beer. Dry hopping with traditional whole hops is also effective in some of the stronger ales, giving positive floral aromas.

Getting the Most out of Hops

- **Buy** in a pack size as close to the brew length usage as you can. Aroma is lost once the pack is opened. For smaller needs buy in fresh packs or vacuum packs in double silver foil.
- **Ask** the age of the hops. Buy the latest harvest hops.
- **Store** in a deep freeze, refrigerator or cold room. Hop bitterness is lost faster at higher temperatures. Pellets are sometimes easier to store than whole hops.
- **Learn** to evaluate hops yourself. To assess or compare hop aroma, make a hop tea, cool it and smell. Hop merchants rub and sniff hops every day, but there are two problems for the novice: hops may smell powerful when rubbed in the hand, yet may not be so powerful when in the beer; and minor differences in the rub can mean big differences in the beer.

- **Test-brew** with the new hop alone to see where it fits on the bitterness, aroma and intensity scales. Test it in a 100% pale malt beer with a standard water treatment so that the hop aroma shows through clearly. Adjust the portion quantities by the alpha content of the new hop and start with a comparison of the flavour at about 28 International Bitterness Units (similar to commercial ales).
- **Build** a hop grist by looking at the grists of beers you like and experimenting. Track down recipes in home-brewing books and on the internet. Remember, when mixing a grist, that aromas from different hops can sometimes "average out" and dilute the effect. Single-hop beers usually (but not always) have more aroma definition than mixed-varietal beers.
- **Choose** your alpha hop carefully. Some alphas have strong aromas in spite of their early addition to the boil that may alter the final hop character.
- **Look** closely at your yeast. The same hop can taste different when used with a different yeast. Make sure your yeast is compatible with the beer you are trying to make.
- **Control** your brewing process, or other aromas might hide the hop aroma. Higher alcohols, esters, diacetyl and hydrogen sulfide will all disguise or overlay your hop aroma.

All the above information and far, far more is available on the National Hop Association of England website, **www.hops.co.uk**.

Hop Merchants

- **Botanix**, Hop Pocket Lane, Paddock Wood, Kent TN12 6DQ; Tel 01892 833415.
- **Charles Faram**, The Hopstore, Monksfield Lane, Newland, Worcs WR13 5BB; Tel 01905 830734.
- **Wealden Hops**, Congelows, Benover Road, Yalding, Kent ME18 6ET; Tel 01622 817175.
- **Lupofresh Ltd**, Benover Road, Yalding, Kent ME18 6ET; Tel 01622 815720.

More hop merchants can be contacted via the National Hop Association of England.

Chapter Six

How to Get to Market: Draught Sales

Realistically, where can you sell your beer? You may be based in a pub, or at least have one that acts as your brewery tap, but these sales alone won't necessarily make you a living. To get your beers out into the trade, you therefore need to understand the structure of the market. This chapter will deal with the "on-trade" – pubs, clubs and so on – and will therefore be mainly concerned with sales of draught beer.

There are two contrasting points of view here. One says that an overcrowded small brewing sector and the iron grip of the tied system mean that the traditional route to market – sales of draught beer to pubs – is dead, and that new brewers have to seek alternative outlets. The opposing view is that the long-term health of the sector as a whole demands that the tied house system be cracked open. They are not mutually exclusive. You can continue to seek draught sales to pubs at the same time as seeking new opportunities. Let us look at both, to start with, the draught beer opportunity.

There are around 180,000 on-licensed premises in Britain, not just pubs and clubs but restaurants, casinos, hotels, village halls, golf clubs, sports centre bars, theatre bars, airport bars and God knows what other varieties of bars. Few of them will have any relevance to your business. Some may provide niche opportunities, but the ones that really matter are the country's 55,000 or so pubs (but dwindling at a rate of around 30 a week during the recession) and 15,000-odd sports and social clubs. And be warned: not many of them will be buying beer from you.

As we have already seen, ownership in the pub trade has changed dramatically since the 1990 Beer Orders that followed the big Monopolies Commission enquiry into the nation's beer supply. There used to be brewery-owned tied houses – some run by managers directly employed by the brewery, others by self-employed tenants – and owner-operated free houses, many of which had accepted low-interest loans from a brewery in return for stocking only its beers, the old-fashioned "loan tie". Not any more. It's not so simple now.

The Local Free Trade

When you first decided to investigate becoming a local brewer, part of the attraction may well have been the cheery relationships you saw yourself enjoying with your local publicans, and indeed their customers, as you turned up each week with your regular beer delivery. If that's the case, disabuse yourself now. It's extremely unlikely that you'll be able to generate enough sales to sustain your business through the local free trade alone.

Perhaps 12,000 of the country's pubs are genuinely owner-operated free houses with the discretion to stock your ales. Some of them, although perhaps not as many as in the past, will be restricted by a tied brewery loan. Others buy strictly on price, or are unadventurous and favour well-known national and big regional brands, or have clienteles that are just not interested in real ale. The few that are left will be besieged by people like you. To make matters worse, breweries and pub companies are currently offering inflated prices for free houses that come on the market, thus cornering yet more of the trade.

Having said that, a guaranteed local sale, however limited, is an essential precursor to starting up: it creates awareness of your beers (and indeed of your existence) and for the first few weeks or months might be the only cash-flow you have. So even if you intend in the longer term to sell your beer much further afield, it's absolutely imperative that you research your local market thoroughly:

- How many genuine free houses are there within, say, a 20-mile radius?
- What sort of range do they stock currently – is it all from national and regional brewers, or are they apparently micro-friendly?

- How many handpumps do they have?
- Do they, or could they, stock changing guest ales?
- How many of the local free traders who blithely agree to give your beers a whirl will actually, when it comes to it, place an order – and how often will such orders be repeated?

Most parts of the country have a cadre of free trade landlords whose pubs attract diehard beer aficionados and who love to stock as widely as they can, filling six, seven, eight or even more handpumps with a never-ending rotation of exotic guest ales. (Although not everywhere: in regions where the tie has always been strong, such as Greater London and Surrey, the free trade is negligible.) Pubs like this will invariably give your beer a try, and are a useful place to be seen, but part of their unique selling point is their rapid turnover of brands, and you'll be lucky to get more than infrequent orders from them. But do take note from the case studies in Chapter Two that a single licensee in Kettering is responsible for giving a flying start to at least two local micros (actually many more); strive to meet and befriend his equivalent in your own neck of the woods.

Owner-operators

Perhaps more important is the rather more numerous breed of owner-operators who like to stock a decent if not extravagant selection that will include a local product if at all possible. It's in pubs like this that you stand your best chance of building up the steady trade you'll need; and in many cases this kind of loyal regular account was only stocking better-known regional brands before a genuinely local brewer came along and wormed his way into a regular slot. So don't be deterred if your local free house only stocks the usual suspects – Adnams, Fuller's London Pride, Marston's Pedigree, that sort of thing; it could end up as your best outlet.

You may already know most of the qualifying licensees in your area; to meet more, join the local branch of CAMRA – you can sign up online at **www.camra.org.uk** – to share local knowledge with fellow members and get personal introductions to the right retailers. Do your groundwork thoroughly, and try to establish a coterie of two or three local free houses that will have one or more of your beers permanently on tap and maybe half-a-dozen more that will order regular guests from you. But always bear in mind that only a handful of small brewers – mainly those that operate in very rural counties

Case study: Brewery with Large Local Free Trade – Hobson's, Cleobury Mortimer, Shropshire

When Nick Davis decided to make the switch from licensed trade property surveyor to local brewer, he had already decided on his business strategy – and that was, to remain firmly local.

That was back in 1993, when there was still a booming market in guest ales among national brewery tenants following the 1990 Beer Orders, and before the new generation of real ale wholesalers had really got into its stride. It made sound sense then to concentrate on building up a direct delivery route among strictly local outlets, and Nick determined not to canvass business further than an hour's drive from his business.

Nick's choice of location helped. The Davis family lived in the Bristol area, where Nick's parents ran a pub. But in deciding to move the 100-odd miles north to Shropshire, Nick was targeting a rural district where bigger breweries owned comparatively few tied houses and where there was therefore a strong free trade. It was dominated at the time by Banks's of Wolverhampton (now part of the neo-national group that includes Marston's of Burton-on-Trent and Jennings of Cumbria). But there were few microbreweries in the region (there are plenty now!), and Nick was certain that a locally brewed competitor to Banks's Bitter would be welcomed by many licensees and their customers.

It was a long haul, but he was proved right.

"At first it was just a question of going round letting publicans know that we were in business and making beer," he says. "It was hard work – a lot of doorknocking, and always keeping our eyes and ears open while we were out delivering."

Time on the road proved invaluable in finding out about new prospects, says Nick – often a trade customer would suggest new sales leads and just as often, pub customers would.

"You'd stop in the bar for a cup of tea after making the delivery and one of the regulars would tell you that the pub they played darts against last week desperately needed some decent beer," says Nick.

Within two years, production was up to 30 barrels a week, providing a living for Nick himself and one employee. Then in 1996 Hobson's Best was named CAMRA's West Midlands Beer of the Year, following up with a gold medal in its class in 1997's Champion Beer of Britain awards.

Competition success led to approaches from The Beer Seller and other wholesalers, says Nick, but despite being tempted he turned them down.

"The Beer Seller wanted 40 firkins straight way and the temptation to say yes was massive," he says. "The downside is that you may never see half of the casks again, which more than wipes out anything you might make on the sale."

Concentrating on the local market has allowed Hobson's to build up a strong following for a range that includes Town Crier at 4.2 per cent alcohol, Old Henry at 5.2 and more recently a 3.2 per cent traditional dark mild. In recent years its trade has come under pressure from aggressive purchasing by pubcos, which were snapping up every free house that came on the market at ridiculously inflated prices. As a result of the price inflation that they themselves have caused, the pubcos have now drawn back somewhat; and to make up for the loss of accounts Hobson's has been able to replace much better-known brands on the bars of the surviving free houses.

"The free trade cake may be smaller, but the local brewers' slice of it is much bigger," says Nick. "Brands like Banks's Bitter, Tetley Bitter and Courage Best, which used to be the big sellers, are losing popularity because people want a genuinely local beer."

Drinkers feel reassured if they have a link with the brewery, says Nick, even if it's a tenuous one. "They might know the brewer himself, but even knowing the farm where we get our hops or the mechanic who services our delivery van creates a connection," he says. "It's rather like buying your meat from a farmers' market. It's certainly not cheaper than what you'd get in a supermarket; it might not even be better. But it comes with people attached."

www.hobsons-brwery.co.uk

such as Shropshire and Devon, where the tie has never been strong – can depend on enough business in the local free trade alone to make a living. And as the number of local breweries continues to grow, the pressure on the genuine free trade increases. You will therefore, almost certainly, need to find other markets.

Brewery Tied Estates

These days, and contrary to public belief, breweries actually own remarkably few pubs. Of the four multinationals, only Scottish & Newcastle still has a retail division (actually owned by the Royal Bank of Scotland and only leased to S&N, but that's another story). Greene King and Marston's, the two "neo-national" brewers (that is, regional brewers whose estates have surpassed the

A Woodfordes pub

old Monopolies Commission ceiling of 2,000) have about 2,500 pubs each, while the smaller regionals own another 4,500-odd between them. In these brewery-owned estates the tie is rigorously imposed: guest ales might be permitted, but only from the brewery's own list; any tenant buying outside the tie is liable to be evicted. So if there's a regional brewer's name on the pub sign, don't try and sell your beer there.

However, not all brewery tied houses belong to regionals that won't stock other brewers' brands: microbrewers themselves account for about 400 pubs. As we saw in Chapter Two, many small brewers are based in or associated with a pub, which in most cases stock a range of guest ales from other brewers too. These pubs are never going to shift huge amounts of your beer; but it's still worth trying to get the odd order out of them as a profile-raiser because they tend to attract enthusiasts who will take note of and seek out your beers in future. Similarly, some smaller breweries also have mini-estates of their own in which they usually stock not only their beers but also guests from other brewers. They don't do this out of charity: the sort of customer who seeks out their pubs is going to want a good range of different ales to try, preferably including as large a number as feasible of changing guest ales. You may very well find yourself knocking at open doors if you approach these brewers with ales of top quality; so worth a quick call, especially if they are local to you, are:

- **Banks & Taylor**, Shefford, Beds; Tel 01462 815080.
- **Bath Ales, Warmley**, Bristol; Tel 0117 947 4797.
- **Beartown Brewery**, Congleton, Cheshire; Tel 01260 299964.
- **Burton Bridge,** Burton upon Trent; Tel 01283 510573.
- **Butcombe**, Wrington, Bristol; Tel 01934 863 963.
- **Evan Evans**, Llandeilo, Carmarthen; Tel 01558 824455.
- **Hop Back,** Downton, Wilts; Tel 01725 510986.
- **Leadmill**, Denby, Derbys; Tel 01332 883577.
- **Milk Street**, Frome, Somerset; Tel 01373 467766.
- **Milton Brewery**, Milton, Cambs; Tel 01223 226198.
- **Oakham Ales**, Peterborough; Tel 01733 370500.
- **Ossett Brewery**, Ossett, W Yorks; Tel 01924 261333.
- **Vale**, Haddenham, Bucks; Tel 01884 290008.
- **Whitstable**, Grafty Green, Kent; Tel 01622 851007.
- **Wickwar Brewery**, Wickwar, Glos; Tel 0870 777 5671.

Non-brewing Pub Chains

But if fewer than a quarter of Britain's pubs still fit the traditional "vertical integration" model of brewery ownership and exclusive supply, that doesn't mean the tied house system is dead, or even feeling a little unwell. The non-brewing pub companies that between them own well over 30,000 of Britain's pubs range from giants like Punch Taverns with 10,000 down to Head of

Steam with just five. The smallest chains are often very receptive to local micros, but like the brewery-owned estates of old, the big chains are operated either by directly employed managers or by lessees or tenants. And like the brewery-owned estates of old, they are firmly tied; so you can't just roll up at the door and try to talk the licensee into buying your beer.

As we shall see, there are ways of getting your beer on the bar in pubs owned by the various tenanted pubcos. But you can write off almost all the directly managed town-centre "style bar" operators. Their customers would rather fill the gutters with regurgitated shots, alcopops and the like – sugary, synthetic concoctions the chain buyers can procure for less than the price of bottled water, but for which they can charge the punter as much as chateau-bottled claret – than your ale. A handful of high street chains such as All Bar One might have a solitary handpump lurking forlornly among the lager fonts, serving a musty sample of a national or leading regional brand. But by and large the high street is Budweiser territory (and I don't mean Budvar), and is barred to you and, indeed, pretty much all cask beer.

Big "family dining" managed house brands such as Harvester and Beefeater are equally unwelcoming to the craft brewer. They do, mostly, list a real ale; but inevitably it will be a cheap national brand that bears as much relation to the nectar you brew as their food does to... well, food.

JD Wetherspoon

Uniquely among big managed house chains, the JD Wetherspoon Organisation has always been a keen supporter of small brewers, but there's a limit to how many brewers' beers it can stock in its 670 pubs.

Wetherspoon's was founded in the late 1970s by Tim Martin, a barrister who decided that running pubs would be more rewarding and more socially useful than practising law. Martin was one of a handful of radical entrepreneurs such as David Bruce of the Firkin chain and Michael Cannon of Inn Leisure who set out to challenge the stranglehold then exerted over the London pub scene by Allied, Watney's, Bass, Whitbread and Courage; and his legal training was to stand him in good stead.

His chosen route was not to buy run-down pubs and transform them, but to lease derelict shopfronts, filling stations and other high street properties, and turn them into stylish bars where good real ale was on sale at a reasonable price. It was a bold strategy: in those days magistrates refused to grant new licences where other pubs were already operating. This attitude harked back to the temperance days of 50 years previously and was intended to prevent "proliferation"; and the magistrates maintained that where there were already pubs, there was no "need" for new ones. Martin single-handedly overturned the policy, successfully arguing in court after court that the existing Big Six tenancies, run-down, restrictive and overpriced as they were, didn't answer the consumer's "need" for better pubs. His applications for new licences were invariably opposed by all vested interests – brewers and licensees afraid of the competition as well as anti-alcohol campaigners who opposed every application as a matter of principle. But he was always prepared to appeal when he was refused, and I can't think of a single case in those early days when he lost an appeal (although he has lost one or two since).

His formula worked, and in the 1980s and the first half of the 1990s Wetherspoon pubs appeared throughout London and then throughout Britain. There were even rumours of a venture in France at one stage. Wetherspoon's expansion slowed as other operators built on Martin's success at getting new licences and started competing aggressively for a finite number of suitable premises. You could even argue that Martin was personally responsible for the explosion of city-centre "drinking barns" of the last 15 years, and the company diversified out of its original music-free, TV-free, community-oriented pubs into more youthful bars (Lloyd's Number One) and even lodges. But it has always stuck to its principle of patronising local and regional brewers, sporting rows of six or more handpumps serving guest ales from all over Britain and Europe, and holding regular beer festivals.

Getting your beers into Wetherspoon's is harder now than it used to be, simply because there are more breweries competing for slots, but the company is still a great patron of local brewers. Its real ales are sourced by East-West Ales, an independent company based in Paddock Wood in Kent (Tel 01892 834040; Fax 01892 838553); the people you need to impress there are Dave Aucutt and Janet Cheeseman.

Leased and Tenanted Pubcos

The biggest of the modern chains, though, run their pubs as quasi-traditional tenancies or leaseholds. These, too, are tied; but in this case it's generally the bigger chains that allow their licensees the most freedom. Ted Tuppen, founder of Enterprise Inns, said in his early days that he would be happy for his tenants to stock whatever their customers would buy, provided it

SIBA Direct Delivery System (DDS)

Launched in December 2003, the Society of Independent Brewers' Direct Delivery Scheme followed a long campaign aimed at winning access for local brewers to pubco-owned tied estates.

Previously, small brewers had been frozen out by the big pubcos' highly centralised ordering and logistical systems, which favoured the national and bigger regional companies. Protests by small brewers had failed to prize open the crucial pubco market, so SIBA's Nick Stafford, who runs the Hambleton Brewery in North Yorkshire, decided on a co-operative approach instead and set out to find a way of enabling small brewers to meet big pubcos' trading requirements. The system he worked out, SIBA DDS, has at the time of writing been taken up by retailers including Admiral Taverns, Punch Taverns, New Century Inns and Enterprise Inns among pubcos and, in the take-home trade, Edinburgh Woollen Mills and Asda; the list continues to grow.

The aim of SIBA DDS is to allow small brewers to sell their beer to pubco-owned pubs in their neighbourhoods directly, without having to go through the pubco's central listing, ordering, stocking and delivery systems. It allows participating brewers to make their sales pitch direct to participating licensees, deliver the beer to the pub itself rather than to a regional depot, and collect their empties themselves rather than have to wait months for them to trickle back through the pubco's logistical chain. As well as saving time and effort, it allows small brewers to work in close partnership with publicans and increase trade to the benefit of all parties. Since its launch, SIBA DDS has proved that when pubco lessees have the chance to stock local beers from local brewers, they can enhance their businesses and increase their cask beer sales by offering their patrons a wider and more attractive range. Another attraction for the pubcos is that creating a single point of contact between their head offices and an organisation representing literally dozens of small brewers minimises their administrative burden and costs.

So how does it work? Well, it does depend on its members being relatively IT-savvy and very conscientious about keeping their admin up to date. Essentially, once the member brewer has struck up a trading relationship with a pubco tenant, the licensee orders his beer from the pubco's telesales department in the normal way. The pubco then places the order with SIBA, which promptly issues a delivery note to the brewer. It may seem a trifle circuitous, but because it's all done on the internet the order can be with the brewer within hours of the licensee placing it. And because the order is added to the licensee's regular statement from the pubco, payment should be equally quick – no more wasting hours and even days chasing an ancient invoice for a single firkin!

It all sounds too good to be true and of course there are drawbacks. For a start, not every tenant of every participating pubco is allowed to take advantage of it: in most cases, before he can stock beer from the local micro, the tenant has to get his regional manager's approval, which for many reasons may not always be forthcoming.

And SIBA DDS is not without its administrative burden. It requires standardised e-forms that the member brewers have to learn to use. They have to have the right software (specially created for DDS) too, and hardware that can read it. They have to check their e-mails frequently and respond promptly and correctly, whether they're exhausted at the end of a long day or not. They have to pay a £250 registration fee (plus VAT, of course). And they have to accept a fixed price, agreed individually between SIBA DDS and each participating retailer, that may not be as high as what they would usually charge. This is a big sticking point for some brewers, who have decided not to join SIBA DDS on the strength of it. But the effectively discounted price has to be offset against greatly improved cash-flow and vastly reduced exposure to bad debt.

According to SIBA, DDS is a system that benefits everyone – pubcos, their main national distributors and brewers alike. To find out more, visit **www.siba.co.uk** and follow the link to "SIBA Direct Delivery Scheme".

www.siba.co.uk

all came from one supplier and at the right price. For unlike the brewers of old, these pubcos have no supply chain of their own: beers are delivered by third-party distributors such as Trade Team, Carlsberg UK and the Scottish & Newcastle-owned Waverley TBS. The range that these companies can stock and distribute is pretty big: Waverley TBS has claimed in the past to carry 2,000 draught beers from 300 breweries. However, these are mostly the large or medium concerns that can keep up with the logistics and meet the prices demanded, and few of the newer brewers have geared themselves up to operate on the scale and in the manner necessary to penetrate the pubco market successfully unaided.

The bigger pubcos have regional lists featuring beers from local brewers as well as seasonal ales drawn from a wider supply base and they sometimes host promotions that they call beer festivals, during which they temporarily allow their tenants to stock from a wider list still. But generally speaking your best way of getting your beers into their pubs is via the Society of Independent Brewers' Direct Delivery Scheme.

That accounts for the bigger pubcos. But there are many smaller ones as well. Some are run as property companies that squeeze as much rent as possible out of their tenants while buying the cheapest beer they can find. Not much opportunity for you in these cases – but on the other hand some of the smaller locally based chains are extremely friendly to local brewers and indeed specialise in stocking their beers. Tynemill in the East Midlands, David Bruce's Capital Pub Company in London, Market Town Taverns in West Yorkshire, Brunning & Price in Cheshire and North Wales, and English Inns in Bedfordshire and Hertfordshire are all good examples. But they probably own fewer than 300 pubs between them, and in trying to sell to them you are joining a very long queue.

Listed below is a selection of micro-friendly pub companies. There may well be other small chains of a similar bent in your area. If you know of any pubs that seem to serve a wider than usual range of ales and don't obviously belong to a brewery, ask the licensee who the owner is. It may be one of the national giant pubcos but it may well be a smaller local outfit that can be persuaded to stock your beer.

- **Brunning & Price**, Yew Tree Farm Buildings, Saighton, Chester CH3 6EG; Tel 01244 333100. 15 pubs in the north-west and north Wales.
- **Capital Pub Co**, 1 Relton Mews, London SW7 1ET; Tel 0207 589 4888.

Enquiries@capitalpubcompany.com. Founded by Firkin brewpub entrepreneur David Bruce. 26 pubs in London.

- **Cascade Public House Management**, 5 Merlin Way, Bowerhill Trading Estate, Melksham, Wiltshire SN12 6TJ; Tel 01225 704734. cascade@blueyounder.co.uk. 14 pubs in the South-west. Sister company of Moles Brewery.
- **Chapman Group**, Syon House, High Street, Angmering, W. Sussex BN16 4AG. Tel 01903 856744. Vicki@thechapmansgroup.co.uk. 44 pubs in the South-east and Gloucester.
- **English Inns**, 5 Mill Meadow, Langford, Beds SG18 9UR; Tel 01462 701750. Seven pubs in Bedfordshire, Hertfordshire, Cambridgeshire and Warwickshire.
- **Sir John Fitzgerald**, Café Royal Buildings, 8 Nelson St, Newcastle on Tyne NE1 5AW.; Tel 0191 232 0664. 28 pubs, mainly in the North-east.
- **Head of Steam**, Manesty, Leazes Lane, Hexham, Northumberland NE46 3AE; Tel 01434 607393. Tony@theheadofsteam.co.uk. Four railway-themed managed pubs in the North of England.
- **Market Town Taverns**, 6 Green Dragon Yard, Knaresborough, North Yorkshire HG5 8AU; Tel 01423 866100. office@markettaverns.co.uk. Eight pubs in Yorkshire.
- **Tynemill Inns**, Victoria Hotel, Dovecote Lane, Beeston, Notts NG9 1JG; Tel 0115 925 3333. 17 pubs in East Midlands; founded by former CAMRA National Chairman Chris Holmes.

The Wholesale Trade

Not all that long ago, cask ale brewers were deeply suspicious of the wholesale trade. Brewers were understandably paranoid about the way their beers – living, breathing products, after all – were being handled. How long did they take to work through the distribution chain? How many drops and pick-ups were there between the brewery and the beer's final destination, the pub? What temperature control, if any, was there in the supply chain? What state would the casks return in, and when? The wholesale trade did little to allay their suspicions.

But the way the market was changing left small brewers, and indeed many regional brewers, with little alternative but to trust the wholesale trade. The guest ale market that opened up in the 1990s was a truly national market:

ales from Kent were called for in Cumbria and vice versa, and only the independent wholesale trade could handle the traffic.

It was at this time that independent wholesalers specialising in real ale such as The Beer Seller, Flying Firkin, East-West Ales, Small Beer, Little Ale Cart and many others set up in business. Some disappeared; others prospered – The Beer Seller, in particular, became a major national player, supplying not only small free traders but also the big pubcos. It has now been snapped up by Scottish & Newcastle and renamed Waverley TBS, Waverley Vintners having been S&N's existing wholesale division. That leaves Flying Firkin – northern-based, but now with a much longer reach having acquired the non-Wetherspoon business of East-West Ales and its southern customer base – as by far the leading independent.

The new generation of specialist wholesalers did their best to speed up turnaround times so that the beer arrived at the retailer reasonably fresh and the casks got back to the brewery reasonably quickly. They also sought, mostly although by no means universally, to introduce refrigerated storage and transport so that the problem of beer-barrels exploding on wholesalers' lorries, which had actually happened during the very hot summer of 1996, occurred no more.

These new wave distributors existed alongside a big national network of well-established locally rooted general licensed trade wholesalers, some of them family firms several generations old, who dealt in beer and lager as well as wines, spirits, soft drinks, bag-snacks and sundries. Many of these older companies still exist, and 26 of them with 53 depots in England and Wales between them are now members of a consortium called National Drink Distributors (NDD). They deal in a wider range of beers than they used to, running guest and seasonal ale programmes for their 25,000 regular accounts, and in many cases trying to stock at least some local products; so if they haven't traditionally been big players in the microbrewing world, they are well worth cultivating now.

Before tackling the wholesale trade, though, you have to ask what it will require of you. The answer, in a nutshell, is reliability. That's why most wholesalers won't handle your beers until you've been in business for a while: they don't want to go to all the effort and expense of offering their customers a beer that may very well not be available tomorrow, so they'll want to know that you're sound and solvent. And they want reliable quality as well as reliable supply: nothing upsets them more, as you can imagine, than getting a load of returns from an angry licensee because the beer tastes like vinegar. So even if, as often happens, your very first brew is enthusiastically greeted with a clutch of CAMRA Beer of the Festival awards, most wholesalers will want to be sure you're thoroughly bedded in before they commit resources and energy to pushing your beers.

Selling through wholesalers does have its drawbacks. You have no control over the quality of your beer as it passes through the supply chain. You have to share your margin, which may be slim enough already, with a middleman. You may have to wait quite a while to get your casks back. And you will almost certainly have to wait to get paid, especially if you're dealing with some of the big national chains. They might claim to have a credit period of 60 days, but a glitch – carelessness, laziness or simply the inevitable cases of human error – can wreak havoc with your cash-flow. Marc Bartram tells a story of chasing his payments from the very biggest chain for month after month, only to find out entirely by accident that his cheques were being sent to a very bemused Buffy's Brewery, which, like him, could get no sense at all out of the bureaucrats in the wholesaler's accounts department. These kind of glitches can take a lot of time and effort on your part to sort out; Marc is not the only brewer who swears he will never sell to a wholesaler again unless they pay upfront – which, of course, they don't.

But there's a limit to how much effort you can put into sales yourself;,and as your business grows you may well find the services of a wholesaler indispensable. To meet reliable wholesalers, join SIBA, it has many of them among its associate membership, and Flying Firkin in particular is commendably eager to give beers from new breweries a go. There's also a useful if rather dated listing on **www.quaffale.org.uk/php/wholeslaresmenu.php**; **www. nationaldrinks.com** is the site of the National Drink Distributor network.

A last word on the wholesale trade concerns brewery swaps. Many small breweries try to vary the repertoire of beers they can offer their customers and, at the same time, to get their beers more widely known, by swapping beers with other breweries. This isn't quite the same thing as straightforward wholesale distribution, and it doesn't in itself increase your sales volume. But it's a trading model that has worked very well for very many small brewers for very many years; a little further down the line, perhaps when you're more established, it could prove a handy boost for you too.

Case study: Using Wholesalers, but Cautiously – Mordue Brewery, North Shields, Tyne & Wear

Things went a bit mad for Garry and Matt Fawson of Mordue Brewery when their best bitter, Workie Ticket, won CAMRA's Champion Beer of Britain competition in 1997. The brewery had only been open for a couple of years, and the brothers simply weren't ready for the demand the award generated.

It was a mad scramble for a while, and even when the rush had settled down it was still obvious that the original site wasn't big enough. In 1998 Mordue moved to bigger premises, and Garry and Matt were able to concentrate on building up sales in a more measured way. So In 2005 they had to move again, to a new 12,000 sq ft, £1.5 million development.

In those early days, anyone who called themselves a wholesaler and owned a van was knocking at Mordue's door demanding to be allowed to buy its beer. Producing enough to satisfy them all was a nightmare. A nice problem to have, you might think. But the trouble with an award like CBoB is the weight of expectations it carries with it. Yours is officially the best beer in the country, so if it's less than perfect the customers aren't just going to shrug and try something different – they're going to feel cheated. And, says Garry: "They're not going to blame the landlord; they're not going to blame the wholesaler – they're going to blame the brewery."

Early on, then, the Fawsons learnt not to trust the wholesale trade – not blindly, at least. They wanted to be sure their beers were being treated as reverently as the reigning CBoB deserved, so customers always got the quality pint they were expecting. And while it was beyond their power to check every pub where Workie Ticket was sold, they could at least check all the wholesalers who delivered it. What they wanted was cold storage, proper stock control and the reasonably speedy return of their precious empties; and to make sure they got it they insisted on vetting new wholesale customers before agreeing to supply them.

Their experience was that many smaller wholesalers simply didn't have the facilities to handle a living product like cask beer properly, so they stopped dealing with them. These days, around half of Mordue's 8,000-barrel a year output is delivered through third parties, but they're third parties the brothers can trust. Something like 30 per cent of the output is carried by hauliers to the depots of big pubcos such as Punch Taverns and JD Wetherspoon, but the Fawsons won't use groupage hauliers who deliver to and collect from central hubs. Instead, they only use hauliers they know. Everything goes on overnight deliveries direct to the customers' depots, a bit of fastidiousness that means every pallet of 18–24 firkins costs around £40 to send out rather than the £20 it would cost on economy.

Wholesalers buy about 20 per cent of the brewery's output. Mordue sells to the biggest of them, the Scottish & Newcastle-owned Waverley TBS, and Garry says standards at the company have increased dramatically in recent years. "They've got temperature-controlled vehicles as well as depots and they promote our beer properly so that it turns over quickly and we don't get returns that are past their expiry dates," he says.

Flying Firkin, the Lancashire-based specialist in microbrewery beers, is another favoured customer, as is the National Drinks Distributors network of local independent wholesalers. "They're very strict on quality, and very good," says Garry. Mordue also sells to a handful of small local outfits such as Small Beer of Lincoln, but only because the brothers have personally inspected their facilities and are satisfied with their standards.

"My advice to anyone starting out in the business is not to be tempted by wholesalers you don't know and haven't vetted," says Garry. "It may look like a way of generating revenue quickly, but it's not a long-term strategy because quality is so important. Some of them are pretty good, but you have to be sure."

Another drawback of distributing so widely through third parties is the demands it places on your cask population. Mordue, although not a huge brewery, has more than £500,000 tied up in its stock of around 10,000 firkins.

"It's quite possible for your cask population to be worth more than your actual brewery," says Garry. "It takes six to eight weeks to get your casks back if you're selling through the larger wholesalers, longer if you've sold them to smaller companies. That's something that many people setting up in the business don't realise – but it's all got to be built into your costings and your cash-flow forecasts."

www.morduebrewery.com

Niche Opportunities

One of the very first new breweries to be established, way back in the early 1970s, was the Miners Arms at Priddy, Somerset. It wasn't a pub, though; despite the name, it was a restaurant. And you'd think, wouldn't you, that hotels and restaurants would be keen to offer tourists and diners craft-made local products? Well, in 99 per cent of cases, they're not, and on the rare occasions when they are, they tend to be more interested in bottled beer than draught, so perhaps we'll deal with them in the next chapter alongside the tourist gift shops and other miscellaneous outlets.

The Club Trade

One large part of the on-trade that hasn't really been penetrated by local brewers, though, is the club trade. Not nightclubs, but Britain's 15,000-odd traditional sports and social clubs.

In theory, your local traditional workingmen's club ought to be the ideal home for your ales. You're a local outfit, maybe employing local people, which should appeal to the committee that decides what beers to stock. You should be able to offer an attractive price: if you brew less than 3,000 barrels you qualify for 50 per cent duty relief, which you can share with a big, steady customer such as a club. And the club is big, and usually busy, and full of thirsty working-class drinkers who like their ale; so your beer will turn over quickly enough to ensure that it's always in excellent condition.

Workingmen's clubs, though, have remained stubbornly resistant to the advances of local brewers. Many are still loan-tied, for a start; even if they're not, committees tend to remain loyal to traditional suppliers who often offer not inconsiderable inducements. An all-expenses-paid annual day out at the races, complete with champagne buffet and executive marquee, for the entire club committee including spouses may not actually qualify as bribery, but it's not the sort of jaunt the average working family would indulge in if the brewery wasn't paying. The wholesale price clubs have to pay is one you would find hard to match, even with your duty relief. And finally, they may be big, busy and full of good, steady drinkers, but the drink they drink these days tends to be lager rather than ale. And the ale they do sell tends to be keg rather than cask, for ease of handling.

Even at the traditional end of the club trade, though, this resistance is beginning to crack. The truth is that membership of workingmen's clubs,

Royal British Legions and the like, is tumbling, despite the cheap beer, because their offering is simply not up-to-date. Leatherette banquettes, scruffy lino floors, keg ale, bad singers with obvious comb-overs, and bingo are just not attractive any more, and clubs are having to raise their game to stay alive. Some of them are now offering equal rights to women. There is no reason why real ale shouldn't be part of the equation, especially if it's locally brewed. So it's up to you to go to see your local club steward and secretary, demonstrate that stocking real ale is perfectly possible (even if there isn't a proper cellar, there's bound to be a cold room), and persuade them that well-priced and properly promoted cask beer will attract members. They'll give you a hearing, and the worst they can say is no. Then you go back next year and see if they've changed their minds yet.

You will probably have less trouble getting a sympathetic hearing at sports clubs. There are two sorts here, though: those whose bars are only busy – or in some cases only open at all – on match days aren't going to stock cask ale, even from a local brewer. But the larger, busier and – though I hardly dare utter the words – more middle-class establishments such as golf clubs are proving fruitful territory for those cask ale brewers who actually try to tackle them. Middle-class men tend to drink real ale rather than lager, it's a fact. They also tend to be more appreciative of lesser-known and local brewers whose products have the cachet of, if not exclusivity, certainly rarity.

So, don't ignore the club trade. Clubs may not be easy accounts to crack, and they may not pay top dollar, but they are in general a growth area for real ale, and listing one or two local sporting or social clubs among your regular outlets will pay off in terms of long-term, reliable, regular business.

Outside bars

Running outside bars at events private and public is an opportunity that more and more small breweries are learning to exploit. It's an area that offers two main advantages: the overheads are comparatively low and the margins are comparatively high. It also has its drawbacks, as we shall see.

The half-full glass first. Even at public events such as village shows, your overheads are likely to be minimal. In capital terms, you need a strong trestle table, an awning of some sort, a stillage system on which to mount your casks, some cooling jackets and a biscuit-tin for the cash. If you're selling ale racked off bright into polypins rather than from the cask you can even dispense with the stillage, although a reliable cooling system is still indispensable. These will all involve in you a modest one-off outlay. You might also need some assistants, who will want paying. To offset the expenses you get the full retail price of the beer – £180 a firkin rather than the £50–60 you get wholesale – and if you can't make a nice margin on that, you're doing something wrong.

There are drawbacks. You will need a personal licence (see Chapter Eight), but then you should get one of those anyway. It takes time to set up and take down. There will be the occasional disaster when only half the predicted numbers turn up; and if you've racked beer off specially then the unsold surplus will, unless you have another outside bar the very next day, be spoiled (you can get duty drawback on it, but that's not much help). (I have heard of brewers sneaking very small quantities of freshly racked ale back into the system, but it's risky. You never know what infections are lurking in the sort of barns where ceilidhs are often held, and you certainly wouldn't want them in your brewery. If you really can't overcome the temptation to spread unsold bright beer among a few casks, make sure it's from unbroached containers only. It's safer just to stand the loss, though.)

As well as the cash they generate, though, outside bars have a promotional value. In brewing as in life, you can never have too many friends; outside bars spread your name around in the neighbourhood. So: hard work; chancy; but a good sales opportunity and an equally good profile raiser.

Marketing

Naturally, your first efforts in marketing are going to be concentrated on finding outlets for your beers. But equally important, and in some ways more difficult, is making an impression on the beer-drinking public. Getting repeat orders from your trade customers will depend on how much of your beer they can sell to their patrons and although you might say that they're the retailers and it's up to them to promote themselves, there's a great deal you can do to help.

Your marketing effort starts at the simplest possible level – with the names of your beers, and the design of your pump-clips. In most of the pubs where your beer is on sale, your pump-clip is likely to be the only way you have of communicating directly with the public and the only chance you will get to persuade people who have never heard of you to buy your beer. What sort of people are they likely to be, and what sort of message are they most likely to respond to?

Branding

In the early days, many microbrewers chose branding that was blokeish, jocular and often rustic. Beers had names like The Dog's Bollocks, Piston Bitter (a variation on pissed 'n' broke) and Old Fart, and the pump-clips were often not much more than photocopies of the head brewer's late-night attempts at postcard art. Often it seemed all too crass and amateurish but it struck a chord with an ale-drinking public that was itself, in many cases, blokeish and jocular. Real ale in those days belonged in the same cultural cage as rugby club dinners and dwyle flonking; today, with beer-drinking generally in decline, reading and catching a market is a much more subtle and demanding business.

This is no place to lecture you on design, on what colours to choose, on what note to strike. Suffice it to say that unless the former life you're going into brewing to escape was in graphic design, you should hire a professional. It does make sense, though – and it's surprising how many brewers have let this obvious point fly past them – to maintain uniformity of branding across your range. In a crowded bar on a busy night, the size of the type identifying the pump-clip as yours will defy the cursory inspection that may be all that is possible. Unless all your pump-clips have the same shape and colours, it will not be apparent that the best bitter on tap is one of yours; anybody who tried and liked your cooking bitter and would try more of your beers if given the chance will remain in ignorance. So establishing a clearly recognisable identity via a uniform pump-clip design will be a great help to drinkers who want to sample your range and to publicans who want to sell it. Some breweries take it a step further and give their whole range a common theme: Cotleigh, with its birds of prey, is perhaps the supreme example. That may be a little excessive – it seems to me a little hasty to narrow your possibilities without good reason – but for the perfect example of unobtrusive yet clearly identifiable branding across the range, check out Tunnel Brewery, see **www. tunnelbrewery.co.uk**.

As for names, jokes for blokes are as much of a turn-off as a come-on these days. Craft-brewed beer is trying to get serious and to press a whole range of contemporary buttons: it's foodie-friendly; it's got good green credentials; it's the very antithesis of all that's corporate and globalised. And perhaps because so many of these issues resonate so strongly with women, more and more of them are drinking real ale. You are not going to appeal to them by christening your beer Maiden's Ruin, Willie Warmer or Old Horizontal (all genuine examples).

An example of a Tunnel Brewery label

Working with CAMRA

Having created a range with names and branding calculated to appeal to the customers you have in mind, you need to find cost-effective ways of getting your name around. I have already mentioned CAMRA membership as a way of making contact with local micro-friendly licensees but CAMRA can do more for you than that.

The Brewery Liason Office (BLO)

The first thing your local CAMRA branch should do for you is appoint a brewery liaison officer, or (BLO). The origins of this office lie far back in the mists of the Campaign's early days, when new breweries were rare and tender shoots that CAMRA branches felt they had to nurture and fuss over. The BLO's job was to check in with the brewer from time to time, make sure that everything was all right, and report back to the branch with news of new brews or looming problems. In the best of cases, the relationship between brewery and BLO would develop much further, with the BLO taking responsibility – in return for free pints and being made to feel special – for publicising and promoting the brewery. In the worst of cases the very opposite happened, and the BLO turned out to be a curmudgeon for whom everything the brewery did was a mockery. In these, thankfully few, cases, the BLO was very soon made persona non grata at the brewery. More often, the BLO turned into a valued and indeed valuable friend who even, on occasion, ended up as a partner or employee. So provided your BLO is bearable, cultivate them. Give them things to do like writing press releases or delivering leaflets to your retail customers. They will not resent it or regard it as imposition; they will be genuinely thrilled to help.

Every CAMRA branch also organises an annual beer festival – and some of them run a winter ales festival as well. Your local branch will undoubtedly order one or more of your range for its festival. In volume terms this is insignificant – three or four firkins at most, unless you're in one of these places like Peterborough, Cambridge, Worcester where the local beer festival is huge. So although there's not likely to be a huge amount of money involved, a presence at local festivals is great for public exposure. The local media – broadcast as well as print – will often seize on a new local brewery as the news "hook" on which to hang their festival report, especially if you have an unusual or catchy story to tell. More important still, even quite small festivals attract CAMRA members from surprisingly far afield, who are always on the look-out for new brews and will spread the news of your arrival – and their opinion of your ales – to other CAMRA members, beer festival organisers and micro-friendly licensees back home. Winning the Beer of the Festival award is better publicity still, and it's surprising how often the title goes to a new local brewery. These things are supposed to be unfixable, and in the most obvious sense they are (waving brown envelopes is likely to be counter-productive, I'm happy to affirm). But sentiment and local loyalty often play their part and who's going to complain about that?

Public Relations

Using the media is something local brewers are often very bad at. There are only 24 hours in the day, and at least two or three of them should be spent asleep; media relations tend to come far down the busy brewer's list of priorities. It shouldn't be that way, though: building strong local awareness is one way you can help your trade accounts shift your beer, which will help you win new accounts as well.

There's no publicity like free publicity, and putting out a constant stream of news stories is one good way of getting it. Some local breweries even hire public relations agencies to do it for them, and to good effect: Wood's of Wistanstow in Shropshire has used local PR agency Seabury Salmon for years and has become one of the best-known brewers in the West Midlands as a result.

If you're doing it yourself, you need to get to know your media. Start with the CAMRA branches in your trading area: they almost all publish local newsletters – the larger branches print thousands of them – which are

Writing a Press Release

One way to assure yourself of plenty of newspaper coverage is to learn how to write a press release. Don't worry about whether you have a newsworthy story: if you read your local paper regularly you'll already know that the down-page stuff isn't necessarily all that exciting. And surprisingly often, the selection criteria for stories to prop up the bottoms of inside pages have nothing to do with news values anyway. If there's a bit of copy to hand that can be slotted quickly and neatly into the available space, in it goes. Even local papers are put together under pressure these days, and if you can supply press releases written like news stories – even if they're not about anything in particular – then the sub-editors who lay out the pages will be eternally in your debt.

The rules are simple. Basically, the subs want to trim the story to fit space they have, quickly, easily and, if possible, without having to read it. But a news story must also be complete in itself, leaving no questions unanswered and requiring no extraneous knowledge to be intelligible. So, two things to watch: structure and content.

The structure should be what we journos call an "inverted pyramid". This means that all the information you need to understand the story should be in the first paragraph, or "intro", which should also never be more than 35 words long. A good example of a self-contained intro might be: "A single mum was taken to hospital suffering from smoke inhalation last night after rescuing her two-year-old daughter from a fire at their home in Blogton." And there you have it: 28 words which, with the addition of the mum's name, could go into the paper as a standalone news in brief paragraph (or "nib") if that was the only space available. Then you can go into detail such as: "Theresa Bloggs, 21, managed to drag little Shania out of their third-floor flat on the Blogton Towers estate and used her mobile phone to summon firefighters before collapsing."

You can see how the process works: you start with the kernel of the story, then add detail after detail in order of importance, remembering that the subs may want to cut it from the bottom.

As for content: well, the paper has to be filled and if the only story to hand at the vital moment seems to be a trivial one, so be it. I have written a story before now about a pub putting up hanging baskets.

Almost anything can be newsworthy on the right day: the installation of a new fermenting vessel, especially if it's a tight squeeze; the appointment of a local youth as apprentice brewer, even if he's really only making tea and scrubbing down the tiles; any one-off brew, especially if it's in aid of a local good cause.

One golden rule: if your news release is lacking a single piece of information, even a trivial one, the chances are it'll end up on the spike. A reporter is not going to bother to phone you to chase up the second brewer's surname; quicker and easier to reach for the next press release on the pile. A caption that reads something like this is worse than useless: "Bloggs's Brewery boss Billy Bloggs is pictured with Red Lion landlord Alf Stubbs and barmaid Rita." The missing bits of information here are: which is Billy and which is Alf; and what is Rita's surname? The caption should read: "Pictured from left are Red Lion landlord Alf Stubbs, barmaid Rita Bubbles, and Bloggs's Brewery boss Billy Bloggs." Note that everyone in the caption is fully identified with first name, surname and descriptor.

Anyway, let's do the full press release. The story is that you've sponsored a competition in which drinkers in your free trade accounts are asked to vote for the bar person with "Blogton's sunniest smile".

Start with a little headline. This isn't the head that will appear in the paper; it's there to catch the eye of the reporter sifting through the day's crop of press releases. How about: "Radiant Rita has Blogton's Sunniest Smile".

"Radiant barmaid Rita Bubbles could be bathing in beer after drinkers in Blogton pubs voted her smile the town's sunniest.

Rita, 32, who has been pulling pints at the Red Lion in Hogwash Way for five years, has won a barrel – that's 36 gallons – of Best Bitter from competition sponsor Blogg's Brewery after topping the punters' poll.

More than 200 drinkers in the four Blogton pubs that stock Bloggs's beers -- the Red Lion itself, the Cloak & Dagger, Bond Street; the George & Dragon, Knight Street; and the Cholmondely Arms, Featherstonehaugh Avenue – took part in the poll, with Rita scoring 69 votes to her nearest rival's 42.

And as she measures only five foot nothing in her highest heels, Rita reckons she's won enough ale to fill her bath."

distributed around ale-friendly pubs for customers to browse in odd moments. Find out who the editor of your local newsletter is and keep him or filling these publications can be difficult and the editor will be glad of news of new brews, new members of staff, funny stories and the like. You may even get your brewery featured in a profile article.

You (or even your BLO, if he or she is canny, aware and willing) should also try to develop a relationship with a favoured reporter at each of your local newspapers and radio stations. This is, remember, a two-way street: the reporters will help you by getting you free publicity, and you will help the reporters by establishing their reputation as a keen and productive newshound.

As for what kind of stories local media are looking for – well, buy your local paper and see for yourself. New beers, especially charity brews (Wood's, that PR-canny outfit, is one of many that regularly creates special brews with part of the proceeds going to newsworthy local causes), new recruits, the brewery cat's mouse-hunting prowess – it's all grist to the local reporter's mill.

Ask yourself, also, what format your local media want to get their information in. A story is more likely to make it into the paper or onto the airwaves if it's presented in a way that needs minimum processing – as a proper press release (*see* panel piece on page 130). In the old days these would be hard copies posted by snail mail to the newsdesk; these days, a Word document attached to an email (not a cut and paste job, preferably) addressed personally to your pet reporter is probably your best bet.

Advertising

Advertising is a trickier business altogether. You're not Carlsberg, spending a fortune to establish and maintain a national brand; and you're not a scaled-down version of Carlsberg, either, trying to achieve locally what it does nationally. Brand advertising doesn't work like that: it has to make your brand stand out from the others, and if it's not ubiquitous and relentless, it's a waste of money. It also only works if your brand already has excellent distribution – there's no point advertising a product no one can buy! So don't be tempted to take out big ads for your brands in the local paper, or even in specialist media such as *Beers of the World* or *What's Brewing*. That's for the future, perhaps, but for now it's simply not effective.

That doesn't mean you shouldn't advertise at all; but to repay the investment, your advertising needs to be highly market-specific and well planned.

- First, make a forward planner highlighting events such as your open day/beer festival, the launch dates of special or seasonal beers, important local dates where your beers can be highlighted, and joint promotions with stockists.

- Second, set a budget. This will be based on the advertising rates of the local media you intend to use, but remember – nobody but a mug pays the ratecard price. Discounts are always available, based on repeat or regular advertising. Once you've made your budget, stick to it. You might want a small contingency fund to exploit unforseen events, but don't be tempted by slick sales patter into spending more than you have allocated.

- Third, choose your medium, basing your decision on "bangs per buck" – not the overall readership or audience of the medium, but what proportion is likely to buy your beer. Always remember: a small ad strategically placed is more effective than a big ad in a vacuum. And one sure way of testing the effectiveness of each medium is to include a money-off voucher in some of your adverts (but not all of them – promotional discounts are part of your advertising budget, which is unlikely to be huge) and analyse the redemption rate.

Local CAMRA branch newsletters, distributed in hundreds to local pubs to be picked up and put down by drinkers whiling away a few idle moments, are ideal vehicles for your advertising because everybody who reads them is ipso facto in a pub and willing to buy. Local A5 newsletters of the type that are appearing in villages all over the country are also cheap and well-read; but here, as with local newspapers and local commercial radio, you need to tie your advertising to a particular event. Is the local CAMRA beer festival being covered? Is a pub where your beers are on sale being profiled? Is a special feature being published or broadcast on drinking and dining out in the district? Supporting this sort of coverage with a well-designed ad is effective both in raising your public profile and earning brownie points with your retail partners. Then there are specialist national media: not only beer-related titles such as *What's Brewing* and *Beers of the World*, but all sorts of hobby and special interest media too. Do your beers, for instance, have a steam theme, or are you involved in a promotion with a local preserved railway? Are you donating part of the proceeds of a special ale to a good cause? Invariably there is a magazine or newsletter that will give your efforts exposure to relevant consumers, and normally at a reasonable rate too.

Even where there's no editorial involved, working with your stockists makes advertising more effective. One of your best accounts may be advertising its quiz nights, or a forthcoming beer festival, or a special menu for Valentine's Day or Father's Day. Share the cost and get your name in the ad, and you both save money and share the benefit.

One design tip: keep your ad simple. When you're paying by the column centimetre, the urge to cram in as much information as possible is almost irresistible. But do resist. Save the lingering descriptions of your hop varieties, your malt grist, your pure well-water and the rest for your website, your brochures and your back-label. Your ad should be clear, uncluttered and eye-catching. You only have a split second of your customer's attention, so use it wisely! And if in doubt, use a professional graphic designer – traditionally a service provided free or at little extra cost by local newspapers.

Promotions

As with advertising, organising promotions jointly with your retail partners (and do try to think of them as partners) is often more rewarding than going solo, spreading the work and the cost and sharing the benefit. You might provide prizes – free pints, for instance, or merchandise, or brewery tours – for pub promotions such as quiz nights or charity raffles. But don't go mad with money-off or free-pint offers: they can turn out to be more popular than you anticipated and end up blowing a hole in your promotional budget.

If one of your stockists is running a beer festival, you can be of practical help by pulling pints (staff are always short on occasions like this) and providing technical support. Naturally, your beers will be on sale, and you might also be allowed to leave your dray prominently sited in the pub car park for the duration, and to put up a few posters or distribute your leaflets. If you want to run a beer festival or open day at the brewery but don't have a liquor licence of your own, a friendly publican might act as licensee for the event and also help out with cellar and dispense equipment in return for a cut of the profits and some publicity for the pub. Involving a local charity is also a good idea: it guarantees publicity, and volunteer fundraisers will both provide a workforce and drag their friends and family along.

It's all about mutuality, building relationships, creating bonds that will last. There's only a certain amount you can do alone, especially if you're a one-man band, so work with your stockists, your CAMRA branch, and local voluntary groups, share both the burdens and the benefits – and make every casual customer a regular.

Electronic Marketing and Promotion

Marketing and promotion doesn't depend entirely on the old-fashioned print and broadcast media these days. More and more, they make use of websites, blogs and emails.

A website of your own is pretty much a must these days. It's a low-cost, low-maintenance shop window, and one that the entire world can mooch past and gaze into. And not only does it show the world what you have to offer, it can also invite them in to buy. We'll deal with e-commerce later: if you decide that it's one of your main routes to market, you'll soon find that it has problems and peculiarities of its own. But as a complement to your core business, it can be a very useful way of generating sales and awareness. It's also one way of announcing new launches and other promotions and developments.

However a website is not cost-free: designers charge, and a webmaster will also charge to keep the site up to date. You can pay anything from £200 to £2,000 or even more, and in web design as in life, you get what you pay for. A cheap designer will produce a cheap-looking site that will probably break down. The best advice is to shop around and get plenty of quotes; fortunately, web designers are very easy to find. You can either Google "web designers", and literally hundreds will come up, or you can be a bit more selective and revisit a few sites you've been impressed by in the past. They'll normally have the designer's name and contact details on them somewhere (it would be odd if they didn't!) and the designers' own sites should have links to other sites they've designed.

Website Content

But before you rush in to getting quotes from designers, think of what you want your site to do. First, you want it to say who you are and what you do. A nice, chatty site with plenty of background detail is more effective than a dry, terse, and straightforwardly factual one. You want potential customers to get involved with you and your venture on a personal level – it makes the beer taste better and seem cheaper! Having engaged the public's attention, give them the facts about your beers and where people can actually buy them; keep them abreast of new and forthcoming beers, new outlets, events of your own such as brewery open days and third-party events such as beer festivals where your ales will be on sale. Using the site for e-commerce we have already touched on; but you can also use it for trade telesales, with a password-controlled page where customers can not only place orders but also pay for them.

Another way of using new media to establish a link with your trade customers is to set up an email newsletter. This is free, takes hardly any time at all, and communicates with all your stockists at once at the click of a mouse. You simply tap all their email addresses into your system, and every time you have a new product or promotional price or any other information you need to communicate to them, just write a little sales letter and click on "send". It couldn't be simpler, it couldn't be more tightly targeted, it couldn't be more effort-efficient. And it's not strictly speaking spam, either, since your customers will have given you their email addresses voluntarily.

Chapter Seven

How to get to Market: Bottled Sales

L ocal brewers have always been associated in the public mind with cask-conditioned beers or, to use the vernacular, real ale. But bottled beer sales are becoming more and more important both to the brewing industry as a whole and for smaller brewers in particular. Ten years ago I sat down with a set of statistics detailing the trend in draught versus packaged beer sales volumes. At that time packaged sales (bottled and canned) represented fractionally over a third of all volume, but the trend was gradually upwards. I worked out that on a straight-line graph, packaged volume would overtake draught in 2007. I haven't seen the most recent statistics; but by 2002, according to the British Beer & Pubs Association, packaged volume had reached 41.7 per cent of all sales, so my prediction was on track at the halfway stage.

For not only have take-home sales continued to grow at the expense of pub sales (not least because beer is so much cheaper in supermarkets than in pubs), but in a large section of the on-trade – the town-centre drinking barns – bottled beer sales have been growing at the expense of draught. I cannot myself see the advantage of necking a 330ml bottle of Budweiser when a whole pint of Stella costs not much more, and proportionately rather less, but apparently I am in a minority.

Bottling some or all of your output is a second, and increasingly important, string to your commercial bow, and does have several advantages over draught. Bottling extends a beer's life from a few days to a few months; it gives you something to stock your own shop with, if you have one; and some shops in your area – small independent grocers, especially – can usually be persuaded to stock a case or two as a showcase for (or gesture towards) local produce. Bottled versions of your range make great trade samples when you're out on the road trying to drum up new business. And it's relatively efficient in that you don't have to worry about your empties as you will, constantly, with casks.

But as with the pub trade, so with the bottled trade. Most of it, quite simply, will remain firmly closed to you. The Competition Commission adamantly refuses to accept that the "multiple grocers" warrant investigation, even though the Big Five supermarkets control as large a slice of the market as the Big Six brewers did back in the late 1980s, when they were found to be a complex monopoly operating against the public interest. To pursue the analogy, the independent sector – effectively, Thresher's and second-string supermarket chains such as Budgen's, Somerfield and the Co-op – is just as restrictive as the regional brewery tied estates of the 1980s were. And the take-home equivalent of the free trade – small family-run convenience stores and corner shops – is largely supplied by cash and carries that will be closed to you as firmly as Tesco or Morrisons.

Nevertheless, there are opportunities out there that will almost certainly make bottling some or all of your beers – either yourself, or by a contractor – worth investigating. But before we explore these opportunities, let's take a look at the practicalities.

Bottling Your Beers

Bottling on a small scale is time-consuming and monotonous, and unless it's done carefully the beer is very prone to infection and oxidisation. On the other hand, starter-level bottling and corking machines are almost ridiculously cheap: an initial outlay of £600 will provide you with all the equipment you really need.

The most primitive four-headed hand-bottler will cost you about £320 + VAT and stands quite happily on a trestle table, leaving plenty of room for a simple crown capper (about £165 + VAT) to stand next to it. The bottle filler is

Case study: New line beer filling line at Highgate Brewery.

Brewing commenced at Highgate Brewery on 1st July 1899 and the company's first two employees were Fred Broadstock and Bill Jones, representative and drayman. In recent years the brewery has been subject to buyout by Smethwick-based Global Star which has given "a new breath of life" to the Sandymount Road brewery. The company owns more than 100 pubs in the region.

As part of the new era at Highgate Brewery it was decided to invest in a new beer bottling line which was designed and supplied by specialist bottling equipment supplier; Enterprise Tondelli based in Bedfordshire with head office and manufacturing in Italy.

The new modern line rated at 2,000 bottles per hour has been specified to give premier labelling capability and also very high beer filling quality. With this in mind Enterprise supplied a three station rotary self adhesive labeller. This is sited before the filler to ensure no poor labelling due to condensation on a filled bottle. The labelling unit can apply both a body, back and also neck label onto a variety of bottles. A rotary unit was selected to achieve the high labelling accuracy not possible on an in-line labelling machine. Coding is carried out by hot foil printing on the label before application.

The filler manufacturer specialises in beer fillers and has references with some of the major continental brewery groups. The filler at Highgate is a modern monobloced bottle rinser, filler and crowner and is a compact single unit to reduce space required and also allow easy access for the operator. The filler has a double pre-evacuation filling valves which in tests carried out in Leuven University in Belgium the filler picked up less than 50 parts per billion of oxygen during the filling process. The filler also has a closed circuit cleaning in place facility for sanitation and to ensure good hygiene. The base frame of the rinser/filler/crowner unit is in stainless steel to give a long life and improve hygiene around the filling area. A mini hopper on the crowner reduces the need for constant operator loading of crowns.

A shrinkwrapper unit for secondary packaging was included as part of the line to reduce the carbon footprint rather than cartons. The shrinkwrapper is complete with conveyor for palletising.

Highgate Brewery believe that the high specification of the line will ensure that it give best quality to their own brands such as Davenports, Fox's Nob, Old Ember etc and allow them to offer a quality contract bottling service for other smaller and micro breweries. In fact they have already secured several new contracts for bottling for other breweries and brands.

Mr.Stephen Brooks who used to brew at Marston's said: "Although I came into the project quite late on in the day I was impressed by the equipment supplied and the service and attention to detail given by Enterprise Tondelli. I understand that they usually supply medium and large bottling lines but they put the same effort into our project. We believe we have a great line here that will be very helpful in expanding the business and the range of services we can offer in the industry. In fact this is the first of several site and production developments that will be coming through in due course.".

The complete project was supplied by Enterprise including all the conveyors to give a turn key project. Enterprise Tondelli supply lines from 500 bottles to 5,000 bottles per hour. For high speed lines Enterprise can supply up to around 66,000 bottles per hour.

We understand at the time of writing Enterprise Tondelli are just completing major equipment deliveries on other beer bottling lines rated at 24,000 bph and 42,000 bph – both in the UK.

www.highgatebrewery.com
www.enterprisetondelli.com

connected directly to a beer barrel or conditioning tank; the operative simply holds the bottles to the spouts, two at a time, and pays enough attention to make sure they don't overfill. Two operatives, one on the filler, one on the capper, can easily fill 1,500 bottles (more than an entire pallet) a day on this simplest of items; or, if you're a one-person band, you can do the whole job yourself and fill 750, which is the equivalent of nearly 10 firkins. If you do the whole thing yourself, though, remember to swap from filler to capper frequently: not only does it make the job marginally less boring, but the longer the bottles stand around without caps, the likelier they are to pick up an infection. And however bored you get, remember that if you're retailing the beer yourself, either through your own shop or at farmers' markets (see below), your day equates to sales of £1,500 or more, depending on the strength of the beer.

Of course, you'll need slightly more equipment than that, but none of it is expensive. If you're filling bottles direct from the shrink-wrapped pallet on which they were delivered they shouldn't even need sterilising. But if you're only bottling a few cases at a time, and the bottles are likely to stand around unprotected for any period before use, a simple rinser using an odourless peracetic fluid costs £30 and a plastic draining tree £24.

Consumables

Then there are the consumables, which unfortunately are more expensive than you might think. If you're buying in bulk – and by bulk I mean a container-load of 50-plus pallets of 1,200 bottles apiece – you can probably get your bottles for 15–16p each, with delivery thrown in. If, though, you can only afford and store a pallet or two at a time you'll have to pay top dollar, with £45–50 a pallet delivery on top, so you may be paying more than 20p for a simple brown 500ml bottle. (Always use brown glass, by the way: beer kept in clear or even green bottles is affected by ultraviolet light, producing an off-flavour known as "light-struck".) Crown corks cost a penny apiece in quantities of 1,000 or less; you could pay less than half that if you could afford and store a minimum order of 10,000. (From this I think you're beginning to see that you could get your consumables much more cheaply if you joined forces with two or three other local breweries.)

Labels

Labels are more problematic still. In bulk, they're quite cheap – but bulk, in this case, does mean quite improbable quantities. There are several firms that specialise in typesetting and printing reel upon reel of bottle labels, but the origination can be expensive. Designs stored on your personal computer (and do get a professional designer: amateur labels are rarely good enough in a market where presentation is much more important than many small brewers think) can be emailed as PDFs or taken on a disk to a local commercial printer and turned into self-adhesive labels at 8–9p each. The drawback is that these have to be applied by hand (the bottles carry a line to help you position the labels accurately), which you may well find repetitive and time-consuming enough to make you rethink your new career entirely. However, an entry-level automatic labelling machine can set you back £1,800, so perhaps it's something for later on. And it's worth reflecting as you toil that the bottle, label, and cork for a package that can retail at £2.50 should only cost about 30p.

A final point on hand-bottling: the expiry date. There is no legal formula for deciding this: most breweries opt for 12 months, or 18 months for beers of 6 per cent alcohol or more. But it's up to you. Set too short an expiry date and you can have trouble selling the beer to wholesale and retail accounts who are especially picky; too long and you risk beer being on the shelf when it really shouldn't, which can harm your reputation.

Which brings us neatly to bottle-conditioned ales (BCAs): in the case of the strongest BCAs, expiry dates are a complete irrelevance, since the beer is still gently working and often improves over 10 or even 20 years.

Bottle-conditioned Ales (BCAs)

Bottle-conditioned ales are those that are unfiltered, unpasteurised, and uncarbonated, and bottled with a certain amount of live yeast – either the original yeast with which they were fermented, or a special flocculating culture that will sink to the bottle of the bottle and form a sediment. Sometimes they are also primed with a tiny dose of sugar to help the yeast continue to work.

Some customers don't like the sediment, but if the beer is poured carefully the yeast should stay put in the shoulder of the bottle. Actually, though, it's packed with Vitamin B and is very good for you; its only deleterious effect is that it makes the beer cloudy in the glass. An old trick is to pour the beer carefully and indeed theatrically, expertly leaving all the sediment behind – then to swirl the bottle with a triumphant flourish and tip the yeast into your otherwise brilliantly clear ale.

Bottle-conditioned ales are promoted by CAMRA as "Real Ale in a Bottle" or "RAIB" (although what's wrong with the technical expression is beyond me: RAIB is a singularly graceless set of initials), and are now quite common, but until a few years ago they were in danger of dying out. When CAMRA was founded in 1972 the only BCAs (a far less clumsy expression than RAIBs, so I shall stick with it) on the market were Guinness, Gale's Prize Old Ale, Courage Russian Imperial Stout, Eldridge Pope Thomas Hardy's Ale and Worthington White Shield. Bottled Guinness is now pasteurised and carbonated, and has been for over a decade. Gale's has been bought by Fuller's, which seems disinclined to produce any more of the marvellously rich and vinous 9 per cent alcohol Prize Old. The last vintage of Imperial Russian Stout was brewed in 1993, although there have been periodic rumours of another brew. Eldridge Pope of Dorchester first brewed Thomas Hardy's Ale in 1968 to commemorate the centenary of the novelist's birth but shut down long ago; the beer is now brewed across the border in Devon by O'Hanlon's. Finally, Worthington White Shield is a classic Burton pale ale whose production has been shunted from brewery to brewery over the last decade. It was briefly contract-brewed by King & Barnes in Sussex, but when King & Barnes was closed White Shield went home to Burton, where it is now produced at the small demonstration brewery (part of the Coors Brewing Museum) that bears its name.

That was then. Thanks almost entirely to microbrewers, bottle-conditioning is now popular again, and thank goodness for that. For BCAs are usually much more complex and less gassy than pasteurised and carbonated beers, and some of the stronger ones can be laid down like a claret and will improve for years. CAMRA's 2004 *Good Bottled Beer Guide* listed over 600 examples from 143 breweries and the number continues to grow (and most CAMRA festivals these days have a bottled beer bar that stocks only BCAs, which means a few more sales and a bit more exposure for you). Some brewers won't touch BCAs because they think they're tricky to bottle and are easily spoilt, but keep everything spotless and your BCAs should be fine. Opting to bottle-condition your beers will also save you the not inconsiderable expense of installing filtration, pasteurisation and carbonation equipment.

So you've bottled your beer. Now it's time to sell it.

Supermarkets

Supermarkets generally are not regarded with much fondness by microbrewers, who often claim they are either exploited or frozen out altogether. To be fair to the big multiples, though, there is only a limited amount of shelf space they can devote to premium bottled ales (PBAs), although the fact that their wine aisles are several times longer than their beer and cider aisles seems bitterly unfair. And it's logical that most of the space allotted to PBAs (a fraction of the beer aisle, most of which is filled with "slab packs" of cut-price canned lager) should go to beers from the regionals, which are cheaper for the supermarkets to buy and just as attractive to an undiscerning public.

Most of the bigger chains are beginning to shift, though, if only at the pace of a turning supertanker. Many of them now have "regional lists", and Asda has even joined SIBA-DDS. Tesco and Asda also run competitions whose winners are assured a six-month national listing, which often leads on to listings with other chains and a good steady national sale. But there are some 600 brewers banging at the buyers' doors, and without a seismic and frankly unforeseeable change in their attitude to beer retailing, they are never going to find shelf space for more than a couple of dozen of them.

And frankly, even if you do get on a supermarket's regional list, it can be a mixed blessing. The surge in demand can be hard to satisfy and, unless you get a batch or two of beer expensively contract-bottled, may mean letting down your regular customers – always something to be wary of. As with the national wholesale giants, getting paid can be a nightmare: there's a huge bureaucracy involved, in which it's all too easy for your invoice to get lost – more so if you're not a regular supplier – and mistakes once made are hard to get straightened out. Then again, it may boost your sales volumes if your beer is put on a four-for-five promotion or even declared a BOGOF, but don't think the retailer is absorbing the discount. It gets passed down to you, and even the slim margin the supermarket allows you can easily be swallowed up in this way.

Having said that, the supermarket buyers I know say they don't deal with regionally listed micros quite as harshly, if that's the right word, as they do with bigger, more efficient, brewers. They say that once they've decided that stocking a range of local products is in their commercial interest, they'd be stupid to put their local suppliers out of business. Hence the margins should be somewhat better for small local brewers, and their beers are unlikely to be put on promotion.

And of course, some independent brewers do very well out of the supermarket trade. Refresh UK, which supplies the Brakspear, Wychwood

Case study: Brewery that Deals Extensively with Supermarkets – Arran Brewery, Cladach, Isle of Arran

A sculptor and artist who fell in love with a Scottish island after being taken there by his Glaswegian wife, Richard Roberts is the last person you'd expect to be thriving in the cut-throat world of the multiple grocer. But seven years after he founded Arran Brewery on the Isle of Arran, that's how things have panned out.

Richard, originally from High Wycombe in Buckinghamshire, hit on the idea of founding a brewery on Arran almost by accident.

"It was about 12 or 13 years ago, when a new independent distillery had just been built on the island, and I thought to myself: 'What this place needs now is a brewery!'" he says. And so he started work.

Originally, and like almost every other would-be microbrewer, Richard intended to brew real ale for local pubs. But during the five years he took to plan, finance and develop the project his thinking changed, and by the time he took possession of his purpose-built brewery complex on January 1 2000, his business model had evolved in a completely different direction. Most of the pubs and hotels in the area were wedded to lager and keg ale, he found; and they changed hands so often that even if he had made many converts to cask beer, he would have had to devote a huge amount of effort to making converts of the new owners. So, and still thinking about a mainly local trade, Richard had decided to major on bottled beers, creating a visitors centre and shop for tourists and selling beer to the many other gift-shops and grocers on the island.

Soon after opening, he had a completely unexpected call from Waitrose. Somehow, a sample of his 5 per cent ABV Blonde had fallen into the hands of the category buyer, who liked it. "It came completely out of the blue," he says. "We hadn't set out planning to tackle the supermarket trade – it tackled us. We had only just started up and such a big order was frankly scary."

Richard bit the bullet anyway; since he only had a primitive hand-bottler he decided to have the Waitrose order contract-bottled, sending a tanker of Blonde to Belhaven of Dunbar. Contract bottling spared him the risk of investing in a whistles-and-bells bottling line on the strength of a single order that might or not become regular. It also eased the cash-flow problems inherent in dealing with supermarkets' elastic credit-periods, since the beer went from the bottler to a bonded warehouse, and duty wasn't due until after it left the warehouse for the supermarket depot.

Waitrose was followed by Sainsburys, where Arran Blonde proved a good steady seller. Others followed, and Blonde is now on sale in every multiple in Scotland except M&S, and most of the bigger chains in England. It has been educational for the romantic artist-turned-brewer, but Richard has proved equal to every challenge thrown at him not only by the supermarkets but also by his contract bottlers. A change of bottling line at Belhaven forced him to move briefly to Forth Brewing in Alloa and Robinson's of Stockport, but the contract ended up at Cameron's of Hartlepool, where it remains.

As for dealing with the supermarkets, Richard says you have to learn to think like they do: "You're expected to be proactive." That doesn't mean cutting the ratecard price of his beer, which he says would "devalue the brand". But with most of them, Blonde is on a three-for-two or similar promotion for two or three months of the year, during which he only breaks even. But he isn't cynical: he believes the promotions don't just help the supermarkets but also encourage consumer trial and, with luck, repeat purchase of his brand. Efficiency in the brewery – and he has a list of improvements "as long as your arm" that he'd like to put in place – may keep his unit cost down; but hitting a (confidential) sales target reduces it "quickly and dramatically", so the sales volume generated by promotions of this kind is of critical importance.

Anyway, "export" sales of Arran Blonde to the mainland multiples now account for 90 per cent of his 5,000-barrel annual output – although he says he'd never turn his back on cask beer altogether. Cask versions of Arran beers are regulars (and medal winners) at CAMRA beer festivals both local and national.

Clearly it's unusual – and a testament to the quality of Arran Blonde – that the supermarkets beat a path to a brewer's door rather than have to be wooed like a coy maiden. But Richard, sculptor and artist, is happy with his lot.

www.arranbrewery.com

and Duchy Original brands and is perhaps not so small, is hugely successful in this field; last time I met any of its directors, they weren't looking too hard up. Hop Back Summer Lightning, Arran Blonde and Coniston Bluebird are also pretty ubiquitous. What these brewers have in common is the efficiency to work on slim margins, promotional discounts and long credit periods. In short, they're geared up for it.

But suspicion remains: for every supermarket-friendly small brewer there are a dozen who say from experience that no spoon is long enough to sup with this particular devil. Anyway, don't build the supermarket trade into your business plan: it'll be a year or two before you're ready to start submitting samples to them, if then.

Local Stockists

Far more important to the start-up small brewer – and, indeed, the established small brewer – is to build up a strong local trade. Looking round the retail scene in your trading area, this may not at first seem too promising a strategy: you can get canned Carling anywhere, but how many off-licences stock a local beer?

That's in large part due to the fact that the big cash and carries used by many independent retailers are even less micro-friendly than the supermarkets. But in East Anglia there's a dedicated band of small brewers who have joined forces to create an alternative market for their bottled beers, under the radar of the supermarkets and cash and carries, and perhaps everybody could learn a few dodges and wrinkles from the East Anglian Brewers' Co-operative (EAB).

EAB was founded in 2002, principally as a buying consortium, and now has around 40 brewery members. It sources all kinds of equipment, services and ingredients for its members, including barley from one of the region's top growers, which is specially (and separately) processed by Crisp's, a traditional floor-maltings at Great Ryburgh, Norfolk, thus guaranteeing traceability. EAB soon evolved from a buying consortium into a marketing operation helping to build collective sales of its members' bottled output, although their cask beers still compete freely in the pub trade. The philosophy is simple. While a pub may have only three or four handpumps and can only stock beers from one or two brewers at a time, beer shops and off-licences benefit from having as wide a variety of beers on the shelf as space allows. Therefore, while the EAB's members fight merrily for pub accounts, they see the wisdom of collaborating in the take-home trade. Being a "secondary co-operative", or one made up of independent members, EAB also qualifies for grants and other help from the region's Social Enterprise Board. It's been a highly successful experiment, albeit one that small brewers in other regions haven't copied.

When EAB was founded, the take-home trade in the region was as hard to penetrate as anywhere else. The group therefore set about targeting a new area of the trade: farm shops, garden centres, gift shops, post offices, delicatessens, camp-site shops and bars, traditional butcher's shops – any retailer, in fact, with a demand for genuine craft-made local produce. Many of these outlets aren't licensed: EAB therefore pays for them to get licences. The £400 it costs can quickly be recouped, and a whole new layer of retail opportunities is gradually being created.

Even if you're not a member of a co-operative like EAB, it can still be worth your while paying a shop of this kind to get a licence, and if you're paying, you can then institute an exclusive supply arrangement – a sort of tie, in fact. You might even share the cost with a local craft cidermaker or vineyard whose products will complement yours rather than compete with them. And if the shopkeeper is still a little wary, there's another step you can take: instead of selling them the beer in the normal way, you stock their shelves yourself and pay them commission on everything they sell. That way, the shopkeeper doesn't even have to pay upfront for stock and is taking no risk whatever. An inexpensive advertisement or two in the local CAMRA branch newsletter, with the cost perhaps shared by the shopkeeper, should generate enough custom to make the venture worth everybody's investment.

Farmers' Markets

Farmers' markets grew up as an evolution of farm shops, and in response to the difficulties farmers encounter in getting a decent price for their produce from the country's high street retailers. There are now around 500 regular markets throughout the UK, half of which are certified by the National Farmers' Retail & Markets Association (FARMA – **www.farmersmarkets.net**).

In their purest form, farmers' markets such as those certified by FARMA insist that stalls are only available to bona fide growers and producers, and there is sometimes an additional requirement that stallholders must be genuinely local. This is a source of much contention, often reaching Byzantine levels of intricacy. The purists say that shoppers who are led to believe that they're buying only local produce need to be protected from carpetbaggers who aren't really producers and aren't really local. But many small independent traders say that it only needs to be clear that all the stallholders are small and independent, and complain that they are often excluded from farmers' markets on mere technicalities. You may well think that the ideology of farmers' markets obscures their real point – that they're not Tesco; that shoppers are guaranteed a range of interesting, unusual and top-quality products; and that producers frozen out of the mainstream can find an outlet for their products. Be that as it may, farmers' markets are proving a useful outlet for more and more small, independent brewers.

The advantages are many. The overheads are low, for a start. Your stall can be as simple or as elaborate as you wish, but even the most ornate is only a comparatively modest one-off cost, and your pitch fee is likely to be £50 or less – much less, in some cases. Your margin will be good: one small brewer I know charges £2.50 for a 500ml bottle of a 5 per cent ABV beer, which is 70p more than a supermarket would charge for a similar product; and of course without the middleman, all the profit margin is his to keep.

There are drawbacks, though, says this same brewer. Markets are quite expensive in terms of time, he warns. Don't forget that you have to put up and take down your stall, which can add many hours to the proceedings. You also want to be the only brewer at that particular market: competition from a local cidermaker or vineyard is one thing; but there's only so much people can carry away from the market, and if they're buying beer you want to be sure it's your beer. Then again, you are very much in the hands of the weather and the organiser. A run of rainy market-days can see takings plunge, and if the organiser is no good at promotion you can stand there for an awfully long time without any customers. My friendly brewer's advice, though, is to stick it out for a while – if your first stall at a particular market doesn't work, give it two or three more attempts. Your first bad day may have been a one-off, so persist for long enough to see whether it's usually a busy event or not.

In licensing terms, you'll need a personal licence to run your stall (see Chapter Eight). What sort of licence the promoter needs is a much more complicated question. It could be argued that the marketplace needs a premises license, which is a virtual impossibility. It is theoretically possible to licence an open space, but the owner of the marketplace (normally the district council, which also happens to be the licensing authority) is unlikely to go to the trouble. On the other hand, it might be permissible to hold a farmers' market with only a temporary event notice (TEN), and indeed many are held on precisely that basis. However, a TEN only allows for 500 people to attend at a time. Either way, there is a "due diligence" defence for the stallholder, and provided you've done your absolute best to ensure you're operating legally, you'd be very unlucky to be prosecuted. As to whether the licensing authority would prosecute the promoter or the landowner (which is usually, as we've seen, the licensing authority) – well, Kafka must be chuckling in his grave. Meanwhile we await either a test case or, preferably, new guidance from the Department for Culture, Media and Sport (DCMS), which inexplicably is in charge of liquor licensing.

Assuming the current state of uncertainty in the licensing regime hasn't put you off, you need to find your nearest farmers' market. The FARMA website mentioned above is the best place to start, but it's an unregulated and largely unorganised (as opposed to disorganised) activity, and simply Googling "farmers' markets" will throw up many useful sites such as **www.lfm.org.uk** (farmers' markets in London) and **www.scottishfarmersmarkets.co.uk** (farmers' markets in Scotland). Other than that, it's largely a matter of local knowledge. Is there a farmers' market in your area? Has it got a brewery stall? If the answers are (a) yes and (b) no, then pounce.

Specialist Shops

Dotted around the country are 100 or so specialist beer shops, ranging from the enormous Beers of Europe in its vast complex of former granaries at Setchey just outside King's Lynn to the tiny Beer Essentials squeezed into a pedestrianised street in Horsham town centre.

Their number is slowly growing, but the amount of beer most of them can realistically be expected to order is measured in cases rather than pallets, and getting a few cases to an outlet on the other side of the country is prohibitively expensive. There are a handful of wholesalers that specialise in bottles, such as Beer Direct of Newcastle-under-Lyme (Phil Johnson, Tel 0116 273 4408 or email **peterjaye@beerdirect.co.uk**) and Beer Paradise, also the parent company of the Yorkshire-based BierRitz off-licence chain (**sales@beerparadise.co.uk**). So far, though, no one seems to have investigated the same sort of beer swaps for bottled beers that Crouch Vale and others do for cask beers; perhaps it's time someone tried. In the meantime you might consider pooling deliveries with one or more of your small brewing neighbours to target specialist shops in other parts of the country. If you can jointly

Case study: A brewery that only does Bottles – Uncle Stuart's, Lingwood, Norfolk

It was the continual pestering of friends who'd enjoyed their beers at parties that finally persuaded keen home-brewers Stuart and Lisa Evans to take their hobby seriously and, in 2002, to register their brewery as a commercial operation. But with a young family to feed, the couple couldn't give up their day jobs – Stuart managed a furniture shop in Norwich and Lisa was a child-minder – so for the first three years Uncle Stuart's was strictly a nice little earner on the side.

But brewing part-time brought its own constraints: competing with Norfolk's myriad better-established microbrewers for custom in the pub trade, with all the toing and froing delivering and collecting casks it implied, was out of the question. Uncle Stuart's therefore became the country's only brewery, so far as I know, to sell only bottled beers. It also saved Stuart and Lisa a considerable investment in casks and cask-washing equipment.

Soon after registering the brewery, Stuart and Lisa had made the acquaintance of Brendan Moore of Iceni Brewery, evangelist of the East Anglian Brewers' co-operative and apostle of developing new retail markets. That meant persuading local grocers, post offices and gift shops – and Norwich's independent department store, Jarrold's – to stock their beers. In time, it also led to the establishment of their own shop, the Little Beer Shop on the Blofield Leisure Village just off the A47 at Lingwood, and the abandonment of Stuart's day job.

Says Lisa: "The business was growing by leaps and bounds, but we didn't want to fight other brewers for a slice of the pub trade – we prefer the co-operative approach, and the idea of a shop was perfect for that. "Actually, the owner of the leisure village approached us. There's already a camping equipment shop and a farm shop and a coffee shop on the site, and now we have our own little log cabin there as well."

Blofield Leisure Village concentrates on selling as much local produce as possible, including locally made garden furniture, and the Little Beer Shop fits the concept perfectly. All the beers the shop sells are locally brewed, mostly but not all by fellow EAB members, and Stuart and Lisa also stock Whin Hill Cider from Wells-next-the-Sea and Norfolk fruit wines. For a while, Uncle Stuart's was also the EAB's e-commerce and mail order arm. But Stuart and Lisa gave it up after finding that it didn't generate enough sales to compensate for the harassment and anxiety involved – "Couriers," says Stuart, "seem unable to read the words 'glass' and 'fragile'!"

Actually, Uncle Stuart's does have a tiny population of casks, but they only ever go to local beer festivals and the brewery has not been tempted to enter the pub trade fray. The brewery itself produces eight beers, all sold bottle-conditioned, and the plant may well move from the Evanses' home to the Leisure Village in due course. And although theirs is a highly unusual and possibly unique business model, it's one Stuart and Lisa are committed to.

"We can fill 500 bottles an hour if we all pitch in," says Lisa. "The kids bring the bottles from the pallet, Stuart fills them, and I cap them, and we have a fast labelling machine. We've got a good rhythm going, and it's a right little hive of activity here on bottling days!"

As for making it pay without venturing into the cask trade – well, it's viable and growing, but it hasn't been an overnight sensation. "The shop made a profit in its first year, although not quite a living," says Lisa, who still has an evening job. "But that's a good record for a retail venture like this, and we're on course to make a living as well as a profit by the end of our second year. And if we do move the plant to the Leisure Village, we aim to do brewery tours as well."

www.littlebeershop.co.uk

rustle up an order of 60–70 cases (and in some cases, small shops will "share" orders with others) it's worth making up a pallet, which can be delivered anywhere in the country by a groupage distributor such as Palletways or Palletline for less than £50.

For complete details of specialist off-licences refer to the *Good Bottled Beer Guide* by Jeff Evans published by CAMRA.

Hotels and Restaurants

Brewers large and small have long bemoaned the fact that however good their beers are, the foodie end of the on-trade simply won't take them seriously. Wine lovers are well catered for: no restaurant would be caught dead with Piat D'Or or Blue Nun on its list. But ask for a beer in a restaurant with a wine list that starts at £20 and you're likely to be offered a bottled international lager, take it or leave it. Chefs and sommeliers are, by and large, horribly ignorant about beer: I was consulted on what real ales Gordon Ramsay Holdings should stock in its new pub in north London, the Warrington, and Ramsay's executive chef suggested Caffrey's! I also once, many years ago, had the temerity to complain that there were no American beers on sale in the American Bar at the Savoy; I might at least have expected Budweiser or Miller, although I suppose Sierra Nevada or Rogue would have been too much to hope for. I got a very haughty reply saying that these beers were too expensive. So does the Savoy buy its wines on price?

National newspapers are willing conspirators in this neglect of beer: all the broadsheets have wine writers; not one has a beer writer. And if, grudgingly, the food and drink editor condescends once in a while to include a piece about beer, the writing is generally deputed to the wine writer. This doesn't happen in Belgium, where top chefs as well as humble proles place craft-brewed beer among the nation's glories and regularly use it in cooking, as well as stocking it in their restaurants. In desperation, the British brewing industry declared 2004 as "The Year of Beer and Food", laying on food and beer banquets, dishing out recipe and beer-matching cards, and promoting food-friendly beers alongside the fine and not-so-fine wines in the dining rooms of their managed houses. It was a promotion that frankly sank without trace, not through lack of effort or lack of merit, but through the total indifference of the media and the catering trade. True, a couple of high-profile restaurateurs sourced pretty skimpy beer lists almost as a token gesture. But the fact that

Michel Roux jnr turned to InBev for all the beers on the highly publicised list he introduced at Le Gavroche demonstrates the scale of ignorance about beer at the top end of the catering trade.

Bottled beers ought to be the ideal way for hotels and restaurants to introduce foreign visitors and native gastronauts alike to the "wine of the country". Bottles are easy to store and dispense; they have a long shelf-life, so they won't go off; and they can be bought tentatively, a case or two at a time, so the financial risk is no more than the chef's teenage daughter's pocket-money. And for a restaurateur, a beer list alongside the wine-list creates consumer interest and is a good point of difference.

These are strong plus points with which enterprising small brewers can tackle the more enlightened hoteliers and restaurateurs in the district. But there's more: your beer's local provenance ought to be another attraction in these days of eco-consciousness; and if that isn't enough to make the sale, you could always offer the same deal you've offered the farm shop: no money upfront, but a commission on sales. But if this is a market you've decided to try, you might have to work harder still to make your sales. Offer to create a beer list tailored to the individual restaurant's cuisine, with full tasting notes and a description of each beer (not too gushing, though – adjectives exist to shore up a bad product, and a good product shouldn't need them). If it doesn't work, you've wasted nothing but time; if it does, you've got your beer into a high-profile outlet that will benefit your reputation as well as your balance sheet.

Mail Order and Web Sales

Mail order has always been a classic route to market for small manufacturers and traders in all sectors, including food and drink, who for one reason or another have found it difficult to break into the high street. And since the arrival of the internet mail order, or more properly e-commerce, has become an even more important alternative sales platform.

For obvious reasons, though, bottled products and couriers tend not to mix. Even those who claim to be specialists in the field can be more than a little heavy-handed. This has not deterred wine merchants, many of whom have long been enthusiastic exponents of mail order. But there's a good reason for their enthusiasm. Packaging bottles to withstand the rough handling they will undoubtedly suffer is an expensive and time-consuming business.

Couriers aren't cheap, either. But when you're selling high-value merchandise such as a case of 12 bottles of good-quality wine at £6 or £7 the bottle, the additional cost of packaging and delivery is a fairly, or at any rate acceptably, small addition to the price and the consumer is happy to pay it. However, the costs are exactly the same for a case of 12 bottles of beer at £2 or £3 the bottle, and suddenly the value doesn't look quite so good.

The cost of sending cases of beer around the country, and more particularly its effect on the consumer's perception of value, is one factor that deters many small brewers from getting involved in e-commerce. Dealing with couriers is an even greater one. It can take a long time to find a courier who understands that glass is fragile, according to Stuart Evans of Uncle Stuart's Brewery of Norfolk. And trying to claim insurance for the inevitable breakages is such a tangle, he says, that given the small sums involved it's not worth the effort. In fact Uncle Stuart's is getting out of ecommerce altogether, having tried a long list of courier companies and every variety of protective packaging under the sun.

Not all small brewers have had such an unhappy experience, though. Pitfield Brewery has had a profitable sideline in mail order sales for a quarter of century, and brewer Andy Skene says that after trying many couriers, the proportion of breakages is now well within acceptable limits. The couriers' most annoying habit, he says, is not informing the brewery of breakages. Either they're not delivered at all and are left in a corner of the depot, with brewer and customer wondering what has happened; or they're delivered, rejected, and returned to the depot as above, with the brewer not knowing anything is wrong and the customer fuming for a replacement or refund.

Having said that, there are still one or two highly successful ecommerce beer sellers, probably the biggest being Beers of Europe (BoE) of Setchey in Norfolk. It did take a lot of chopping and changing before the company found a courier it could trust (it won't divulge the company's name, though); and BoE's packaging is second to none.

Not only is BoE a big company itself (by the standards of the sector, at any rate), it's also part of a much bigger one. That means there's a lot of waste cardboard on its vast site – enough to justify investing in a shredder that cost "several thousand pounds". BoE now delivers its beers in two boxes, the outer being of chemically toughened cardboard, and the whole parcel is stuffed with shredded card which not only cushions the contents against the courier's buffeting but also efficiently soaks up the spillage when a bottle does get broken. This has proved so successful that BoE now collects and shreds waste cardboard from other factories and warehouses in the area. It's not without cost, though: BoE charges its customers a standard £7.49 per delivery, of whatever size. In theory the smaller orders subsidise the larger ones; actually the charges never quite cover the expenditure. On the plus side, the standard charge encourages customers to place bigger orders, so it's six of one and half-a-dozen of the other.

In conclusion, is ecommerce worth your while? Having spoken to two or three mail order/e-commerce specialists, I think Uncle Stuart's has been exceptionally unlucky; perhaps the way to find out whether your luck is equally bad is to give it a try. Certainly there are enough brewers and retailers engaged in selling beer around the country by the case to suggest it's worth their while. And thanks to the world wide web, you can now dip a toe into the mail order business without too much financial risk. In the past you had to advertise widely, persistently, and expensively to get a worthwhile response, but these days your website should generate enough orders to give you sufficient experience to base a longer-term decision on.

A final word on mail order, and perhaps one that might sway you one way or the other: it's specifically mentioned as a licensable activity in the latest guidance notes from the DCMS, and that means you now need a premises licence to do it. Having said that, getting a premises licence for a mail order operation where the public don't actually come on site should (according to my local council's licensing officer) be a pretty simple procedure, and you're probably getting a premises licence anyway to enable you to hold open days and beer festivals.

Chapter Eight
A Place of Your Own

There's a widely held view in small brewing these days that anyone who opens a brewery without a pub is mad. That's because the sector has become so competitive that custom is increasingly hard to come by and wholesale beer prices have actually fallen to £50 a firkin or even less. As we saw in Chapter Two, though, owning or leasing a pub of your own isn't necessarily the key to success; in fact the opposite can be true. For a pub is a huge investment – bigger, almost certainly, than the brewery itself; and if it turns out to be a dud, or if you're unlucky enough to appoint an unreliable manager, it can drag the whole enterprise down. The truth is that running a brewery and running a pub are quite different disciplines; despite the superficial appeal of guaranteed retail, most new brewers prefer to concentrate on what they're good at, for the simple reason that they're good at it.

Nevertheless, local brewers are either based at or very closely associated with about 130 pubs. In many of these cases, a publican has decided to turn brewer. Or, as we saw earlier, a brewer has found that a pub's outbuildings make a convenient home. And then there's the handful of local breweries including Beartown, Bath Ales, Ringwood, Butcombe and Hop Back that have made conscious decisions to go into retail wholeheartedly and have set about building up miniature tied estates of their own, although few own more than half-a-dozen or so pubs. But between them, small brewers only own a combined total of about 350 pubs, or 0.7% of the national stock; so they haven't exactly been falling over themselves to invest in licensed real estate.

Still, and even if the hundreds of thousands of pounds it takes to buy a viable or potentially viable pub is a bit rich for your blood, the fact remains that building up a decent delivery route gets harder and harder, making it a good idea to take as much control as you can over the retail of your beer. A pub of your own, though, isn't the only way to achieve it. But the whole process starts with getting a licence.

The 2003 Licensing Act

The Licensing Act 2003 which came into force in November 2005 brought fundamental changes to the system. Its most highly publicised provision, and the original idea that underlay its long and tortuous journey from green paper to enactment, was the abolition of the century-old concept of "permitted hours". Pubs can now, in theory, open whenever they choose – provided, of course, the licensing authority agrees.

And that was the Act's second main provision: it took the licensing function away from the magistrates and awarded it instead to district and borough councils. What this means, in practice, is that there is much wider and more detailed consultation than in the old days. The Act not only demands that licensees understand and uphold public policy on alcohol-related disorder, protection of minors, and so on; it also ensures that the police and fire services as well as the local community are closely involved in granting of liquor licences and imposing conditions.

In one sense this is a headache for licensees. Getting a new licence, or having an existing one varied, is far more costly and time-consuming than it used to be. On the other hand, you only have to jump through the council's hoops once; when you've done it, you're on a much more secure footing than you used to be. Provided you respect the terms of your licence, it's hard for the police or neighbours to get it reviewed or even revoked altogether (although the Act does give the police powers to close "trouble pubs" on the spot). You've filed your flight-plan, as it were, in exhaustive detail and everyone concerned has had a chance to suggest alterations and restrictions.

Everything has been openly negotiated and agreed, and as long as you stick to the operating schedule that the council has approved, nobody (in theory, at least) has a beef.

Another important provision of the 2003 Act was to split liquor licences in two, so you now have to have a personal licence as well as a premises licence. Ill-informed critics claimed this merely added another layer of bureaucracy to an already growing pile; in fact, it ended the cumbersome old system of licence transfers and made it much easier for licensees to migrate from pub to pub. In the old days, when there was just the one licence, a "protection order" had to be granted whenever a pub fell vacant in order to allow it to trade while a new licensee was appointed. This meant a day in court for someone – normally the brewery area manager – and another when a new tenant or manager was finally appointed. If the new appointee was found to be inadequate for some reason, the procedure had to be gone through again; if a pub was proving hard to let or was going through a rough patch, there could be several licence transfers in the space of a few months. Magistrates were often highly critical when they had to hear serial transfers for the same premises, which they occasionally even threatened to close down. Under the new system, the publican and the pub have their own licences, and the whole fiddle-faddle of transfers has been almost entirely eliminated.

Personal Licences

A personal licence is not all that hard to get, and it's worth your while holding one even if you have no immediate plans to acquire a licensed premises. Possession of a personal licence removes an otherwise almost insuperable bar to holding beer festivals or open days at the brewery; and it also allows you to retail liquor on other occasions – outdoor bars or beer-tents at the local village show, for instance. You can also hold the licence for a third party's beer festival – the local Lions Club or Rotary, or even the CAMRA branch of which you ought, by now, to be a member – where your beers will, of course, be prominently on sale. And if, as many local brewers do, you run outside bars at public functions on unlicensed premises – a ceilidh at the village hall, for instance – a personal licence is now indispensable. It is also usually necessary if you sell your beer at farmers' markets: very few of them are held in venues that have premises licences.

National Certificate for Personal Licence Holders

The personal licence is issued by your local council and costs £35. Before you apply, though, you'll need a National Certificate for Personal Licence Holders, and to get one of those you need to attend a one-day training course which has a 40-question multiple choice exam at the end. This will cost about £200. The British Institute of Innkeeping accredits some 500 training providers who run courses at over 5,000 locations all over the country – to find one, visit **www.biiab.org**. These training providers did not appear overnight when the Act came into force; for some time previously, magistrates had been stipulating that the requirement for applicants to demonstrate that they were "fit and proper persons" included not only a clean record but also some modicum of training. Many of those who set up as trainers were extremely experienced publicans or brewery staff, so the Act's training requirement really only codified what had been existing common practice. Many times the fear has been expressed that this compulsory training would prove a turn-off to the kind of individualistic mavericks who had often made top-class licensees in the past. But a quick look at the syllabus reveals it to be an extremely practical affair and one that even the most colourful of would-be publicans should be able to complete without having the individuality entirely squeezed out of them.

The sheer number of training providers means you can shop around for the cheapest, but before enrolling do make sure that they actually teach the one-day course, rather than just the five-day National Certificate in Licensed Retailing course. Not all of them do. For general information on the subjects covered by the course click on "find a qualification" on the left-hand side of the BIIAB home page; then click on "search" under the drop-down box at the foot of the page; and finally click on "Level 2 National Certificate for Personal Licence Holders". To gain a personal licence you will also need a Criminal Records Bureau check, which costs £31. Your local authority's liquor licensing department should give you an application form before you apply for the licence itself.

The best explanation of the 2003 Licensing Act I have come across is at **www.opsi.gov.uk/ACTS/en2003/2003en17.htm**. It's long, but well worth studying in detail, because even if you have been too ambitious on your plans to acquire your own pub, there are other uses for a premises licence.

Premises Licences

Your personal licence gives you leeway to indulge in a limited amount of retail on your premises – you can apply to hold up to 12 brewery open days or beer festivals a year, for instance, by submitting a temporary events notice. Increasingly, though – and especially if you've found a location that is worth visiting in its own right – some more regular form of retail is part of the local brewer's business model. It might just be selling polypins of bright beer at the door; it might be running a brewery shop; it might be establishing a visitors' centre with its own bar; it might be running a thoroughgoing brewery tap open to all and sundry. For any of these activities, you will need a premises licence; for among its many revolutionary aspects, the Licensing Act 2003 swept away two previous distinctions that made a retail operation of limited scope an easy option.

Licence Definitions

The first change was to redefine the term "wholesale". Before the Act came in, this was an expression of quantity, which meant that Majestic Wines outlets didn't need to be licensed because they sold alcohol only in wholesale quantities – by the case. It also meant that breweries and cider farms could sell wholesale quantities – a 36-pint polypin or a five-gallon polycask – to members of the public without a licence. Not any more. The Act has redefined "wholesale" as sales by a producer or distributor to licensed retailers, not to the public – a definition which, you may feel, better reflects the real meaning of the word.

The second was to sweep away the distinctions between full on-licences (for pubs), restricted on-licences (for restaurants) and off-licences. Getting an off-licence used to be a virtual formality – an application supported by a site map would be followed by an inspection by a panel of magistrates, and then a five-minute appearance in court with the payment of a nominal fee. I myself held an off-licence for a while, and getting it was simplicity itself. But all the different categories have now been subsumed under the general heading "premises licence", and the procedure for getting one is the same whether you only intend to sell polypins at the back door or to turn part of your premises into a pub.

As mentioned earlier, the new-look licensing procedure is principally about consultation and ensuring that you understand your responsibilities. There's a fearsome-looking 16-page form to fill in, but if you download it from your local council's website and give it a thorough read you'll see that much of it isn't relevant to you. That's one of the (admittedly slight, in this case) drawbacks to the new one-stop licensing procedure: a single form has to cover every licensable activity including showing films, putting on plays, promoting boxing matches and so on, which makes it a pretty bulky document. But most of it isn't concerned with liquor licensing at all and need not concern you, and the trickier sections, such as those to do with carrying out the council's licensing objectives, will be covered in your training course. (By the way, and although the form doesn't say so, the section covering "performance of dance" specifically excludes folk dancers such as the local morris side and their more extreme variant, molly dancers.)

The form, then, is fairly simple – you shouldn't need a solicitor to help you fill it out, and it should only take you a day or at most two. But the form is only the last part of the application process. You will also need to advertise your application in the manner prescribed by the licensing authority (which is not a new requirement); you will need to submit an accurate and intelligible plan of the premises, although hiring a proper draughtsman to do it probably won't be necessary; and you will need to submit copies to the "responsible authorities" (fire, police and so on) as stipulated by the licensing authority. Just as important as correctly observing the formalities is to consult as widely as possible in advance, both with neighbours (and the term "interested parties" includes schools and businesses as well as residents) and with the "responsible authorities" and the council's licensing officers. As with your planning application, if you do your homework thoroughly the application you finally submit should be bomb-proof.

Council Licensing Officers

The key to dealing with council licensing officers, as with planning officers, is to be calm, rational and friendly, and not to regard them as jobsworths to be either bamboozled or placated or both. If treated with respect they can be – and indeed most of them want to be – extremely helpful, and can give you the advice that makes sure your application succeeds. They can suggest ways in which the four licensing policy objectives can be met, many of which you may not have thought of. They will give you many invaluable tips, such as how to present the general description of the premises (section 3 of the application form) and the more detailed operating schedule as flexibly as possible, so you don't have to keep varying your licence whenever you want to try something new. They will have issues of their own to raise, too: you might, for instance, be in or near an area where public drinking is prohibited, and they may ask what steps you propose to deter customers from buying takeaways to drink in the street. (The best answer to this is to stress that your shop, if you have one, won't be selling cheap cans of lager or cider but extremely expensive bottles of hand-crafted ale – although once you've made this commitment you will be bound by it.).They may very well also want to know what provisions you have in mind for parking, toilets, noise abatement, control of numbers and public disorder contingency planning should you be hoping to run on-site beer festivals or open days. Going into this kind of detail may seem a bit previous, but it's as well to have considered such matters as site layout, advance publicity and limiting numbers even at this early stage.

Brewery Tours

More and more, brewers large and small are treating brewery tourism – guided tours and visitors' centres – as profitable parts of their businesses.

Brewery tours have been with us for many years, but have traditionally been seen, by established mainstream brewers and newcomers, as a sort of bolt-on – something you do as an after-hours profile-raiser for your trade customers and local CAMRA branches.

Typically, the brewer or a member of the brewing staff would be detailed to conduct the tour, which would be followed by a few sandwiches and some free samples in any space that happened to be convenient and available. Larger breweries might take on a retired employee or simply a knowledgeable enthusiast to conduct the tours, but essentially the whole thing would be pretty ad-hoc. Some breweries – especially those that had grown higgledy-piggledy over the years and were an obstacle course of steps, pipes, slippery bits and so on – were unhappy about giving tours at all and only did so as an occasional necessity. But demand grew, because breweries are interesting in a way that hosiery mills and plastic extrusions factories aren't (mainly because of the nature of the product!); slowly brewers came to see that here was a way of marketing themselves not just to key accounts and special interest groups but to the general public as well.

Planning the Tour

If you're going to run tours seriously you need to do it properly, which means devoting time, thought and investment to it. The very basics, in investment terms, are a comfortable and suitably decorated lounge where people can sit and enjoy their samples after the tour, and decent loos. And you need to devote some though to making the tour interesting, too: chances are, if you're a new brewery, that your site and plant aren't going to be too picturesque or have much history, so you need to work at making the tour as entertaining as possible. A confident, well-briefed and characterful tour guide who doesn't mumble but doesn't drone on and on either can make or break the whole thing (this is a branch of showbiz, after all). Samples of hops to smell and malt to chew are essential. Posters or wall-plaques explaining each step in the process create interest. Any "breweriana" you can rustle up adds atmosphere – difficult if you're a newcomer with no history of your own, but not impossible: CAMRA beer festivals usually host breweriana stalls and auctions.

The question with tours, though, is how far to take them. Are they still an after-hours bolt-on and even a bit of a distraction, or are you going to go the whole hog and organise and promote them properly? Often, demand for tours grows by word of mouth, and you may find yourself in the position of having a decision forced on you: are you going to turn down requests for guided tours you can't manage; or are you going to give in and provide the right facilities to meet the demand? And once you've done that, you have to sustain the level of demand, or whatever investment you've made could be wasted. The time to make up your mind about the potential of your brewery itself, then, is early on.

There's also the question of whether offering free samples as part of the charge for the tour constitutes a "licensable activity" under the 2003 Act. My local licensing authority thinks it isn't, because the main purpose of the activity is not the retail of alcohol. Others might think differently, and as there has yet to be a test case to decide who's right, it's wise to check what the local line of thinking is. And even those who think it isn't licensable will warn you against abusing their good will. If you are charging enough for a five-minute tour to cover seven or eight pints as well, it will be counted as "hidden retailing" – a tried and tested concept that goes way back to the days when shops were shut on Sunday except for the sale of perishables. (The test case was a furniture shop convicted of Sunday trading for selling bunches of carrots with free sofas thrown in.)

Brewery Shops

The next logical step is to add a small shop. Visitors like to have something to take away with them – a branded polo-shirt, perhaps, or a brewery beer glass. Or even some of its beer. A little souvenir and merchandise counter is easy enough to organise and adds value to the tour, from both the visitor's point of view and, of course, your own. But selling bottled beer or bright beer in polypins to take away is definitely a licensable activity and one for which you will require a premises licence as well as your own personal licence.

Many breweries now run a shop selling their own beers and branded merchandise and perhaps a little local produce – honey, cheeses, jam, chutneys and the like. It can be a valuable generator of cash-flow, but there are cost implications. The most obvious one is that you have to have someone to run it, even when it's not busy. And it has to be open at the stated times – nothing upsets shoppers, some of whom might have come a long way to buy your beer, like turning up when the shop says it's going to be open only to find it's shut. So someone has to be there all the time. If it's rarely busy, and you have someone at the brewery to run the office – to do the paperwork and take telephone orders – they might as well answer the bell too. The shop can also be the collection point for customers who have ordered polypins of bright beer for parties and other functions. The critical decision comes when the shop gets too busy to be run as an adjunct to your book-keeper's job description but not busy enough to justify a full-time employee. That's the point at which you have to decide which way to jump – whether to close down a profitable sideline, or invest in making it a separate profit-centre in its own right.

A handful of brewers have jumped in with both feet and expanded their on-site retail sideline into a thorough-going beer shop selling not only their own products but beers from other breweries, traditional ciders, country wines and imported speciality beers as well. It's a big investment, though: if you visit Hog's Back Brewery in Tongham, Surrey, or Tucker's Maltings in Newton Abbot, Devon (which is also home to the Teignworthy Brewery), you will find not hastily kitted-out sheds but beautifully designed and decorated boutiques with huge ranges of all sorts of wonders. They were not cheap to develop; they are not cheap to keep stocked; they are not cheap to staff; and they are not cheap to promote. Such places often acquire legendary status and generate significant custom simply by word of mouth, but you can't build that into your business plan!

Customer Car Parking

One key area for consideration when planning a shop is customer parking. There are two matters arising from this. One is that neighbours may object to your licence if they think it will mean customers will have to park in the surrounding streets. Another is that customers buy more when they can load their purchases straight into their car boots. Hackney Council's decision to ban parking in Pitfield Street was a contributory factor in the demise of the Beer Shop in Hoxton. But at Beers of Europe at Setchey near King's Lynn, which has enough parking for a fleet of trucks, customers browsing among the treasure-packed aisles aren't deterred from trying one of these and a couple of those by the knowledge that they've got to carry the whole lot 500 yards back to their cars. In addition, the knowledge that there's plenty of parking brings avid beer-lovers to Setchey from astonishing distances. So if you plan to make a shop a significant part of your business, you will need adequate customer car parking.

Brewery Visitors' Centres

The need to entertain tour parties saw sample-rooms morph first into shops and then into hospitality suites with bars and loos and displays of brewery memorabilia ferreted out from dark corners – when Greene King closed its maltings, for example, enough material came to light to fill an entire museum.

Breweries had often made a modest charge for tours, to cover the guide's pay and the cost of the free samples. But they had still seen tours more as a marketing tool than as a paying part of the business. Now they saw income from extra drinks for tour parties over and above the free samples, and sales of bottled beer and branded merchandise as profitable activities in their own right. In the last 15 years many established breweries have opened visitors' centres – there's a partial list in Chapter One – in a bid to slot themselves into the wider tourism industry.

In time, then, your well-conducted tours and small shop counter might

Case Study: A Brewery Licensed to the Hilt – High House Farm Brewery, Matfen, Northumberland.

Steve Urwin and Sally never really planned to become brewers. They were quite happy running their 200-acre family farm on Hadrian's Wall, where they grew wheat and barley and ran small beef herd and a flock of 150 sheep. But then in 2001 foot and mouth disease struck, and the Urwins realised they needed another string to their bow if the farm was to survive.

At the time the Hadrian's Wall Walk had just been completed, and a public footpath ran to it through the farm, so the Urwins were quite used to casual visitors and serious ramblers hiking through their yard. And a lovely yard it is to hike through, too, with its early Victorian stone buildings, all Grade II listed, and its glorious setting in the rolling Northumbrian hills. It was those natural advantages that decided the Urwins not just to install a brewery and join the competition for the local free trade (although as things have turned out, High House has enjoyed enviable success in gaining local distribution). Instead, they wanted to share everything they had with the thousands of visitors who flock to the region.

The brewery opened in 2003, after an 18-month planning process in which the Urwins overcame the local council's deep reservations by lining up as much support as they could and getting their application honed to the last detail. Crucially, their supporters included English Heritage, which co-operated with their plans to reroof and repoint the sturdy farm buildings sympathetically to make room for a purpose-built 10-barrel brewery, and backed their application for listed building consent.

Creating a visitors' centre was always part of the business plan, says Steve, but while he originally thought it would take five years to get round to it, the brewery was so successful that in fact it only took three. And what a visitors' centre the Urwins have developed! There's scarcely a whistle or a bell that High House doesn't have except perhaps B&B and a campsite, which might have been pushing it a bit.

As well as tours at a nominal charge per head, there's an exhibition of the brewing process and the farm's history in the old malt loft (and incidentally, High House beers are all brewed from the farm's own barley, which is malted by Thomas Fawcett at Castleford in Yorkshire).

Then there's a well-patronised coffee-shop where light meals are also served; a shop that sells High House beers alongside beer mustard, beer chutney, beer pickles, beer chocolate and even beer ice-cream, all locally made; a bar which is open to the general public as well as brewery visitors; a farm walk; and a function room.

All this has cost the Urwins a pretty penny – £300,000 all told. But then they already owned the premises, and the buildings were in good condition to start with, which all kept the bills down. And it's paid off handsomely. Within minutes of opening in September 2006, High House had been named Rural Retailer of the Year in the Countryside Alliance's Diversification Awards and had won bronze in the North-East England Tourism Awards. And while the Urwins had reckoned on 3,500 visitors in their first year, they actually saw more than 9,000 in their first 10 months, despite the rotten weather.

And after a patchy relationship with the local planning authorities, Steve describes the licensing process as "one of the easier bits". "We got on very well with the licensing authority," he says. "They were happy to work with us, and we got a licence for off-sales, on-sales, entertainment and music, with opening hours from 10am to midnight every day."

Not that High House actually runs all the activities for which it has approval, but the Urwins took very good advice to apply for more than they needed. "Apply for more than you want because you never know how the operation will evolve, and it's easier to get it all in one than have to go back later on," says Steve. "Even though you might never use all the permissions you apply for, get them anyway. Having to go back is expensive and time-consuming, and you never know – you might get knocked back!"

www.highhousefarmbrewery.co.uk

grow into a fully fledged visitors' centre, open throughout the day. This is a different level of operation – requiring paid staff, for one thing. Whether to take this step depends very much on your location and premises. If you're in a new unit on an industrial estate on the edge of a northern industrial town, the chances that you'll make much of a tourist attraction are pretty slim (although even northern industrial towns have their tourism initiatives these days, so don't dismiss the possibility out of hand). If you're in a historic barn on a picturesque farm in Devon, though, or in a converted 18th-century silk-mill in a quaint old Cotswold town, it's a very different proposition. Either way, before making plans, consult those who know. The local council, the local tourist board and Businesslink (never forget Businesslink!) will all be able to provide useful information on local visitor numbers, levels of investment in local tourism, and the possible availability of grants. The council and the tourist board will also be able to offer ongoing practical help in marketing and promoting your visitors' centre. You may even find that a sound and well thought out proposal to develop your brewery as a visitor attraction is a plus-point in your planning application – especially as promoting self-sustaining rural communities is one of the 2003 Licensing Act's stated objectives.

And finally, never forget the marketing value of welcoming people into your brewery and sending them away with a story to tell their drinking buddies and, hopefully, your logo emblazoned on their sweatshirts. You've entered the tourism industry now, and it's essential to send your visitors away satisfied. That means never doing anything half-heartedly. If visitors feel they've had a substandard experience at your brewery, the feeling of dissatisfaction will embrace your products as well – and they'll be telling their friends and neighbours bad things about you when they get home.

Your Pub

All this brings us back rather neatly to where we started – whether or not to invest in a pub of your own. Running a pub, as I have said, is a very different business from running a brewery:

- You will be face to face with the public, and if you're no good at it you'll soon come unstuck.
- You will be hiring staff – maybe a manager for the pub, certainly bar staff and cleaners and possibly kitchen staff as well – and employment law is a whole new area of knowledge in itself.

- You will need to maintain investment in customer facilities – scuffed carpets and chipped urinals need to be replaced.
- There is an unimaginable tangle of compliance issues – you wouldn't believe the amount of time the average publican spends on paperwork these days. It's not something you want to slide into.

But just by running brewery tours, a shop and maybe a visitors' centre, you will be gradually acquiring the marketing, planning, budgeting, administrative and supervisory skills you'll need to run a pub – or pubs. One of the best ways to learn is to do, and gradually stepping up the retail side of your brewery will enable you to learn a step at a time, even leaving yourself leeway to fail without failing too disastrously. You are also, at each stage of development, increasing the sale value of your business without investing too much at a time.

Buying a pub may be your next logical step, but it's a big one. It's a very expensive and extremely complicated business and calls for detailed professional advice from one of the many specialist estate agents, correctly termed licensed trade property brokers, such as Christie & Co, Fleuret's, Guy Simmonds or Humberstone's. Like ordinary estate agents, they also offer financial advice, and in some cases run full licensed trade training courses as well. The best way of contacting them – and of browsing a huge number of pubs for sale – is to visit the sites of the licensed trade newspapers, the *Morning Advertiser* (**www.morningadvertiser.co.uk**) and *The Publican* (**www. thepublican.com**). It's a good idea anyway, as we saw in Chapter One, to subscribe to both of them.

Freehold or Leasehold

Buying outright has been made much more difficult by the fact that freehold prices have soared in recent years. This is largely thanks to the intervention of acquisitive pubcos, which snap up freeholds for silly prices. An alternative is to lease from a pubco instead; but although the ingoings are much, much lower, it's probably a bad idea. For a start, rents are sky-high, and you may soon find yourself struggling to pay them. And although few pubcos these days have a formal "upwards only" clause in the rent review section of their leases, in practice it is extremely difficult to get a reduction! Worse, you may well find that you can't even sell your own ales in your own pub. For these leases are invariably tied; and even if you negotiate an exemption, there's

Case Study: When Owning a Pub Didn't Quite Work Out – Rebellion Brewery, Marlow, Buckinghamshire

It seemed a golden opportunity for Marlow's Rebellion Brewery when the lease of the Three Horseshoes just 500 yards away came up.

Rebellion had been running successfully for 10 years and had built up a big local following with its shop, tours, beer club and open days. It had already had to move once, but there was no scope to develop a brewery tap on the site, and the pub's sudden availability was a godsend. True, the Three Horseshoes was owned by Enterprise Inns, but property prices in the area made an outright freehold purchase prohibitive. And as the pub had been closed for three months when partners Tim Coombes and Mark Gloyens heard the lease was for sale, Enterprise was lenient with the premium.

It all looked pretty good. But four years later, Rebellion abandoned the experiment and sold the lease to pub manager Nigel Douglas, who still stocks the brewery's beer. What had gone wrong?

Well nothing, really. The relationship with Enterprise worked well. Nigel turned out to be a great manager. Locals were delighted that their neighbourhood brewery had its own tap at last and flocked there, and in 2005 the local CAMRA branch voted it Pub of the Year. Diners gave it their seal of approval, too: although the cooking had no pretensions to haute cuisine, it was all top-quality stuff at sensible prices. The pub quickly got busy.

Despite the pub's success, though, it was a constant worry.

"Nigel was a great manager, but it was always in the back of your mind that he might decide to move on, or fall under a bus," says Tim. "These things happen, and the thought of having to find a new manager as good as him was a constant source of stress.

"There are other worries with a pub, too: there's a massive amount of cash and some very high-value stock in any pub; no matter how good your control systems, if someone decides to start pilfering there's precious little you can do about it. We never had that problem. But it's all part of the risk, and running a pub is a big risk.

"Staff turnover is another headache. There's a very fast rate of staff turnover in the pub trade because the wages are so poor, but if you pay a decent wage your margin disappears. "It might seem a better idea to put in a tenant or lessee rather than a manager. That way, all the problems with staff and so on are his, not yours, but the trade-off is that you lose control over the style of operation. The lessee could turn it into a restaurant or a young people's pub and you'd still get your rent, but your ale sales would fall."

Running the pub was actually far more stressful than running the brewery, says Tim. It absorbed a huge amount of time and energy and, worse, it didn't make much money.

"The amount of profit it made for the brewery relative to its turnover was negligible," says Tim. "We paid better than average wages to get and keep good staff, and we invested heavily in beer quality. If you're setting out your stall as a showcase for your beers, the quality has to be spot-on all the time. We hired a cellar services contractor to clean and inspect all the lines every week, and that isn't cheap and we allowed Nigel unlimited ullage – So after four years Rebellion sold the lease to Nigel, with a tie, and got its original investment back without losing any sales – a good result all round. And Tim isn't entirely downbeat about running a pub of your own.

"Potentially there are huge advantages to having a flagship for your brewery," he says. "And lots of breweries have done really well with it. Some of them have even built up little tied estates of five or six really cracking pubs doing five barrels a week each, and if you can do that you're straight up to your 3,000-barrel duty relief limit with no further effort.

"But you need to go into it with your eyes open. Expect it to take up a third of your time at least. Expect to invest double the capital you'd originally planned, and then some. And budget for success – if you aim double the dining trade, say, the kitchen has to be able to cope. If you can get all that right, and get the right people in, there are potentially huge benefits – not least that it vastly increases the value of your brewery should you need or want to sell up.

"But it's a big investment in a specialist operation, and if you're not a specialist yourself you have entrust what is a huge part of your business to someone else, someone you probably don't know all that well. And in the end, we decided that it wasn't for us. It's all worked out okay in the end, but I don't think we'll ever get another pub."

www.rebellionbeer.co.uk

no guarantee it will last. One brewer I know did just that and built up a very successful and popular business – until the pubco sold the pub over his head to a regional brewer, which immediately ordered him to take his beers off the bar and revert to tied status. He tried to argue his corner, but legally he didn't have a leg to stand on and found himself saddled with an expensive lease that was no good to his brewery at all. His is not the only case of brewers getting into trouble by leasing pubs rather than buying them freehold. Having said that, there are a small number of free-of-tie leasehold pubs around, often belonging to a private owner. The National Trust, for instance, owns a scattering of historic pubs around the country, one of which – the 15th-century King's Head in Aylesbury – is run by the Chiltern Brewery. The opportunity to acquire a free-of-tie lease like this comes but rarely, although it's worth keeping an eye out in case one comes up.

A third course of action is to acquire an unlicensed premises and turn it into a pub. This is exactly how the JD Wetherspoon empire was founded: Tim Martin, a barrister by training, started out in the 1970s by acquiring old shoe-shops, garages and minimarts and turning them into characterful local pubs. His legal background stood him in good stead, because in those days it was extremely difficult to persuade magistrates to grant new licences. It's easier now, thanks in large part to him; indeed Wetherspoon's has made a speciality out of acquiring character properties such as disused banks and cinemas and turning them into splendid and often award-winning pubs: the Winter Gardens in Harrogate is a brilliant example. But it's almost certainly far too ambitious for anyone at entry level. Having said that, many smaller brewers have bought less grandiose historic properties, often in industrial heritage sites, and made wonderful pubs of them. Grainstore's brewery and pub next to the railway station in Oakham is an outstanding example, as is the old station at Codsall in the West Midlands, turned into a fantastic pub by local family brewer Holden's. In terms of cost, this may well be your best way into the pub trade. Certainly there are more than a few microbrewers who have successfully turned a part of their brewery into a successful bar. The drawback is that projects of this kind can easily become all-consuming in terms of your time and energy, and of capital, distracting you from the core business of running and growing your brewery.

Transfer of Premises Licence

Most of the steps described above assume that you're seeking a completely new premises licence to develop the retail activities based on your brewery site. If you're taking over an existing pub or shop, of course, you won't need a new licence; you can simply transfer the existing one.

I use the word "simply" here advisedly. The sections of the 2003 Act dealing with premises licence transfer look incredibly involved, largely because the Act is seeking to cover all possible eventualities. Actually the transfer is effected by the outgoing and incoming licensee signing a single form and one of them (you, probably) paying the council a small administration fee.

That's not the end of it, though. When you move in the existing premises licence will still be in force. That covers the opening hours, including seasonal variations as detailed in the operating schedule, and the previous licensee's choice of licensable activities – for instance, you may find you can have a disco but not a folk night, because the existing licence permits dancing but not live music. That means that if you want to change the way your new pub is run not just substantially but even slightly, you may very well need to change the terms of the premises licence too. You can get an application form to vary the licence from the council; when you do you'll find it's almost identical to an entirely new application.

Before you fill it in, it's wise to go through a thorough consultation exercise with the interested parties and responsible authorities. You might perhaps drop a letter through all the doors within reach asking residents if they had any reservations about the way the pub was run in the past and what improvements, if any, they would like to see. Check with the local police, too – there's normally an officer detailed to deal with licensing matters – to find whether the pub had a bad record and, if so, what steps they would recommend to clean it up.

Many might find this sort of consultation tedious or even an unwarranted intrusion. But remember: the best pubs are at the heart of their communities. Your neighbours are also going to be your regulars – unless, that is, you start off by picking a fight with them.

Case Study: A Classic Brewpub – The Chequers, Binham, Norfolk

When Steve and Alex Chroscicki finally found the Chequers at Binham in the rural depths of North Norfolk, it was the end of a two-year hunt for pub to site a brewery in.

Steve, an engineer by trade, had been made redundant by Parisa Café-Bars, an ambitious venture intended to be a chain of 250 boutique breweries across the world. Only one ever opened, in exotic Putney, and Steve ran it. By the time it had run its course, the brewing bug had bitten.

Steve and Alex took the lease of the Chequers – which is, rather unusually, owned by a local charity – in 2003 and originally planned to renovate its barn as the site of the planned brewery. After much havering, though, their bank wouldn't lend them enough on the security of an unassignable lease, so the Front Street Brewery (the pub is in Front Street) was installed in the old ladies' loo across the yard instead.

From the start, there were issues of size. A five-barrel brewery was squeezed into the building, but cask washing and bottling on a tiny hand-bottler have to be carried out in the pub's cellar. And as the local waterworks hadn't been expanded since it was built in the 1940s or 50s, the water company even tried to stop the brewery opening on the grounds that the drainage was inadequate. In the end Steve challenged the company to set him an effluent limit. It did – but such a small one that any spoiled beer has to be taken away to be disposed of elsewhere.

The local council, by contrast, was a delight. The planning officers even told the Chroscickis that they didn't need planning permission as brewing would be ancillary to pub use. A lot of councils probably wouldn't agree, but the only town hall official who came on site after that was the building inspector!

Size issues have continued to dog the brewery's progress. Binham is extremely rural, and there's no public transport, so the Chequers has never become the magnet for beer-hunters that more accessible brewpubs have. Trade is good in summer, but never quite good enough to justify hiring staff to cover the bar while Steve is brewing. And in winter sales are so low that Steve has to sell through wholesalers just to keep the whole thing ticking over. That means he has to keep a stock of nearly 100 casks at £50–£80 each, many of which spend months out in trade and some 10 per cent of which vanish every year.

As a result of all this, Steve is desperate to expand, off-site if necessary.

"It's been interesting and worthwhile but I think the lesson is not to start a brewery at a small rural pub," he says. "There is money to be made – your own beer is cheaper than beer you buy in, and you can use it to do swaps with other breweries too, but you need to be of a size where you can take on bar staff and concentrate on the brewing.

"Any good-sized wet-led town pub could do well out of its own brewery, but to make the best of the brewery here I definitely need to expand."

www.the-chequers-inn.hostingbt.com

The Microbrewers' Directory

We have done our best to provide the most comprehensive list of microbreweries in the UK, at the time of going to press (May 2009). The Society of Independent Brewers (SIBA) defines a microbrewer as one that produces up to 5,000 HL per annum. It's not an exact science, but we have tried to be as accurate as we possibly can in compiling this list. Inevitably some breweries may have slipped through the net, and some may be reproduced here that fall outside of SIBA's definitions. We hope you will let us know.

ENGLAND

BEDFORDSHIRE

B&T Brewery Ltd
The Brewery, Shefford, SG17 5DZ
01462 815 080
www.banksandtaylor.com

Potton Brewery Co
10 Shannon Place, Potten, Sandy, SG19 2PZ
01767 261 042
www.potton-brewery.co.uk

White Park Brewery
Perry Hill Farm, Bourne End Road,
Cranfield, MK43 0BA
01223 911 357
www.whiteparkbrewery.co.uk

BERKSHIRE

Butts Brewery Ltd
Unit 6a Northfield Farm Industrial Estate,
Wantage Road, Great Shefford,
Hungerford, RG17 7BY
01488 648 133
www.buttsbrewery.com

Loddon Brewery Ltd
Dunsden Green Farm, Church Lane, Dunsden,
Reading, RG4 9QD
01189 481 111
www.loddonbrewery.com

West Berkshire Brewery Co
The Old Bakery, Yattendon,
Thatcham, RG18 0UE
01635 202 968
www.wbbrew.co.uk

Zerodegrees Reading
9 Bridge Street, Reading, RG1 2LR
01189 597 959
www.zerodegrees.co.uk

BRISTOL

Arbor Ales Ltd
The Old Tavern, Blackberry Hill, Bristol, BS16 1DB
07970 920 627
www.arborales.co.uk

Bath Ales
Units 3-7 Caxton Industrial Estate,
Tower Road North, Bristol, BS30 8XN
01179 474 797
www.bathales.com

Bristol Beer Factory
The Beer Factory, Unit A The Old Brewery,
Durnford Street, Bristol, BS3 2AW
01179 026 317
www.bristolbeerfactory.co.uk

Butcombe Brewery Ltd
Butcombe, Bristol, BS40 5PA
01275 472 240
www.butcombe.com

The Avon Brewing Company Ltd
Unit 4 Lawrence Hill Industrial Estate,
Russell Town Avenue, Bristol, BS5 9LT
01179 553 353
www.avonbrewing.co.uk

Zerodegrees Bristol
53 Colston Street, Bristol, BS1 5BA
01179 252 706
www.zerodegrees.co.uk

BUCKINGHAMSHIRE

Chiltern Brewery
Nash Lee Road, Terrick,
Aylesbury, HP17 0TQ
01296 613 647
www.chilternbrewery.co.uk

Concrete Cow Brewery
59 Alston Drive, Bradwell Abbey, Milton
Keynes, MK13 9HB
01908 316 794
www.concretecowbrewery.co.uk

Old Luxters Farm Brewery
Chiltern Valley Vineyard, Hambledon,
Henley-on-Thames, RG9 6JW
01491 638 330
www.chilternvalley.co.uk/brewery.html

Oxfordshire Ales
12 Pear Tree Farm Industrial Units, Bicester
Road, Marsh Gibbon, Bicester, OX27 0GB
01869 278 765
www.oxfordshireales.co.uk/bottledales.htm

Rebellion Beer Company
Bencombe Farm, Marlow Bottom,
Marlow, SL7 3LT
01628 476 594
www.rebellionbeer.co.uk

Vale Brewery Co
Tramway Business Park, Brill, HP18 9TY
01844 290 008
www.valebrewery.co.uk

CAMBRIDGESHIRE

Cambridge Moonshine Brewery
28 Radegund Road, Cambridge, CB1 3RS
07906 066 794

City of Cambridge Brewery
Ely Road, Chittering, Cambridge, CB5 9PH
01223 864 864
www.cambridge-brewery.co.uk

Devil's Dyke Brewery
8 Fair Green, Reach, Cambridge, CB25 0JD
01638 743 816

Hereward Brewery
50 Fleetwood, Ely, CB6 1BH
01353 666 441

Kilderkin Brewing Company
1 Mill Road, Impington, CB24 9PE
www.kilderkin.co.uk

Milton Brewery
Unit 111 Norman Industrial Estate,
Cambridge Road, Milton,
Cambridge, CB4 6AT
01223 226 198
www.miltonbrewery.co.uk

Oakham Ales
2 Maxwell Road, Woodston,
Peterborough, PE2 7JB
01733 370 500
www.oakhamales.com

Son of Sid Brewery
The Chequers, 71 Main Street, Little
Gransden, Sandy, SG19 3DW
01767 677 348

Tydd Steam Brewery
Kirkgate, Tydd St. Giles,
Wisbech, PE13 5NE
01945 871 020

Uffords Ales
Ye Old White Hart, Main Street, Ufford nr
Stamford, PE9 3BH
01780 740 250
www.ufford-ales.co.uk

CHESHIRE

3 Rivers Brewery Ltd
Delta House, Greg Street, Stockport, SK5 7BS
0161 477 3333
www.3riversbrewery.co.uk

Beartown Brewery
Bromley House, Spindle Street,
Congleton, CW12 1QN
01260 299 964
www.beartownbrewery.co.uk

Betwixt Beer Co Ltd
The Brewery, 8 Pool Street,
Birkenhead, CH41 3NL
0151 647 7688
www.betwixtbeer.co.uk

Blakemere Brewery
Blakemere Brewery, Blakemere Craft Centre,
Chester Road, Sandiway, CW8 2EB
01606 301 000
www.norbrew.co.uk

Bollington Brewing Co Ltd
c/o Vale Inn, Adlington Road, Bollington, SK10 5JT
01625 575 147
www.valeinn.co.uk

Borough Arms Brewery
The Borough Arms, 33 Earle Street,
Crewe, CW1 2BG
01270 254 990
www.borougharmscrewe.co.uk

Brimstage Brewing Co Ltd
Home Farm, Brimstage Lane,
Brimstage, CH63 6LY
0151 342 1181
www.brimstagebrewery.com

Dunham Massey Brewing Company
100 Oldfield Lane, Dunham Massey,
Altrincham, WA14 4TY
0161 929 0663
www.dunhammasseybrewing.co.uk

Frodsham Brewery
Lady Heyes Craft Centre, Kingsley Road,
Frodsham, WA6 6SU
01928 787 917
www.frodshambrewery.co.uk

Shaw's Brewery
The Old Stables, Park Works, Park Road,
Dukinfield, SK16 5LX
0161 330 5471

Spitting Feathers Brewery
Common Farm, Common Lane, Waverton,
Chester, CH3 7QT
01244 332 052
www.spittingfeathers.org

Storm Brewing Co Ltd
2 Waterside, Macclesfield, SK11 7HJ
01625 431 234

The Coach House Brewing Co Ltd
Wharf Street, Warrington, WA1 2DQ
01925 232 800
www.coach-house-brewing.co.uk

WC Brewery
3 Micklegate, Mickle Trafford,
Chester, CH2 4TF
www.wcbrewery.com

Weetwood Ales Ltd
Weetwood Grange, Weetwood,
Torporley, CW6 0NQ
01829 752 377
www.weetwoodales.co.uk

Wincle Beer Co Ltd
Heaton House Farm, Heaton, Rushton
Spencer, Macclesfield, SK11 0RD
01260 226 166
www.winclebeer.co.uk

Woodlands Brewing Company
Unit 3 Meadow Lane Farm, London Road,
Stapeley, Nantwich, CW5 7JU
01270 841 511
www.woodlandsbrewery.co.uk

CORNWALL

Atlantic Brewery
Treissaac Farm, Treissaac, Newquay, TR8 4DX
0870 042 1714
www.atlanticbrewery.com

Blackawton Brewery
Unit 7 Peninsular Park, Forge Lane, Moorlands
Trading Estate, Saltash, PL12 6XL
01752 848 777
www.blackawtonbrewery.com

Blue Anchor
50 Coinagehall Street, Helston, TR13 8EL
01326 562 821
www.spingoales.com

Coastal Brewery
Unit 9b Cardrew Industrial Estate,
Redruth, TR15 1SS
07875 405 407
www.coastalbrewery.co.uk

Driftwood Spars
Trevaunance Cover, Quay Road,
St Agnes, TR5 0RT
01872 552 428
www.driftwoodspars.com

Keltek Brewery
Candela House, Cardrew Industrial Estate,
Redruth, TR15 1SS
01209 313 620
www.keltekbrewery.co.uk

Lizard Ales Ltd
Old Bunker, Treleaver, Coveack,
Helston, TR12 6SE
01326 281 135
www.lizardales.co.uk

Organic Brewhouse
Unit 1 Rural Workshops, Higher Bochym,
Cury Cross Lanes, Helston, TR12 7AZ
01326 241 555
www.theorganicbrewhouse.com

Penpont Brewery
Inner Trenarrett, Altarnun,
Launceston, PL15 7SY
01566 86 069
www.penpontbrewery.co.uk

Penzance Brewing Co Ltd
Star Inn, Crowlas, Penzance, TR20 8DX
01736 740 375

Ring O'Bells Brewery Ltd
Pennygillam Way, Pennygillam Industrial
Estate, Launceston, PL15 7ED
01566 777 787
www.ringobellsbrewery.co.uk

Skinner's Brewing Co Ltd
Riverside, Newham Road, Truro, TR1 2DP
01872 271 885
www.skinnersbrewery.com

The Doghouse Brewery Co
Scorrier, Redruth, TR16 5BN
01209 822 022

Wooden Hand Brewery
Unit 3 Grampound Road Industrial Estate,
Grampound Road, Truro, TR2 4TB
01726 884 596
www.woodenhand.co.uk

CUMBRIA

Abraham Thompson's Brewing Co
Flass Lane, Barrow-in-Furness, LA13 0AD
07708 191 437

Barngates Brewery Ltd
Barngates, Ambleside, LA22 0NG
01539 436 575
www.barngatesbrewery.co.uk

Beckstones Brewery
Upper Beckstones Mill, The Green,
Millom, LA18 5HL
01229 775 294
www.beckstonesbrewery.co.uk

Blackbeck Brewery
Blackbeck Hotel, Blackbeck,
Egremont, CA22 2NY
01946 841 661
www.blackbeckbrewery.co.uk

Castle Brewery
Cockermouth, CA13 9NE
01900 823 214
www.jenningsbrewery.co.uk

Cumberland Breweries Ltd
The Forge, Great Corby, Carlisle, CA4 8LR

Cumbrian Legendary Ales
Old Hall Brewery, Hawkshead,
Ambleside, LA22 0QF
01539 436 436
www.cumbrianlegendaryales.com

Dent Brewery
Hollins, Cowgill, Sedburgh, LA10 5TQ
01539 625 326
www.dentbrewery.co.uk

Derwent Brewery
Units 2a-2b Station Road Industrial Estate,
Silloth, Wigton, CA7 4AG
01697 331 522

Foxfield Brewery
Prince of Wales, Foxfield, Broughton in
Furness, LA20 6BX
01229 716 238
www.princeofwalesfoxfield.co.uk

Geltsdale Brewery Ltd
Unit 6 Old Brewery Yard, Craw Hall,
Brampton, CA8 1TR
01697 741 541
www.geltsdalebrewery.com

Hardknott Brewery
The Woolpack Inn, Boot, Holmrook, CA19 1TH
01946 723 230
www.woolpack.co.uk

Hawkshead Brewery Ltd
Mill Yard, Staveley, LA8 9LR
01539 822 644
www.hawksheadbrewery.co.uk

Hesket Newmarket Brewery
Old Crown Barn, Hesket Newmarket, CA7 8JG
01697 478 066
www.hesketbrewery.co.uk

Keswick Brewing Co
The Old Brewery, Brewery Lane,
Keswick, CA12 5BY
01768 780 700
www.keswickbrewery.co.uk

Kirkby Lonsdale Brewery
Old Station Yard, Kirkby Lonsdale, LA6 2HP
01524 272 221
www.kirkbylonsdalebrewery.com

Loweswater Brewery
Kirkstile Inn, Loweswater, Cockermouth, CA13 0RU
01900 85 219
www.kirkstile.com

Strands Brewery
Strands Hotel, Wasdale, Seascale, CA20 1ET
01946 726 237
www.strandshotel.com

The Bitter End Pub & Brewery
15 Kirkgate, Cockermouth, CA13 9PJ
01900 828 993
www.bitterend.co.uk

The Coniston Brewing Co Ltd
Coppermines Road, Coniston, LA21 8HL
01539 441 133
www.conistonbrewery.com

The Great Gable Brewing Co Ltd
Wasdale Head Inn, Wasdale Head,
Seascale, CA20 1EX
01946 726 229
www.greatgablebrewing.com

Tirril Brewing Ltd
Red House Barn, Long Marton, Appleby-in-
Westmorland, CA16 6BN
01768 361 846
www.tirrilbrewery.co.uk

Ulverston Brewing Company
Diamond Buildings, Pennington Lane,
Lindal-in-Furness, LA12 0LE
01229 584 280
www.ulverstonbrewing.co.uk

Watermill Brewing Company
Watermill Inn, Ings, Kendal, LA8 9PY
01539 821 309
www.watermillinn.co.uk

Whitehaven Brewing Co Ltd
Croasdale Farm Barn, Ennerdale, Cleator, CA23 3AT
01946 861 755
www.twbcl.co.uk

Yates Brewery
Ghyll Farm, Westnewton, Wigton, CA7 3NX
01697 321 081
www.yatesbrewery.co.uk

DERBYSHIRE

Amber Ales Ltd
PO Box 7277, Ripley, DE5 4AP
01773 512 804
www.amberales.co.uk

Ashover Brewery
1 Butts Road, Ashover, Chesterfield, S45 0EW
01246 590 888
www.ashoverbrewery.com

Blue Monkey Brewing Ltd
Unit 1 Enterprise Court, Manners Ave,
Manners Industrial Estate, Ilkeston, DE7 8EW
07500 555 595

Bottle Brook Brewery
10 Church Street, Kilburn, Belper, DE56 0LU
07971 189 915

Brampton Brewery Ltd
Unit 5 Chatsworth Business Park,
Chatsworth Road, Chesterfield, S40 2AR
01246 221 680
www.bramptonbrewery.co.uk

Derby Brewing Co Ltd
Masons Place, Nottingham Road, Derby, DE21 6AQ
01332 242 888
www.derbybrewing.co.uk

Derventio Brewery
Trusley Brook Farm, Sutton on the Hill,
Ashbourne, DE6 5JP
07816 878 129
www.derventiobrewery.co.uk

Falstaff Brewery
24 Society Place, Derby, DE23 6UH
01332 342 902
www.falstaffbrewery.co.uk

Funfair Brewing Company
34 Spinney Road, Ilkeston, DE7 4LH
07971 540 186
www.funfairbrewingcompany.com

Globe Brewery
The Globe, 144 High St West, Glossop, SK13 8HJ
01457 852 417
www.theglobepub.org

Haywood Brewery
Callow Top Holiday Park, Buxton Road,
Sandybrook, Ashbourne, DE6 2AQ
01335 344 020
www.callowtop.co.uk

Howard Town Brewery Ltd
Unit 10 Howard Town Mill, Mill Street,
Glossop, SK13 8PT
01457 869 800
www.howardtownbrewery.co.uk

John Thompson Inn and Brewery
Ingleby Lane, Ingleby, Melbourne, DE73 1HW
01332 862 469
www.johnthompsoninn.com

Leadmill Brewery Co
Park Hall, Park Hall Road, Ripley, DE5 8PX
01332 883 577
www.leadmillbrewery.co.uk

Leatherbritches Brewery
Bentley Brook, Fenny Bentley, Ashbourne, DE6 1LF
01335 350 278
www.bentleybrookinn.co.uk

Nutbrook Brewery Ltd
6 Hallam Way, West Hallam, DE7 6LA
0800 458 2460
www.nutbrookbrewery.com

Peak Ales
The Barn Brewery, Chatsworth, Bakewell, DE45 1EX
01246 583 737
www.peakales.co.uk

Spire Brewery
Unit 2-3 Gisbourn Close, Ireland Business
Park, Staveley, Chesterfield, S43 3JT
01246 476 005
www.spirebrewery.co.uk

The Brunswick Brewery Ltd
1 Railway Terrace, Derby, DE1 2RU
01332 290 677
www.brunswickinn.co.uk

The Headless Brewing Company
The Flowerpot, 23-25 King Street,
Derby, DE1 3DZ
01332 204 955

The Hope Valley Brewing Co Ltd
Castleton Youth Hostel, Hope Valley, S33 8WG
0845 371 9628

The Wild Walker Brewing Co Ltd
Unit 1 Victory Parkway, Victory Road,
Derby, DE24 8ZF
01332 766 195
www.wildwalker.co.uk

Thornbridge Brewery
Thornbridge Hall, Ashford-in-the-Water,
Bakewell, DE45 1NZ
01629 640 617
www.thornbridgehall.co.uk

Tollgate Brewery
Unit 8 Viking Business Centre, High Street,
Woodville, Swadlincote, DE11 7EH
01283 229 194

Townes Brewery
Speedwell Inn, Lowgates, Staveley,
Chesterfield, S43 3TT
01246 472 252

Whim Ales Ltd
Whim Farm, Hartington, Buxton, SK17 0AX
01298 849 91
www.whimales.co.uk

Wirksworth Brewery
25 St John Street, Wirksworth, DE4 4DR
01629 824 011
www.wirksworthbrewery.co.uk

DEVON

Barum Brewery Ltd
c/o The Reform Inn, Reform Street,
Barnstaple, EX31 1PD
01271 329 994
www.barumbrewery.co.uk

Bays Brewery Ltd
Yalberton Industrial Estate, Aspen Way,
Paignton, TQ4 7QR
01803 555 004
www.baysbrewery.co.uk

Branscombe Vale Brewery
Great Seaside Farm, Branscombe, EX12 3DP
01297 680 511

Clearwater Brewery
2 Devon Units, Hatchmoor Industrial Estate,
Torrington, EX38 7HP
01805 625 242

Combe Martin Brewery
4 Springfield Terrace, Combe Martin,
Ilfracombe, EX34 0EE
01271 883 507
www.combemartinbrewery.prizaar.com

Country Life Brewery
The Big Sheep, Abbotsham, Bideford, EX39 5AP
01237 420 808
www.countrylifebrewery.com

Dartmouth Brewery
Dartmouth Inn, 63 East Street,
Newton Abbot, TQ12 2JP
01626 353 451

Devon Earth Brewery
7 Fernham Terrace, Torquay Road,
Paignton, TQ3 2AQ
07927 397 871
www.devonearthbrewery.co.uk

Exe Valley Brewery
Land Farm, Silverton, Exeter, EX5 4HF
01392 860 406

Exmoor Ales
Golden Hill Brewery, Wiveliscombe, TA4 2NY
01984 623 798
www.exmoorales.co.uk

Forge Brewery
Ford Hill Forge, Hartland, Bideford, EX39 6EE
01237 440 015
www.forgebrewery.co.uk

Gargoyles Brewery
Court Farm, Holcombe Village, Dawlish, EX7 0JT
07773 444 501

Hunter's Brewery Ltd
Glebe Acres, Orley Road, Ipplepen,
Newton Abbot, TQ12 5SA
01803 814 399

Jollyboat Brewery (Bideford) Ltd
The Coach House, Buttgarden Street,
Bideford, EX39 2AU
01237 424 343

O'Hanlon's Brewing
Great Barton Farm, Whimple, EX5 2NY
01404 822 412
www.ohanlons.co.uk

Otter Brewery
Mathayes, Luppit, Honiton, EX14 4SA
01404 891 285
www.otterbrewery.com

Princetown Breweries Ltd
The Brewery, Station Road, Princetown, PL20 6QX
01822 890 789
www.princetownbreweries.co.uk

Quercus Brewery Ltd
Unit 2n South Hams Business Park,
Churchstow, Kingsbridge, TQ7 3QH
01548 854 888
www.quercusbrewery.co.uk

Red Rock Brewery Ltd
Higher Humber Farm, Humber,
Teignmouth, TQ14 9TD
01626 879 738
www.redrockbrewery.co.uk

Ringmore Craft Brewery
Ringmore Barn, Higher Ringmore Road,
Shaldon, TQ14 0HG
01626 873 114
www.ringmorecraftbrewery.co.uk

Scattor Rock Brewery
Unit 5, Gidley's Meadow, Christow, Exeter, EX6 7QB
01677 252 120
www.scattorrockbrewery.com

South Hams Brewery Co Ltd
Stokeley Barton Barns, Stokenham,
Kingsbridge, TQ7 2SE
01548 581 151
www.southhamsbrewery.co.uk

Summerskills Brewery
Unit 15, Pomphlett Farm Industrial Estate,
Billacombe, Plymouth, PL9 7BG
01752 481 283
www.summerskills.co.uk

Teignworthy Brewery
The Maltings, Teign Road, Newton Abbott, TQ12 4AA
01626 332 066
www.teignworthybrewery.com

The Beer Engine
Newton St Cyres, Exeter, EX5 5AX
01392 851 282
www.thebeerengine.co.uk

The Bridgetown Brewery
The Albert Inn, Bridgetown Close, Totnes, TQ9
5AD
01803 863 214

The Exeter Brewery Ltd
Unit 5 Lionsrest Estate, Station Road,
Exminster, Exeter, EX6 8DZ
01392 823 013
www.theexeterbrewery.co.uk

Union Brewery
Fore Street, Holbeton, Plymouth, PL8 1NE
01752 830 460
www.dartmoorunion.co.uk

Warrior Brewing Co
4 Matford House, Old Matford Lane,
Matford, Exeter, EX2 8XS
01392 221 451
www.jameswarrior.com

Wizard Ales
Unit 4 Lundy View, Mullacott Cross Industrial
Estate, Ilfracombe, EX34 8PY
01271 865 350
www.wizardales.co.uk

DORSET

Art Brew
North End Farm, Venn Lane, Chideock,
Bridport, DT6 6JY
07881 783 626
www.artbrew.co.uk

Dorset Brewing Company
Brewers Quay, Hope Square,
Weymouth, DT4 8TR
01305 777 515
www.dbcales.com

Dorset Piddle Brewery Ltd
Unit 7 Enterprise Park, Piddlehinton,
Dorchester, DT2 7UA
01305 849 336
www.dorsetpiddlebrewery.co.uk

Goldfinch Brewery
47 High East Street, Dorchester, DT1 1HU
01305 264 020
www.goldfinchbrewery.com

Isle of Purbeck Brewery
Bankes Arms Hotel, Manor Road, Studland,
Swanage, BH19 3AU
01929 450 227

Sherborne Brewery Ltd
257 Wesbury, Sherbourne, DT9 3EH
01935 817 307
www.sherbornebrewery.co.uk

Small Paul's Brewery
27 Briar Close, Gillingham, SP8 4SS
01747 823 574

DURHAM

Consett Ale Works
The Grey Horse, 115 Sherburn Terrace,
Consett, DH8 6NE
01207 591 540
www.thegreyhorse.co.uk

Double Maxim Beer Company Ltd
1 Gadwall Road, Houghton Le Spring, DH4 5NL
0191 584 8844
www.maximbrewery.co.uk

Hill Island Brewery
Unit 7 Fowlers Yard, Back Silver Street,
Durham, DH1 3RA
07740 932 584

Jarrow Brewing Company
Robin Hood Inn, Primrose Hill, Jarrow, NE32 5UB
01914 836 792
www.jarrowbrewery.co.uk

The Durham Brewery Ltd
Unit 5a Bowburn North Industrial Estate,
Bowburn, DH6 5PF
01913 771 991
www.durham-brewery.co.uk

The Four Alls Brewery
Four Alls Hotel, Ovington,
Richmond, DL11 7BP
01833 627 302
www.thefouralls-teesdale.co.uk

The Yard of Ale Brewing Co Ltd
Surtees Arms, Chilton Lane,
DL17 0DH
01740 655 724
www.thesurteesarms.co.uk

Wear Valley Brewery Ltd
The Grand Hotel, Holdforth Crest,
Bishop Auckland, DL14 6DU
01388 601 956
www.the-grand-hotel.co.uk

EAST RIDING OF YORKSHIRE

Old Mill Brewery
Mill Street, Snaith, Goole, DN14 9HU
01405 861 813
www.oldmillbrewery.demon.co.uk

The Great Newsome Brewery Ltd
Great Newsome Farm, Winestead,
Hull, HU12 0NR
01964 612 201
www.greatnewsomebrewery.co.uk

Whalebone Brewery
The Whalebone, 163 Wincolmlee,
Hull, HU2 0PA
01482 226 648

EAST SUSSEX

1648 Brewing Co Ltd
Mill Lane, East Hoathley,
Lewes, BN8 6DR
01825 840 830
www.1648brewing.co.uk

Beachy Head Brewing Co Ltd
c/o The Dipperays,
Upper Street,
East Dean, Eastbourne, BN20 0BS
01323 423 906
www.beachyhead.org.uk

Fallen Angel
PO Box 95, Battle, TN33 0XF
01424 777 996
www.fallenangelbrewery.com

Full Moon Brewery
Sharpes Farm, Henley Down, Catsfield,
Battle, TN33 9BN
07832 220 745

Kempton Brewery
Hand in Hand, 33 Upper St. James's Street,
Brighton, BN2 1JN
01273 693 070

Rother Valley Brewing Company
Gate Court Farm, Station Road,
Northiam, Rye, TN31 6QT
01797 253 550

The FILO Brewing Co Ltd
14–15 High Street, Hastings, TN34 3EY
01424 425 079
www.thefilo.co.uk

White Brewing Company
The 1066 Country Brewery,
Pebsham Farm Industrial Estate,
Pebsham Lane,
Bexhill, TN40 2RZ
01424 731 066
www.white-brewing.co.uk

ESSEX

Brentwood Brewing Company
Frieze Hall Farm, Coxtie Green Road,
Brentwood, CM14 5RE
01277 375 577
www.brentwoodbrewing.co.uk

Crouch Vale
23 Haltwhistle Road, Rochford, CM3 5ZA
01245 322 744
www.crouch-vale.co.uk

Farmer's Ales
The Stable Brewery, The Blue Boar Stable
Yard, Silver Street, Maldon, CM9 4QE
01621 851 000
www.maldonbrewing.co.uk

Felstar
Felsted Vineyard, Crix Green, Felsted, CM6 3JT
01245 361 504
www.felstarbrewery.co.uk

Harwich Town Brewing Company
Station Approach, Harwich, CO12 3NA
01255 551 155
www.harwichtown.co.uk

Mersea Island Brewery
Mersea Vineyard, Rewsalls Lane,
East Mersea, CO5 8SX
01206 385 900
www.merseawine.com

Nethergate
Growler Brewery, The Street, Pentlow, CO10 7JJ
01787 283 220
www.nethergate.co.uk

Pitfield Organic Brewery
c/o Ashlyns Farm Shop, Epping Road,
North Weald, Colchester, CM16 6RZ
0845 833 1492
www.pitfieldbeershop.co.uk

Red Fox Brewery Ltd
The Chicken Sheds, Upphall Farm,
Salmons Lane, Coggeshall, CO6 1RY
01376 563 123
www.redfoxbrewery.co.uk

Sticklegs Brewery
The Cross Inn, Ardleigh Road, Great Bromley,
Colchester, CO7 7TL
01206 230 282
www.bromleycrossinn.co.uk

The Famous Railway Tavern
58 Station Road, Brightlingsea, CO7 0DT
01206 302 581
www.geocities.com/famousrailway

The Hart of Stebbing Brewery Ltd
White Hart, High Street, Stebbing,
Dunmow, CM6 3SQ
01371 856 383
www.hartofstebbingbrewery.co.uk

The Mighty Oak Brewing Co Ltd
14b West Station Yard, Maldon, CM9 6TW
01621 843 713

The Shalford Brewery
c/o 3 Broome Close Villas, Shalford,
Braintree, CM7 5EY
01371 850 925
www.shalfordbrewery.co.uk

Wibblers Brewery Ltd
Joyces Farm Buildings, Southminster Road,
Mayland, CM3 6EB
01621 789 003
www.wibblers.com

GLOUCESTERSHIRE

Battledown Brewery
Keynsham Works, Keynsham Street,
Cheltenham, GL52 6EJ
07734 834 104
www.battledownbrewery.com

Cotswold Spring Brewery Ltd
Dodington Spring, Dodington Ash,
Chipping Sodbury, BS37 6RX
01454 323 088
www.cotswoldbrewery.com

Eagles Bush Brewery
The Salutation, Ham, Berkeley, GL13 9QH
01453 810 284

Festival Brewery
Unit 17 Malmesbury Road, Kingsditch Trading
Estate, Cheltenham, GL51 9PL
01242 521 444
www.festivalbrewery.com

Freeminer Brewery Ltd
Whimsey Industrial Estate, Steam Mills,
Whimsey, Cinderford, GL14 3JA
01594 827 989
http://website.lineone.net/~freeminer.brewery/

Goff's Brewery Ltd
9 Isbourne Way, Winchcombe,
Cheltenham, GL54 5NS
01242 603 383
www.goffsbrewery.co.uk

Nailsworth Brewery Ltd
The Village Inn, Bath Road,
Nailsworth, Stroud, GL6 0HH
07878 448 377
www.nailsworth-brewery.co.uk

Severn Vale Brewing Company
Lower Knapp Farm, Woodend Lane,
Cam, Dursley, GL11 5HS
01453 547 550
www.severnvalebrewing.co.uk

Stanway Brewery
Stanway, Cheltenham, GL54 5PQ
01386 584 320
www.stanwaybrewery.co.uk

Stroud Brewery Ltd
c/o 141 Thrupp Lane, Thrupp,
Stroud, GL5 2DQ
07891 995 878
www.stroudbrewery.co.uk

The Halfpenny Brewery
The Crown Inn, High Street,
Lechlade, GL7 3AE
01367 252 198
www.halfpennybrewery.co.uk

Uley Brewery Ltd
The Old Brewery, 31 The Street, Uley,
Dursley, GL11 5TB
01453 860 120
www.uleybrewery.com

Whittingtons Brewery
Three Choirs Vineyard,
Welsh House Lane, Castle Tump,
Newent, GL18 1LS
01531 890 223
www.whittingtonbrewery.co.uk

Wickwar Brewing Company
The Old Brewery, Station Road,
Wickwar, GL12 8NB
01454 294 168
www.wickwarbrewing.co.uk

GREATER LONDON

Brew Wharf
Brew Wharf Yard, Stoney Street,
London, SE1 9AD
020 7940 8333
www.brewwharf.com

Bunker
41 Earlham Street, Covent Garden,
London, WC2H 9LD
020 7240 0606
www.bunkerbar.com

Horseshoe Brewery
The Horseshoe, 28 Heath Street,
London, NW3 6TE
020 7431 7206

Sambrook's Brewery Ltd
Units 1 & 2 Yelverton Road,
London, SW11 3QG
020 7228 0598
www.sambrooksbrewery.co.uk

Sweet William Brewery
William IV, 816 High Road, Leyton,
London, E10 6AE
020 8556 2460

The Battersea Brewery Co Ltd
43 Glycena Road, London, SW11 5TP
020 7978 7978
www.batterseabrewery.com

The Florence Brew House
133 Dulwich Road, London, SE24 0NG
020 7326 4987
www.florencehernehill.com

Twickenham Fine Ales
Ryecroft Works, Edwin Road,
Twickenham, TW2 6SP
020 8241 1825
www.twickenham-fine-ales.co.uk

Zerodegrees Blackheath
29-31 Montpelier Vale, Blackheath,
London, SE3 0TJ
020 8852 5619
www.zerodegrees.co.uk

GREATER MANCHESTER

Hornbeam Brewery
Unit 1-1c Grey Street, Denton,
Manchester, M34 3RU
0161 320 5627
www.hornbeambrewery.com

Marble Brewery
73 Rochdale Road, Manchester, M4 4HY
0161 819 2694
www.marblebeers.com

Phoenix Brewery Ltd
Green Lane, Heywood,
Manchester, OL10 2EP
01706 627 009
www.phoenixbrewery.co.uk

HAMPSHIRE

Andwell Brewing Company
Lodge Farm, Hook Road, North Warnborough,
Hook, RG29 1HA
01256 704 412
www.andwells.com

Ballard's Brewery
The Old Sawmill, Nyewood,
Petersfield, GU31 5HA
01730 821 362
www.ballardsbrewery.org.uk

Bowman Ales Ltd
Wallop Woods, Sheardsley Lane, Droxford,
Southhampton, SO32 3QY
01489 878 110
www.bowman-ales.com

Irving & Co Brewers Ltd
Unit G1 Railway Triangle, Walton Road,
Portsmouth, PO6 1TH
023 9238 9988
www.irvingbrewers.co.uk

Itchen Valley Brewery Ltd
Unit D Prospect Commercial Park,
Prospect Road, Alresford, SO24 9QF
01962 735 111
www.itchenvalley.com

Oakleaf Brewing Co Ltd
Unit 7 Mumby Road, Clarence Wharf
Industrial Estate, Gosport, PO12 1AJ
023 9251 3222
www.oakleafbrewing.co.uk

Red Shoot Brewery
Linwood, Ringwood, BH24 3QT
01425 475 792

The Flowerpots Brewery
Flowerpots Inn, Cheriton, Alresford, SO24 0QQ
01962 771 534
www.flowerpots.f2s.com

Triple FFF Brewing Co.
Unit 3, Old Magpie Works, Alton, GU34 5AN
01420 561 422
www.triplefff.com

HEREFORDSHIRE

Arrow Brewery
The Wine Vaults, 37 High Street,
Kington, HR5 3BJ
01544 230 685

Marches Ales
The Old Hop Kilns, Claston Farm, Dormington,
Hereford, HR1 4EA
01584 878 999

Oast House Brewery
The Farm, Brockhampton Estate, Whitbourne,
Worcester, WR6 5SH
07974 371 294

Shoes Brewery
Three Horseshoes Inn, Norton Canon,
Hereford, HR4 7BH
01544 318 375

Spinning Dog Brewery
The Victory, 88 St.Owen Street,
Hereford, HR12QD
01432 342 125
www.spinningdogbrewery.co.uk

The Mayfields Brewery
Unit 8 Croft Business Park,
Southern Avenue, Leominster, HR6 0QF
01568 611 197
www.mayfieldsbrewery.co.uk

Wye Valley Brewery
Stoke Lacy, HR7 4HG
01885 490 505
www.wyevalleybrewery.com

HERTFORDSHIRE

Alehouse Pub & Brewing Co Ltd
The Farmers Boy, 134 London Road,
St Albans, AL1 1PQ
07725 138 243
www.alehousebrewery.co.uk

Buntingford Brewery Co Ltd
Greys Brewhouse, Therfield Road,
Royston, SG8 9NW
01763 250 749
www.buntingford-brewery.co.uk

Green Tye Brewery
Green Tye, Much Hadham, SG10 6JP
01279 841 041
www.gtbrewery.co.uk

Red Squirrel Brewery
14b Minram Road, Hertford, SG14 1NN
01992 501 100
www.redsquirrelbrewery.co.uk

Saffron Brewery
Unit 2 Pledgdon Hall Farm, Henham,
Bishop's Stortford, CM22 6BJ
01279 850 923
www.saffronbrewery.co.uk

Sawbridgeworth Brewery
Gate Inn, 81 London Road,
Sawbridgeworth, CM21 9JJ
01279 722 313
www.the-gate-pub.co.uk

The Hertford Brewery
26 Old Cross, Hertford, SG14 1RD
01992 584 911
www.mcmullens.co.uk

The Old Cross Tavern Brewery
Old Cross Tavern, 8 St Andrew Street,
Hertford, SG14 1JA
01992 583 133

Tring Brewery Co Ltd
81-82 Akeman Street, Tring, HP23 6AF
01442 890 721
www.tringbrewery.co.uk

ISLE OF MAN

Bushys
Mount Murray, Castletown Road,
Braddan, IM4 1JE
01624 661 244
www.bushys.com

Old Laxey Brewery
Laxey, IM4 7DA
01624 863 214
www.shorehotel.im

ISLE OF WIGHT

Goddard's Brewery
Barnsley Farm, Bullen Road,
Ryde, PO33 1QF
01983 611 011
www.goddards-brewery.co.uk

Ventnor Brewery
119 High Street,
Ventnor, PO38 1LY
01983 856 161
www.ventnorbrewery.co.uk

ISLE OF SCILLY

Ales of Scilly Brewery
2b Porthmellon Industrial Estate,
St Mary's, TR21 0JY
01720 423 233

KENT

Hopdaemon Brewery Ltd
Unit 1, Parsonage Farm, Seed Road,
Newnham, ME9 0NA
01795 892 078
www.hopdaemon.com

Larkins Brewery
Chiddingstone, Edenbridge, TN8 7BB
01892 870 328

Nelson Brewery
Unit 2, Building 64, Historic Dockyard,
Chatham, ME4 4TE
01634 832 828
www.nelsonbrewingcompany.co.uk

P & DJ Goacher
Unit 8, Tovil Green Buiness Park,
Maidstone, ME15 6TA
01622 682 112
www.goachers.com

Ramsgate Brewery Ltd
Unit 1 Hornet Close, Pysons Road Industrial
Estate, Broadstairs, CT10 2YD
01843 594 758
www.ramsgatebrewery.co.uk

The Millis Brewing Co Ltd
St Margrets Farm, St Margrets Road, South
Darenth, Dartford, DA4 9LB
01322 866 233

The Swan Microbrewery
Swan on the Green, The Green,
West Peckham, Maidstone, ME18 5JW
01622 812 271
www.swan-on-the-green.co.uk

Westerham Brewery Co Ltd
Grange Farm, Pootings Road, Crockham Hill,
Edenbridge, TN8 6SA
01732 864 427
www.westerhambrewery.co.uk

Whitstable Brewery
Little Telpits Farm, Woodcock Lane,
Grafty Green, Maidstone, ME17 2AY
01622 851 007
www.whitstablebrewery.info

LANCASHIRE

Allgates Brewery
The Old Brewery, Brewery Yard, Wallgate,
Wigan, WN1 1JU
01942 234 976
www.allgatesbrewery.com

Bank Top Brewery
The Pavilion, Ashworth Lane, Bank Top,
Bolton, BL1 8RA
01204 595 800
www.banktopbrewery.com

Barearts Brewery
Studio Bar and Gallery, 108-110 Rochdale
Road, Todmorden, OL14 7LP
01706 839 305
www.barearts.com

Bazens' Brewery
The Rees Bazen Brewing Co Ltd,
Unit 6 Knoll Street Industrial Park,
Knoll Street, Salford, M7 2BL
0161 708 0247
www.bazensbrewery.co.uk

Boggart Hole Clough Brewery
Unit 13 Brookside Works, Clough Road,
Moston, M9 4SP
0161 277 9666
www.boggart-brewery.co.uk

Brysons of Lancaster Ltd
Newgate Brewery, White Lund Industrial
Estate, Morcambe, LA3 3PT
01524 394 81
www.brysonsbrews.co.uk

Cambrinus Craft Brewery
Home Farm, Knowsley Park, Prescot, L34 4AQ
0151 546 2226

Derby Brewery
Empire Street, Cheetham, M3 1JD
0161 834 3285
www.joseph-holt.com

Fallons Exquisite Ales
Unit 15 Darwen Enterprise Centre,
Railway Road, Darwen, BB3 3EH
07905 246 810
www.fallonsales.com

Garthela Brewhouse
Beardwood Brow, Blackburn, BB2 7AT
07515 648 630
www.garthelabrewhouse.co.uk

George Wright Brewing Company
11 Diamond Business Park,
Sandwash Close, Rainford Industrial Estate,
St Helens, WA11 8LU
01744 886 686
www.georgewrightbrewing.co.uk

Green Mill Brewery
Queensway Snooker Club, Green Mill,
Well I' Th'Lane, Rochdale, OL11 2LS
07896 702 328
www.greenmillbrewery.co.uk

Greenfield Real Ale Brewery Ltd
Unit 8 Waterside Mills, Chew Valley Road,
Greenfield, Oldham, OL3 7PF
01457 879 789
www.greenfieldrealale.co.uk

Grindleton Brewhouse Ltd
Unit 12 Deanfield Way,
Link 59 Business Park, Clitheroe, BB7 1QU
01200 444 808
www.grindletonbrewhouse.co.uk

Hart Brewery
Cartford Hotel, Cartford Lane, Little
Eccleston, PR3 0YP
01995 671 686
www.hartbreweryltd.co.uk

Higson's Brewery Ltd
Unit 17 Maritime Enterprise Park, Atlas Road,
Liverpool, L20 4DY
0151 922 5640
www.higsonbrewery.co.uk

Hopstar Brewery
11 Pole Road, Darwen, BB3 3LD
01254 703 389

Lancaster Brewery Co Ltd
Unit 19 Lansil Walk, Lansil Industrial Estate,
Lancaster, LA1 3PQ
01524 844 610
www.lancasterbrewery.co.uk

Leyden Brewing Ltd
Lord Raglan, Mount Pleasant, Nangreaves,
Bury, BL9 6SP
0161 764 6680

Lytham Brewery Ltd
Unit 11 Lidun Park Industrial Estate, Boundary
Road, Lytham St Annes, FY8 5HU
01253 737 707
www.lythambrewery.co.uk

Mayflower Brewery
The Royal Oak, 111-113 Standishgate,
Wigan, WN1 1XL
07984 404 567
www.mayflowerbeer.co.uk

Millstone Brewery
Unit 4 Vale Mill, Micklehurst Road, Mossley,
Ashton-under-Lyne, OL5 9JL
01457 835 835
www.millstonebrewery.co.uk

Moonstone Brewery
Ministry of Ale, 9 Trafalgar Street,
Burnley, BB11 1TQ
01282 830 909
www.moonstonebrewery.co.uk

Moorhouse Brewery
The Brewery, Moorhouse Street,
Bucksburn, BB11 5EN
01282 422 864
www.moorhouses.co.uk

Outstanding Brewing Co Ltd
Unit 4b Britannia Mill, Cobden Street,
Bury, BL9 6AW
0161 764 7723
www.outstandingbeers.com

Pennine Ale
Rosendale Brewery, The Griffin Inn,
Haslingden, BB4 5AF
01706 214 021
www.pbcbreweryinstallations.com

Pictish Brewing Co Ltd
Unit 9 Canalside Industrial Estate,
Woodbine Street East,
Rochdale, OL16 5LB
01706 522 227
www.pictish-brewing.co.uk

Prospect Brewery Ltd
120 Wigan Road, Standish,
Wigan, WN6 0AY
01257 421 329
www.prospectbrewery.com

Red Rose Brewery
Unit 5 New Plough Yard,
Queen Street, Great Harwood,
Blackburn, BB6 7AX
01254 877 373
www.redrosebrewery.co.uk

Saddleworth Brewery
Church Inn, Running Hill Gate,
Uppermill, Oldham, OL3 6LW
01457 820 902

Southport Brewery
Unit 3 Southport Enterprise Centre,
Russell Road, Southport, PR9 7RF
07748 387 652
www.southportbrewery.co.uk

Star Brewery
Syke Street, Blackburn, BB1 5BU
01254 686 868
www.thwaites.co.uk

Stringers Beer
Unit 3 Low Mill Business Park,
Ulverston, LA12 9EE
01229 581 387
www.stringersbeer.co.uk

The Bowland Beer Company
The Bowland Brewery, Bashall Barn,
Twitter Lane, Clitheroe, BB7 3LQ
01200 428 825
www.bowlandbrewery.com

Three Bs Brewery
Unit 5 Laneside Works, Stockclough Lane,
Feniscowles, Blackburn, BB2 5JR
01254 207 686
www.threebsbrewery.co.uk

Wapping Beers Ltd
The Baltic Fleet, 33 Wapping, Liverpool, L1 8DQ
0151 709 2247
www.wappingbeers.co.uk

LEICESTERSHIRE

Barrowden Brewing Company
c/o Exeter Arms, Barrowden, Rutland, LE1 5EQ
01572 747 247
www.exeterarms.com

Bees Brewery
c/o Branstons Petroleum Services, 1487 Melton
Road, Queniborough, Leicester, LE7 3FP
01162 607 715

Bell's Brewery & Merchants Ltd
The Workshop, Lutterworth Road, Ullesthorpe,
Lutterworth, LE17 5DR
01455 209 940
www.bellsbrewery.co.uk

Belvoir Brewery
Crown Park, Station Road, Old Dalby, LE14 3NQ
01664 823 455
www.belvoirbrewery.co.uk

Dow Bridge Brewery
2-3 Rugby Road, Catthorpe,
Lutterworth, LE17 6DA
01788 869 121

Langton Brewery
Grange Farm, Thorpe Langton,
Market Harborough, LE16 7TU
01858 545 483

Parish Brewery
6 Main Street, Burrough On The Hill,
Somerby, LE14 2JQ
01664 454 782

Shardlow Brewing Co Ltd
Old Brewery Stables, British Waterways Yard,
Cavendish Bridge, DE72 2HL
01332 799 188
www.shardlowbrewery.co.uk

The Grainstore Brewery
Station Approach, Oakham, Rutland, LE15 6RE
01572 770 065
www.grainstorebrewery.com

Wicked Hathern Brewery Ltd
33 Green Hill, Hathern, Loughborough, LE12 5LD
01509 842 585
www.wicked-hathern.co.uk

LINCOLNSHIRE

Blue Bell Brewery Ltd
Blue Bell Inn, Cranesgate South, Whaplode St
Catherine, Holbeach, PE12 6SN
01406 540 300
www.bluebellbrewery.co.uk

Brewsters Brewing Company
Unit 5, Burnside Industrial Estate,
Turnpike Close, Grantham, LE14 4HR
01476 566 000
www.brewsters.co.uk

Cathedral Ales
Green Dragon Hotel, Broadgate,
Lincoln, LN2 5DH
01522 567 155
www.greendragonpub.co.uk

Dark Tribe Brewery
Dog & Gun, High Street, East Butterwick,
Scunthorpe, DN17 3AJ
01724 782 324
www.darktribe.co.uk

Fulstow Brewery
13 Thames Street, Louth, LN11 7AD
01507 608 202
www.fulstowbrewery.co.uk

Fuzzy Duck Brewery
c/o 6 Northway, Fulstow, Louth, FY6 0ES
07904 343 729
www.fuzzyduckbrewery.co.uk

Grafters Brewery
Half Moon, 23 High Street,
Willingham By Stow, DN21 5JZ
01427 788 340
www.graftersbrewery.com

Highwood Brewery Ltd
Unit 3, Birchams Way, Grimsby, DN31 2SG
01472 255 500
www.tom-wood.com

Leila Cottage Brewery
c/o The Countryman, Chapel Road,
Ingoldmells, Skegness, PE25 1ND
01754 872 268

Malt B Brewery
The Crown Inn, Beesby Road, Maltby le Marsh,
Alford, LN13 0JJ
01507 450 100
www.thecrowninnmaltby.co.uk

Newby Wyke Brewery
Willoughby Arms Cottages, Little Arms
Cottages, Little Bytham, Grantham, NG33 4RA
01780 411 119
www.newbywyke.co.uk

Oldershaw Brewery
12 Harrowby Lane, Harrowby,
Grantham, NG31 9HB
01476 572 135
www.oldershawbrewery.com

Poachers Brewery
439 Newark Road, North Hykeham,
Lincoln, LN6 9SP
01522 807 404
www.poachersbrewery.co.uk

Riverside Brewery
Unit 1, Church Lane, Wainfleet,
Skegness, PE24 4BY
01754 881 288
www.wainfleet.info/shops/brewery-riverside.htm

Swaton Brewery
North End Farm, Swaton, Sleaford, NG34 0JP
01529 421 348
www.swatonbrewery.com

The Blue Cow Inn & Brewery
29 High Street, South Witham,
Grantham, NG33 5QB
01572 768 432
www.thebluecowinn.co.uk

Willys Brewery Ltd
17 High Cliff Road, Cleethorpes, DN35 8RQ
01472 602 145

NORFOLK

Beeston Brewery Ltd
Fransham Road Farm, Beeston,
King's Lynn, PE32 2LZ
01328 700 844
www.beestonbrewery.co.uk

Blackfriars Brewery Ltd
The Courtyard, Mancross Road,
Great Yarmouth, NR30 3NZ
01493 850 578
www.blackfriars-brewery.co.uk

Blue Moon Brewery
The Cock Inn, Watton Road, Barford, NR9 4AS
01603 757 646

Buffy's Brewery Ltd
Rectory Road, Tivetshall St Mary, NR15 2DD
01379 676 523
www.buffys.co.uk

Bull Box Brewery
c/o 1 Brickyard Cottage, Fordham,
Downham Market, PE38 0LW
01366 385 349

Chalk Hill Brewery
Rosary Road, Norwich, NR1 4DA
01603 477 078

Elmtree Beers
Unit 10 Oakwood Industrial Estate,
Harling Road, Snetterton, NR16 2JU
01953 887 065
www.elmtreebeers.co.uk

Fat Cat Inns Ltd
49 West End Street, Norwich, NR2 4NA
01603 624 362
www.fatcatpub.co.uk

Fox Brewery
Fox and Hounds, Station Road,
Heacham, King's Lynn, PE31 7EX
01485 570 345
www.foxbrewery.co.uk

Front Street Brewery
The Chequers Inn, Front Street, Binham, NR21 0AL
01328 830 297
www.frontstreetbrewery.co.uk

Grain Brewery
South Farm, Alburgh, Harleston, IP20 0BS
01986 788 884
www.grainbrewery.co.uk

Humpty Dumpty
Church Road, Reedham, NR13 3TZ
01493 701 818
www.humptydumptybrewery.co.uk

Iceni Brewery
3 Fouldon Road, Ickburgh, IP26 5BJ
01842 878 922
www.icenibrewery.co.uk

Norfolk Cottage Brewing
c/o 22 The Green, North Bulingham, NR13 3DJ
01603 270 520

Norfolk Square Brewery
Unit 7 Estcourt House, Estcourt Road,
Great Yarmouth, NR30 4JQ
01493 854 484
www.norfolksquarebrewery.co.uk

Old Chimney's Brewery
Hopton End Farm, Church Road, Market
Weston, Diss, IP22 2NX
01359 221 013
www.oldchimneysbrewery.com

Ole Slew Foot Brewing Co Ltd
3 Pollard Road, Hainford, Norwich, NR10 3BE
0845 1162 204
www.oleslewfootbrewery.co.uk

Opa Hay's Brewery
Glencot, Wood Lane, Aldeby, Beccles, NR34 0DA
01502 679 144
www.engelfineales.com

Reepham Brewery
Unit 1, Colliers Way, Reepham, NR10 4SW
01603 871 091

Spectrum Brewery
The Cock, Watton Road,
Barford, NR9 4AS
07949 254 383
www.spectrumbrewery.co.uk

The Why Not Brewery
17 Cavalier Close, Thorpe St Andrew,
Norwich, NR7 0TE
01603 300 786
www.thewhynotbrewery.co.uk

Tindall Ale Brewery
Toad Lane, Thwaite, Bungay, NR35 2EQ
01508 483 844

Tipples Brewery
Unit 6, Damgate Lane Industrial Estate,
Acle, NR13 3DJ
01493 741 007
www.tipplesbrewery.com

Uncle Stuart's Brewery
Antoma, Pack Lane, Lingwood, NR13 4PD
01603 211 833
www.littlebeershop.co.u

Wagtail Brewery
New Barn Farm, Wilby Warrens,
Old Buckenham, NR17 1PF
01953 887 133
www.wagtailbrewery.com

Waveney Brewing Co.
Queen's Head, Station Road, Earsham,
Bungay, NR35 2TS
01986 892 623

Winter's Brewery
8 Keelan Close, Norwich, NR6 6QZ
01603 787 820
www.wintersbrewery.com

Wissey Valley Brewery
The Grey House, Lynn Road,
Stoke Ferry, PE33 9FW
01366 500 767
www.wisseyvalleybrewery.com

Wolf Brewery Limited
Rookery Farm, Silver Street, Besthorpe,
Attleborough, NR17 2LD
01953 457 776
www.wolf-brewery.ltd.co

Yetman's Brewery
Bayfield Farm Barns, Bayfield Brecks,
Holt, NR25 7DZ
07774 809 016
www.yetmans.net

NORTH YORKSHIRE

Brown Cow Brewery
Brown Cow Road, Barlow, Selby, YO8 8EH
01757 618 947
www.browncowbrewery.co.uk

Captain Cook Brewery Ltd
White Swan, 1 West End, Stokesley,
Middlesbrough, TS9 5BL
01642 710 263
www.thecaptaincookbrewery.co.uk

Copper Dragon Brewery Ltd
Snaygill Industrial Estate, Keighley Road,
Skipton, BD23 2QR
01756 702 130
www.copperdragon.uk.com

Cropton Brewery
Cropton Pickering, YO18 8HH
01751 417 330
www.croptonbrewery.co.uk

Dark Horse Brewery
Coonlands Laithe, Rylstone, Skipton, BD23 6LY
01756 730 555

East Coast Brewing Company
3 Clay House Yard, Mitford Street,
Filey, YO14 9DX
01723 514 865

Great Heck Brewing Co Ltd
Harwin House, Main Street, Heck,
Goole, DN14 0BQ
01977 661 430
www.greatheckbrewery.co.uk

Hambleton Ales
Unit 2a Barker Business Park, Melmerby
Green Lane, Melmerby, Ripon, HG4 5NB
01765 640 108
www.hambletonales.co.uk

Litton Ale Brewery
Queen's Arms, Litton, Skipton, BD23 5QJ
01756 770 208
www.yorkshirenet.co.uk/stayat/queensarms

Marston Moor Brewery Co
Crown Hotel, Church Street, Kirk Hammerton,
York, YO26 8DD
01423 330 341
www.marstonmoorbrewery.co.uk

North Yorkshire Brewing Co
Pinchinthorpe Hall, Pinchinthorpe,
Guisborough, TS14 8HG
01287 632 000
www.nybrewery.co.uk

Redscar Brewery Ltd
The Cleveland Hotel, 9-11 High Street West,
Redcar, TS10 1SQ
01642 513 727
www.theclevelandhotel.co.uk

Richmond Brewing Co Ltd
The Station Brewery, Station Yard,
Richmond, DL10 4LD
07912 347 946
www.richmondbrewing.co.uk

Rudgate Brewery Ltd
2 Centre Park, Rudgate, Marston Business
Park, Tockwith, YO26 7QF
01423 358 382
www.rudgate-beers.co.uk

The Storyteller Brewery Ltd
The Bay Horse Inn, Terrington, York, YO60 6PP
01653 648 416
www.thestorytellerbrewery.co.uk

Three Peaks Brewery
7 Craven Terrace, Settle, BD24 9DB
01729 822 939

Wensleydale Brewery
Manor Farm, Bellerby, Leyburn, DL8 5QH
01969 625 250
www.wensleybrewery.com

Wold Top Brewery
Hunmanby Grange, Wold Newton,
Driffield, YO25 3HS
01723 892 222
www.woldtopbrewery.co.uk

York Brewery Co Ltd
12 Toft Green,
Micklegate, YO1 6JT
01904 621 162
www.yorkbrew.co.uk

Yorkshire Dales Brewing Co Ltd
Seata Barn Elm Hill, Main Street, Askrigg,
Leyburn, DL8 3HG
01969 622 027
www.yorkshiredalesbrewery.com

Daleside Brewery
Camwal Road, Starbeck,
Harrogate, HG1 4PT
01423 880 041
www.dalesidebrewery.co.uk

Roosters Brewing Co
Unit 3/4 Grimbald Park,
Wetherby Road,
Knaresborough, HG5 8LJ
01423 865 959
www.roosters.co.uk

NORTHAMPTONSHIRE

Alcazar Brewing Company
33 Church Street, Old Basford,
Nottingham, NG6 0GA
01159 785 155
www.alcazarbrewery.co.uk

Caythorpe Brewery
Walnut Cottage, Boat Lane, Hoveringham,
Nottingham, NG14 7JP
01159 664 933

Cherwell Valley Brewery Ltd
Unit 2 St Davids Court, Top Station Road,
Brackley, NN13 7UG
01280 706 888
www.cherwellvalleybrewery.co.uk

Digfield Ales
North Lodge Farm, Thurning Road, Barnwell,
Peterborough, PE8 5RJ
01832 293 295

Frog Island Brewery
The Maltings, Westbridge, St James Road,
Northampton, NN5 5HS
01604 587 772
www.frogislandbrewery.co.uk

Great Oakley Brewery
Bridge Farm, 11 Brooke Road, Great Oakley,
Corby, NN18 8HG
01536 744 888
www.greatoakleybrewery.com

Hoggleys Brewery
Unit 12 Litchborough Trading Estate,
Northampton Road, Litchborough, NN12 8JB
01604 831 762
www.hoggleys.co.uk

Holland Brewery
5 Brown Flatts, Brewery Street,
Kimberley, NG16 2JU
01159 382 685

Julian Church Brewing Company
c/o 38 Nunnery Avenue,
Rothwell, NN14 6JJ
07794 289 559

Milestone Brewing Co
Great North Road, Cromwell,
Newark, NG23 6JE
01636 822 255
www.milestonebrewery.co.uk

Nobby's Brewery
c/o The Ward Arms, High Street,
Guisborough, NN6 8PY
01604 740 785
www.nobbysbrewery.co.uk

Potbelly Brewery Ltd
c/o Corium Leather Co Ltd,
25-31 Durban Road,
Kettering, NN16 0JA
01536 410 818
www.potbelly-brewery.co.uk

Rockingham Ales
c/o 25 Wansford Road, Elton,
Peterborough, PE8 6RZ
01832 280 722
www.rockinghamales.co.uk

The Silverstone Brewing Co Ltd
Kingshill Farm, Kingshill, Syresham,
Brackley, NN13 5TH
01280 850 629
www.silverstonebrewingcompany.com

NORTHUMBERLAND

Allendale Brew Co Ltd
Allen Mill, Allendale,
Hexham, NE47 9EQ
01434 618 686
www.allendalebrewco.co.uk

Hadrian & Border Brewery
Alnwick Ales Ltd, Unit 10 Hawick
Crescent Industrial Estate,
Newcastle-Upon-Tyne, NE6 1AS
0191 276 5302
www.hadrian-border-brewery.co.uk

Hexhamshire Brewery
Leafields, Hexham, NE46 1SX
01434 606 577
www.hexhamshire.co.uk

High House Farm Brewery
High House Farm, Matfen, NE20 0RG
01661 886 069
www.highhousefarmbrewery.co.uk

Northumberland Breweries Ltd
Accessory House, Barington Road,
Bedlington, NE22 7AP
01670 822 112
www.northumberlandbrewery.co.uk

The Ship Inn Brewery
The Ship Inn, The Square,
Newton-by-the-Sea, Alnwick, NE66 3EW
01665 576 262
www.shipinnnewton.co.uk

Wylam Brewery Ltd
South Houghton Farm, Heddon on the Wall,
Newcastle, NE15 0EZ
01661 853 377
www.wylambrew.co.uk

NOTTINGHAMSHIRE

Castle Rock Brewery
Queensbridge Road, Nottingham, NG2 1NB
01159 851 615
www.castlerockbrewery.co.uk

Full Mash Brewery
17 Lower Park Street, Stapleford, NG9 8EW
01159 499 262

Grafton Brewing Company
c/o 8 Oak Close, Worksop, S80 1BH
01909 476 121

Magpie Brewery
4 Ashling Court, Ashling Street,
Nottingham, NG2 3JA
01159 611 556
www.magpiebrewery.com

Mallard
15 Hartingdon Avenue, Carlton,
Nottingham, NG4 3NR
01159 521 289
www.mallard-brewery.co.uk

Maypole Brewery
North Laithes Farm, Kneesall,
Newark, NG22 0AN
07971 277 598
www.maypolebrewery.co.uk

Nottingham Brewery
The Plough Inn, 17 St Peters Street, Radford,
Nottingham, NG7 3EN
01159 422 649
www.nottinghambrewery.com

Springhead Brewery
Old Great North Road, Sutton on Trent,
Newark, NG23 6QS
01636 821 000
www.springhead.co.uk

The Idle Brewery
The White Hart Inn, Main Street,
West Stockwith, DN10 4EY
01427 890 176

OXFORDSHIRE

Adkin Brewery
Wantage
07709 086 149
www.adkinbrewery.co.uk

Appleford Brewery Co Ltd
c/o Iron Bridge House, St Peter's Court,
Appleford, OX14 4YA
01235 848 055
www.applefordbrewery.co.uk

Best Mates Brewery Ltd
Sheep House Farm, Ardington, Wantage, OX12 8QB
01235 835 684
www.bestmatesbrewery.co.uk

Lovibonds Brewery Ltd
19-21 Market Place, Henley-on-Thames, RG9 2AA
01491 576 596
www.lovibonds.com

Pitstop Brewery
Bellingers, Station Road, Grove, OX12 0DH
07870 577 742
www.pitstopbrewery.co.uk

The Cotswold Brewing Company
Foxholes Lane, Foscot, OX7 6RL
01608 659 631
www.cotswoldbrewingcompany.co.uk

The Old Bog Brewery
Masons Arms, 2 Quarry School Place,
Headington, Oxford, OX3 8LH
01865 764 579
www.masonsquarry.co.uk

White Horse Brewery Co Ltd
3 Ware Road, White Horse Business Park,
Stanford-in-the-Vale, SN7 8NY
01367 718 700
www.whitehorsebrewery.com

SHROPSHIRE

Bridgnorth Brewing Co Ltd
The Old Brewhouse, Kings Head Courtyard,
Whitburn Street, Bridgenorth, WV16 4QN
01746 762 889
www.bridgnorthbrewing.com

Corvedale Brewery
Sun Inn, Corfton, Craven Arms, SY7 9DF
01584 861 239
www.suninncorfton.co.uk

Hanby Ales Ltd
The New Brewery, Aston Park Industrial
Estate, Wem, SY4 5SD
01939 232 432
www.hanbyales.co.uk

Ironbridge Brewery Ltd
Unit 7 Merrythought, The Wharfage,
Ironbridge, Telford, TF8 7NJ
01952 433 910
www.ironbridgebrewery.co.uk

Lion's Tale Brewery
Red Lion Hotel, High Street, Cheswardine,
Market Drayton, TF9 2RS
01630 661 234

Offa's Dyke Brewery
Chapel Lane, Trefonen, SY10 9DX
01691 656 889
www.offasdykebrewery.com

Salopian Brewing Co Ltd
67 Mytton Oak Road, Copthorne,
Shrewsbury, SY3 8UQ
01743 248 414
www.salopianbrewery.co.uk

Six Bells Brewery
Church Street, Bishop's Castle, SY9 5AA
01588 638 930
www.bishops-castle.co.uk/SixBells/
brewery.htm

Stonehouse Brewery
Weston, Oswestry, SY10 9ES
01691 676 457
www.stonehousebrewery.co.uk

The Dolphin Brewery Ltd
Dolphin Inn, 48 St. Michael's Street,
Shrewsbury, SY1 2EZ
01743 350 419
www.dolphin-shrewsbury.co.uk

The Ludlow Brewing Co Ltd
Kingsley Garage Yard, 105 Corve Street,
Ludlow, SY8 1DJ
01584 873 291
www.theludlowbrewingcompany.co.uk

Three Tuns Brewery
Salop Street,
Bishop's Castle, SY9 5BW
01588 638 392
www.threetunsbrewery.co.uk

Wood Brewery Ltd
Wistanstow, Craven Arms, SY7 8DG
01588 672 523
www.woodbrewery.co.uk

Worfield Brewing Co
20 Coalport Road, Madeley, TF7 5DP
01746 769 606
www.worfieldbrewery.co.uk

SOMERSET

Berrow Brewery
Coast Road, Berrow,
Burnham-on-sea, TA8 2QU
01278 751 345

Blindmans Brewery Ltd
Talbot Farm, Leighton,
Frome, BA11 4PN
01749 880 038
www.blindmansbrewery.co.uk

Cheddar Ales
Unit 5 Winchester Farm, Draycott Road,
Cheddar, BS27 3RP
01934 744 193
www.cheddarales.co.uk

Cotleigh Brewery
Ford Road, Wiveliscombe, TA4 2RE
01984 624 086
www.cotleighbrewery.co.uk

Cottage Brewing Co Ltd
High Street, West Lydford, TA11 7DQ
01963 240 551
www.cottagebrewing.com

Glastonbury Ales
Grovers Brewhouse, Unit 10 Wessex Park,
Bancombe Road, Somerton, TA11 6SB
01458 272 244
www.glastonburyales.com

Matthews Brewing Co Ltd
Unit 7 Timsbury Workshop Estate, Hayeswood
Road, Timsbury, Bath, BA2 0HQ
01761 472 242
www.matthewsbrewing.co.uk

Milk Street Brewery
The Griffin, Milk Street, Frome, BA11 3DB
01373 467 766
www.milkstreetbrewery.co.uk

Moor Beer Co
Whitley Farm, Stagman Lane, Ashcott,
Bridgewater, TA7 9QW
01458 210 050
www.moorbeer.co.uk

North Curry Brewery
The Old Coach House Gwyon House, Church
Road, North Curry, Taunton, TA3 6LH
07928 815 053
www.thenorthcurrybrewerycouk.com

Odcombe Brewery
The Masons Arms, 41 Lower Odcombe,
Yeovil, BA22 8TX
01935 862 591
www.masonsarmsodcombe.co.uk

Quantock Brewery
Unit E Monument View, Summerfield Avenue,
Chelston Business Park, Wellington, TA21 9ND
07824 860 282
www.quantockbrewery.co.uk

RCH Brewery
West Hewish, Weston-super-Mare, BS24 6RR
01934 834 447
www.rchbrewery.com

Stowey Brewery
The Old Cider House, 25 Castle Street,
Nether Stowey, TA5 1LN
01278 732 228
www.stoweybrewery.co.uk

Taunton Brewing Company
Unit 1f Hillview Industrial Estate,
West Bagborough, Taunton, TA4 3EW
01823 433 999

The Abbey Brewery
Camden Row, Bath, BA1 5LB
01225 444 437
www.abbeyales.co.uk

The Cottage Brewing Co Ltd
The Old Cheese Dairy, Blue Farm,
Lovington, Castle Cary, BA7 7PP
01963 240 551

Yeovil Ales Brewery
Bofors Park, Artilllery Road, Lufton,
Yeovil, BA22 8YH
01935 414 888
www.yeovilales.com

SOUTH YORKSHIRE

Abbeydale Brewery
Unit 8, Aizlewood Road, Sheffield, S8 0YX
0114 2818 712
www.abbeydalebrewery.co.uk

Acorn Brewery
Unit 3 Aldham Industrial Estate, Mitchell
Road, Wombwell, Barnsley, S73 8HA
01226 270 734
www.acorn-brewery.co.uk

Bradfield Brewery
Watt House Farm, High Bradfield,
Sheffield, S6 6LG
0114 2851 118
www.bradfieldbrewery.com

Crown Brewery
Hillsborough Hotel, 54-58 Langsett Road,
Sheffield, S6 2UB
0114 2322 100
www.hillsborough-hotel.co.uk

Glentworth Brewery
Glentworth House, Crossfield Lane, Skellow,
Doncaster, DN6 8PL
01302 725 555

Kelham Island Brewery
23 Alma Street, Sheffield, S3 8SA
0114 2494 804
www.kelhambrewery.co.uk

Little Ale Cart Brewing Company
The Wellington, 1 Henry Street,
Sheffield, S3 7EQ
0114 2 492 295

Morrissey Fox
Ye Olde Punch Bowl, Marton Cum
Grafton, YO51 9QY
01423 322 519
www.morrisseyfox.co.uk

Oakwell Brewery
Unit 11, Pontefract Road, Barnsley, S71 1EZ
01226 296 161

The Brew Company Ltd
G4, 19-21 Carlisle Street East,
Sheffield, S4 7QN
0114 2 709 991
www.thebrewcompany.co.uk

The Concertina Brewery
9a Dolcliffe Road, Mexborough, S64 9AZ
01709 580 841

The Sheffield Brewery Co Ltd
Unit 111 The JC Albyn Complex, Burton Road,
Sheffield, S3 8BZ
0114 2 727 256
www.sheffieldbrewery.com

Wentworth Brewery
The Power House, The Gun Park, Wentworth,
Rotherham, S62 7TF
01226 747 070
www.wentworth-brewery.co.uk

STAFFORDSHIRE

Black Hole Brewery Ltd
Unit 63 Imex Business Park, Shobnall Road,
Burton-upon-Trent, DE14 2AU
01283 534 060
www.blackholebrewery.co.uk

Blythe Brewery
Hamstall, Ridware, WS15 3QQ
07773 747 724
www.blythebrewery.co.uk

Eccleshall Brewery
St Albans Road, Common Road Industrial
Estate, Stafford, ST16 3DR
01785 257 976
www.slatersales.co.uk

Highgate Brewery Ltd
Sandymount Road, Walsall, WS1 3AP
01922 644 453
www.highgatebrwery.com

JHS Traditional Brewers
c/o The Fox Inn, Broadheath,
Tenbury Wells, WR15 8QS
01886 853 189
www.jhstraditionalbrewery.com

Kinver Brewery
Unit 2 Fairfield Drive, Kinver,
Stourbridge, DY7 6EW
07715 842 679
www.kinverbrewery.co.uk

Leek Brewery
Unit 11 & 12 Churnet Court, Churnetside
Business Park, Cheddleton, Leek, ST13 7EF
01538 361 919
www.beersandcheese.co.uk

Lymestone Brewery Ltd
Unit 5 Mount Street Industrial Estate,
Mount Street, Stone, ST15 8LL
01785 817 796
www.lymestonebrewery.co.uk

Morton Brewery
c/o 96 Brewood Road, Coven,
Wolverhampton, WV9 5EF
07988 069 647
www.mortonbrewery.co.uk

Peakstones Rock Brewery
Peakstones Farm, Cheadle Road, Alton,
Stoke-on-Trent, ST10 4DH
01538 750 974
www.peakstonesrockbreweryalton.co.uk

Quartz Brewing
Heart of the Country Village, Swinfen,
Lichfield, WS14 9QR
01543 483 241
www.quartzbrewing.co.uk

The Backyard Brewhouse
Unit 8a Gatehouse Trading Estate, Lichfield
Road, Brownhills, Walsall, WS8 6JZ
07591 923 370
www.thebackyardbrewhouse.com

The Beowulf Brewing Company
Unit 3-4 Chasewater Country Park, Pool
Road, Brownhills, Walsall, WS8 7NL
01543 454 067
www.beowulfbrewery.co.uk

The Burton Old Cottage Beer Co Ltd
Unit 10 Brian Eccleshall Yard,
Eccleshall Business Park, Hawkins Lane,
Burton-upon-Trent, DE14 1PT
07909 931 250
www.oldcottagebeer.co.uk

Titanic Brewery
Unit 5 Callender Place, Lingard Street,
Burslem, Stoke on Trent, ST6 1JL
01782 823 447
www.titanicbrewery.co.uk

Tower Brewery
The Old Water Tower, Walsitch Maltings,
Glensyl Way, Burton-upon-Trent, DE14 1LX
01283 530 695

Townhouse Brewery
Townhouse Farm, Alsager Road, Audley,
Stoke-on-Trent, ST7 8JQ
07976 209 437

SUFFOLK

Bartrams Brewery
Rougham Estate, Ipswich Road,
Bury St Edmunds, IP30 9LZ
01449 737 655
www.bartramsbrewery.co.uk

Cox & Holbrook
Manor Farm, Buxhall, IP14 3DY
01449 073 603

Earl Soham Brewery
Earl Soham, Woodbridge, IP13 7RT
01728 684 097
www.earlsohambrewery.co.uk

Elveden Ales
The Courtyard, Elveden Estate,
Elveden Estate, Thetford, IP24 3TA
01842 878 922

Green Dragon Brewery
29 Broadstreet, Bungay, NR35 1ED
01986 892 681

Green Jack Brewery
Triangle Tavern, 29 St Peters Street,
Lowestoft, NR32 1QA
01502 582 711
www.green-jack.co.uk

Kings Head Brewing Co
The Kings Head, 132 High Street, Bildeston,
Ipswich, IP7 7ED
01449 741 434
www.bildestonkingshead.co.uk

Red Rat Craft Brewery
Broadmere Cottages, Troston,
Bury St Edmunds, IP31 1EH
01359 269 742
www.redratcraftbrewery.co.uk

St. Judes Brewery
2 Cardigan Street, Ipswich, IP1 3PF
01473 413 334
www.stjudesbrewery.co.uk

The Black Adder Brewery
13 Churchfield Road,
Sudbury, CO10 2YA
01787 311 055
www.mauldons.co.uk

The Brandon Brewery
76 High Street, Brandon, IP27 0AU
01842 878 496
www.brandonbrewery.co.uk

The Cliff Quay Brewery
Cliff Road, Ipswich, IP3 0AZ
01473 225 501
www.cliffquay.co.uk

The Mill Green Brewery
White Horse Inn, Mill Green, Edwardstone,
Sudbury, CO10 5PX
01787 211 211
www.millgreenbrewery.co.uk

The Old Cannon Brewery
86 Cannon Street, Bury St Edmunds, IP33 1JR
01284 768 769
www.oldcannonbrewery.co.uk

SURREY

Ascot Ales Ltd
Unit 5 Compton Place Business Centre,
Surrey Avenue, Camberley, GU15 3DX
0845 257 5575
www.ascot-ales.co.uk

Dorking Brewery
Engine Shed, Dorking West Station Yard,
Station Road, Dorking, RH4 1HF
01306 877 988
www.dorkingbrewery.com

Farnham Brewery
104 Upper Hale Road,
Farnham, GU9 0PB
01252 735 278

Hogs Back Brewery
Manor Farm, The Street,
Tongham, GU10 1DE
01252 783 000
www.hogsback.co.uk

Pilgrim Brewery
West Street, Reigate, RH2 9BL
01737 222 651
www.pilgrim.co.uk

Surrey Hills Brewery Ltd
Old Scotland Farm, Staple Lane, Shere,
Guildford, GU5 9TE
01483 212 812
www.surreyhills.co.uk

The Crondall Brewing Co Ltd
Lower Old Park Farm, Dora's Green Lane,
Crondall, Farnham, GU10 5DX
01252 319 000

The Leith Hill Brewery
The Plough Inn, Coldharbour,
Dorking, RH5 6HD
01306 711 793
www.ploughinn.com

Wayland's Brewery
6 Marley Close,
Addlestone, KT15 1AR
07956 531 618
www.waylandsbrewery.co.uk

TYNE & WEAR

Big Lamp Brewery
Grange Road, Newburn,
Newcastle-Upon-Tyne, NE15 8NL
0191 267 1689
www.biglampbrewers.co.uk

Bull Lane Brewing Company
The Clarendon, 143 High Street East,
Sunderland, SR1 2BL
0191 510 3200
www.bull-lane-brewing.co.uk

Darwin Brewery
63 Back Tatham Street, Hendon,
Sunderland, SR1 2QE
0191 514 4746
www.darwinbrewery.com

Mordue Brewery
Units D1 & D2, Narvik Way, Tyne Tunnel
Trading Estate, North Shields, NE29 7XJ
0191 296 1879
www.morduebrewery.com

WARWICKSHIRE

Alexandra Arms Brewery
Alexandra Arms, 72-73 James Street,
Rugby, CV21 2SL
01788 578 660

Birmingham Brewery Ltd
Unit 45 Mount Street Business
Centre, Mount Street, Nechells,
Birmingham, B7 5RD
0121 328 2120
www.birminghambrewery.co.uk

Church End Brewery Ltd
109 Ridge Lane, Nuneaton, CV10 0RD
01827 713 080
www.churchendbrewery.co.uk

Discovery Ales
Brook Farm, Packington Lane, Meriden,
Coventry, CV7 7HN
01675 463 809

North Cotswold Brewery
Ditchford Farm, Stretton-on-Fosse,
Moreton-in-Marsh, GL56 9RD
01608 663 947
www.northcotswoldbrewery.co.uk

Purity Brewing Co
The Brewery, Upper Spernall Farm,
Great Alne, Alcester, B49 6JF
01789 488 007
www.puritybrewing.com

Rainbow Inn & Brewery
73 Birmingham Road, Allesley,
Coventry, CV5 9GT
024 7640 2888

Rugby Brewing Co Ltd
Wood Farm, Willey,
Rugby, CV23 0SL
0845 017 8844
www.rugbybrewingco.co.uk

The Warwickshire Beer Co
Queen Street,
Cubbington, CV32 7NA
01926 450 747
www.warwickshirebeer.co.uk

Tunnel Brewery Ltd
Lord Nelson Inn, Birmingham Road,
Ansley, Nuneaton, CV10 9PQ
024 7639 4888
www.tunnelbrewery.co.uk

WEST MIDLANDS

Black Country Ales
Unit 4, Tansey Green Road, Brierley Hill,
Dudley, DY5 4TL
01384 480 156
www.blackcountryales.co.uk

Enville Ales
Enville Brewery, Cox Green, Hollies Lane,
Stourbridge, DY7 5LG
01384 873 728
www.envilleales.com

Olde Swan Brewery
89 Halesowen Road, Netherton,
Dudley, DY2 9PY
01384 253 075

Sarah Hughes Brewery
129 Bilston Road,
Sedgley, DY3 1JE
01902 883 380

The Slaughterhouse Brewery Ltd
Bridge Street,
Warwick, CV34 5PD
01926 490 986
www.slaughterhousebrewery.com

Toll End Brewery
Waggon & Horses, 131 Toll End Road,
Tipton, DY4 0ET
0121 502 6453

Windsor Castle Brewery
7 Stourbridge Road, Lye,
Stourbridge, DY9 7DG
01384 895 230
www.windsorcastlebrewery.com

WEST SUSSEX

Adur Brewery Ltd
Adur Business Centre, Little High Street,
Shoreham-by-sea, BN44 3DG
01273 467 527
www.adurbrewery.com

Arundel Brewery
Unit 7c, Ford Airfield Industrial Estate, Ford,
Arundel, BN18 0HY
01903 733 111
www.arundelbrewery.co.uk

Dark Star Brewing
Moonhill Farm, Burgess Hill Road, Ansty,
Haywards Heath, RH17 5AH
01444 412 311
www.darkstarbrewing.co.uk

Gribble Brewery Ltd
Gribble Lane,
Oving, PO20 2BP
01243 789 123
www.gribblebrewery.co.uk

Hammerpot Brewery Ltd
Unit 30 The Vinery, Arundel Road, Poling,
Arundel, BN18 9PY
01903 883 338
www.hammerpot-brewery.co.uk

Hepworth & Company Brewers Ltd
The Railway Yard, Nightingale Road,
Horsham, RH12 2NW
01403 269 696
www.hepworthbrewery.co.uk

Rectory Ales Ltd
Streat Hill Farm, Streat Hill, Streat,
Hassocks, BN6 8RP
01273 890 570
www.rectory-ales.co.uk

The Langham Brewery llp
Langham Stables, Langham Lane,
Lodsworth, Petworth, GU28 9BU
01798 860 861
www.langhambrewery.co.uk

W J King & Co Brewers
3-5 Jubilee Estate, Horsham, RH13 5UE
01403 272 102
www.kingbeer.co.uk

Weltons Brewery
1 Rangers Lodge, Oakhill Road,
Horsham, RH13 5LF
01403 242 901
www.weltonsbeer.com

WEST YORKSHIRE

Anglo Dutch Brewery
Unit 12 Saville Bridge Mills,
Mill Street East, Dewsbury, WF13 6QQ
01924 457 772
www.anglo-brewery.co.uk

Atlas Mill Brewery Ltd
Atlas Mill, Atlas Mill Road,
Brighouse, HD6 1ES
01484 720 440
www.atlasmillbrewery.com

Bob's Brewing Co Ltd
The Brewers Pride, Low Mill Road,
Ossett, WF5 8ND
07789 693 597

Briscoe's Brewery
16 Ash Grove, Otley, LS21 3EL
01943 466 515

Eastwood Brewer
Barge & Barrel, 10-20 Park Road,
Elland, HX5 9HP
07949 148 476
www.eastwoodthebrewer.co.uk

Elland Brewery
Units 3-5 Heathfield Industrial Estate,
Heathfield Street, Elland, HX5 9AE
01422 377 677
www.eandsbrewery.co.uk

Empire Brewery
Unit 33 The Old Boiler House,
Upper Mills, Cannal Side,
Huddersfield, HD7 5HA
01484 847 343

Fernandes Brewery
The Old Malthouse, 5 Avison Yard,
Wakefield, WF11UA
01924 291 709
www.fernandes-brewery.gowyld.com

Five Towns Brewery
651 Leeds Road, Wakefield, WF1 2LU
01924 781 887

Fox Beer Company
Fox & Newt, 9 Burley Street,
Leeds, LS3 1LD
01132 454 505

Golcar Brewery
60a Swallow Lane, Golcar,
Huddersfield, HD7 4NB
01484 644 241

Goose Eye Brewery
Ingrow Bridge, South Street,
Keighley, BD21 5AX
01535 605 807
www.goose-eye-brewery.co.uk

H B Clark
Westgate Brewery, Westgate,
Wakefield, WF2 9SW
01924 373 328
www.hbclark.co.uk

Halifax Steam Brewing Company
The Conclave, Southedge Works,
Hipperholme, Halifax, HX3 8EF
01484 715 074

Linfit Brewery
The Sair, Lane Top, Linthwaite,
Huddersfield, HD7 5SG
01484 842 370

Little Valley Brewery Ltd
Turkey Lodge Farm, New Road,
Cragg Vale, Hebden Bridge, HX7 5TT
01422 883 888
www.littlevalleybrewery.co.uk

Mallinsons Brewing Company
Plover Road Garage, Plover Road,
Huddersfield, HD3 3PJ
01484 654 301
www.drinkmallinsons.co.uk

Moorview Brewery
c/o 3 Farr Royd, Burley In Wharfedale,
Ilkley, LS29 7HZ
0845 349 3778
www.moorviewbrewery.co.uk

Naylor's Brewery
Midland Mill, Station Road,
Crosshills, Keighley, BD 20 7DT
01535 637 451
www.naylorsbrewery.com

Old Bear Brewer
Unit 4b Atlas Works, Pitt Street,
Keighley, BD21 4YL
01535 601 222
www.oldbearbrewery.com

Old Spot Brewery Limited
Manor Farm, Station Road,
Cullingworth, Bradford, BD13 5HN
01535 691 144
www.oldspotbrewery.com

Ossetts Brewing Co Ltd
Low Mill Road,
Ossett, WF5 8ND
01924 261 333
www.ossett-brewery.co.uk

Riverhead Brewery Ltd
2 Peel Street, Marsden,
Huddersfield, HD7 6BR
01484 841 270

Rodham's Brewery
74 Albion Street,
Otley, LS21 1BZ
01943 464 530

Ryburn Brewery
c/o Ram's Head, Wakefield Road,
Sowerby Bridge, HX6 2AZ
01422 835 413

Salamander Brewing Co Ltd
22 Harry Street, Bradford, BD4 9PH
01274 652 323
www.salamanderbrewing.co.uk

Saltaire Brewery
The Brewery, County Works, Dockfield Road,
Shipley, BD17 7AR
01274 594 959
www.saltairebrewery.co.uk

Summer Wine Brewery Ltd
Unit 15 Honley Business Centre, New Mill
Road, Honley, Holmfirth, HD9 6QB
01484 665 466
www.summerwinebrewery.co.uk

The Brass Monkey Brewery Co Ltd
Unit 25 Asquith Bottom Mill, West Street,
Sowerby Bridge, HX6 3BS
01422 316 040
www.thebrassmonkeybrewery.co.uk

The Bridestones Brewing Co Ltd
Smithy Farm, Blackshaw Head,
Hebden Bridge, HX7 7JB
01422 847 104

The Leeds Brewery Co Ltd
Units 3-4 Sydenham Road,
Leeds, LS11 9RU
01132 445 866
www.leedsbrewery.co.uk

Tigertops Brewery
22 Oakes Street, Wakefield, WF2 9LN
01924 897 728

WILTSHIRE

Archers Brewing
Penzance Drive, Swindon, SN5 7JL
01793 879 929
www.archers-brewery.co.uk

Box Steam Brewery
Oaks Farm, Rode Hill,
Colerne, SN14 8AR
01225 858 383
www.boxsteambrewery.com

Hop Back Brewery
Downton Business Park, Batten Road,
Downton, Salisbury, SP5 3HU
01725 510 986
www.hopback.co.uk

Keystone Brewery
Old Carpenters Workshop, Berwick St
Leonard, Salisbury, SP3 5SN
01747 820 426
www.keystonbrewery.co.uk

Moles Brewery
5 Merlin Way, Bowerhill,
Melksham, SN12 6TJ
01225 708 842
www.molesbrewery.com

Plain Ales
Bow House, Chitterne, BA12 0LG
01985 851 105
www.plainales.co.uk

Stonehenge Ales
The Old Mill, Netheravon, Salisbury, SP4 9QB
01980 670 631
www.stonehengeales.com

The Downton Brewery Co Ltd
Unit 11 Downton Industrial Estate, Batten
Road, Downton, Salisbury, SP5 3HU
01722 322 890
www.downtonbrewery.com

The Hidden Brewery Ltd
Wylye Road, Dinton,
Salisbury, SP3 5EU
01722 716 440
www.thehiddenbrewery.com

The Ramsbury Brewery
Priory Farm, Axford,
Marlborough, SN8 2HA
01672 541 407
www.ramsburybrewery.com

Three Castles Brewery Ltd
Unit 12 Salisbury Road Business Park,
Salisbury Road, Pewsey, SN9 5PZ
01672 564 433
www.threecastlesbrewery.co.uk

Wessex Brewery
Rye Hill Farm, Longbridge Deverill,
Warminster, BA12 7DE
01985 844 532

WORCESTERSHIRE

Bewdley Brewery Ltd
Units 7 & 8 Bewdley Craft Centre,
Lax Lane, Bewdley, DY12 2DZ
01299 405 148
www.bewdleybrewery.co.uk

Blue Bear Brewery Ltd
Unit 1 Openbarn Farm, Main Road,
Kempsey, Worcester, WR5 3LW
01905 828 258
www.bluebearbrewery.co.uk

Brandy Cask Pub & Brewery
c/o 25 Bridge Street,
Pershore, WR10 1AJ
01386 552 602

Bricktop Brewery
c/o The Gate Hangs Well, Woodgate Road,
Stoke Prior, Brosgrove, B60 4HG
01527 821 957
www.thegatehangswell.co.uk

Buckle Street Brewery
Honeybourne Airfield Trading Estate,
Honeybourne, Evesham, WR11 7QF

Cannon Royall Brewery Ltd
Rear Fruiterer's Arms, Uphampton Lane,
Ombersley, WR9 0JW
01905 621 161
www.cannonroyall.co.uk

Hobsons Brewery & Co
New House Farm, Tenbury Road, Cleobury
Mortimer, Kidderminster, DY14 8RD
01299 270 837
www.hobsonsbrewery.co.uk

Malvern Hills Brewery
15 West Malvern Road,
Great Malvern, WR14 4ND
01684 560 165
www.malvernhillsbrewery.co.uk

St. George's Brewery Ltd
The Old Bakehouse, Bush Lane,
Callow End, Worcester, WR2 4TF
01905 831 316

Teme Valley Brewery
The Talbot, Knightwick, WR6 5PH
01886 821 235
www.temevalleybrewery.co.uk

Weatheroak Brewery Ltd
25 Withybed Lane, Alvechurch, B48 7NX
0121 445 4411
www.weatheroakales.co.uk

Weatheroak Hill Brewery Ltd
Coach & Horses, Weatheroak Hill, Alvechurch,
Birmingham, B48 7EA
01564 823 386
www.coachandhorsesinn.co.uk

Wyre Piddle Brewery
Highgrove Farm, Pinvin,
Pershore, WR10 2LF
01905 841 853

NORTHERN IRELAND
COUNTY ANTRIM

Hilden Brewing Company
Grand Street, Lisburn, BT27 4TY
028 9266 0800
www.hildenbrewery.co.uk

COUNTY DOWN

Clanconnel Brewing Co Ltd
PO Box 316, Craigavon, BT65 9AZ
07711 626 770
www.clanconnelbrewing.com

Whitewater Brewing Co
40 Tullyframe Road, Kilkeel, Newry, BT34 4RZ
028 4176 9449
www.whitewaterbrewing.com

SCOTLAND
ABERDEENSHIRE

BrewDog Ltd
Unit 1 Kessock Workshops,
Fraserburgh, AB43 8UE
01346 519 009
www.brewdog.com

Hillside Brewery
Hillside, Corse, Lumphanan, AB31 4RY
01339 883 506
www.hillside.eclipse.co.uk

The Old Foreigner Brewery
Glenkindie Arms Hotel, Glenkindie,
Alford, AB33 8SX
01975 641 288
www.theglenkindiearmshotel.com

ARGYLL & BUTE

Atlas Brewery
Lab Road, Kinlochleven, PH50 4SG
01855 831 111
www.sinclairbreweries.co.uk

Fyne Ales
Achadunan, Cairndow, PA26 8BJ
01499 600 238
www.fyneales.com

Sulwath Brewery
The Brewery, 209 King Street,
Castle Douglas, DG7 1DT
01556 504 525
www.sulwathbrewery.co.uk

The Oyster Bar & Brewery
Ellenabeich, Easdale, Oban, PA34 4RQ
01852 300 121
www.oysterbrewery.com

AYRSHIRE

Windie Goat Brewery/Failford Inn
Failford Inn, Failford, Ayr, KA5 5TF
01292 540 117
http://www.failfordinn.co.uk/brewery/
aboutus.html

BORDERS

Traquair House Brewery
Traquair House, Innerleithen, EH44 6PW
01896 831 370
www.traquair.co.uk

CLACKMANNAN

Devon Ales Ltd
Mansfield Arms, 7 Main Street, Sauchie,
Alloa, FK10 3JR
01259 722 020
www.devonales.com

Heather Ales
New Alloa Brewery, Kelliebank,
Alloa, FK10 1NU
01259 725 511
www.fraoch.com

EDINBURGH

Fowler's Ale (Prestoungrange) Ltd
The Gothenburg, 227-229 High Street,
Prestonpans, EH32 9BE
01875 819 922
www.prestoungrange.org

Stewart Brewing
Unit 5, 42 Dryden Road, Bilston Glen
Industrial Estate, Loanhead, EH20 9LZ
0131 440 2442
www.stewartbrewing.co.uk
Stewart Brewing, Edinburgh's Independent
brewery, has grown from strength to
strength over the last 5 years. We supply our
award winning premium cask ales (including
the famous Edinburgh Gold), to over 250
local pubs.

FIFE

Fyfe Brewing Company
469 High Street, Kirkcaldy, KY1 2SN
01592 646 211
www.fyfebrewery.co.uk

GLASGOW

Kelburn Brewing Co Ltd
10 Muriel Lane, Barrhead, G78 1QB
0141 881 2138
www.kelburnbrewery.com

HIGHLAND

An Teallach Ale Co
1 Camusnagaul, Dundonell, By Garve, IV23 2QT
01854 633 306

Black Isle Brewery Co Ltd
Old Allangrange, Munlochy, IV8 8NZ
01463 811 871
www.blackislebrewery.com

Far North Brewery
Melvich Hotel, Melvich, Thurso, KW14 7YJ
01641 531 206
www.smoothhound.co.uk/hotels/melvichh

Glenfinnan Brewery Co Ltd
Struth A Lhuilinn,
Glenfinnan, PH37 4LT
01397 704 309
www.glenfinnanbrewery.co.uk

The Cairngorm Brewery Co Ltd
Unit 12 Dalfaber Industrial Estate,
Dalfaber Drive, Aviemore, PH22 1ST
01479 812 222
www.cairngormbrewery.com

The Plockton Brewery
5 Bank Street, Plockton, IV52 8TP
01599 544 276
www.theplocktonbrewery.com

ISLE OF ARRAN

Arran Brewery
Claddach, KA27 8DE
01770 302 353
www.arranbrewery.com

ISLE OF COLONSAY

Colonsay Brewing Co Ltd
The Brewery, Colonsay, PA61 7YZ
01951 200 190
www.colonsaybrewery.co.uk

ISLE OF ISLAY

Islay Ales
The Brewery, Islay House Square,
Bridgend, PA44 7NZ
01496 810 014
www.islayales.com

ISLE OF LEWIS

Hebridean Brewing Company
18a Bells Road, Stornaway, HS1 2RA
01851 700 123
www.hebridean-brewery.co.uk

ISLE OF MAN

The Mount Murray Brewing Co Ltd
The Hop Garden, Mount Murray,
Douglas, IM41JE
01624 661 244
www.bushys.com

ISLE OF MULL

Isle of Mull Brewing Co Ltd
Ledaig, Tobermory, PA75 6NR
01688 302 821

ISLE OF SKYE

Cuillin Brewery Ltd
Sligachan Hotel, Sligachan,
Carbost, IV47 8SW
01478 650 204
www.cuillinbrewery.co.uk

Isle of Skye Brewing Company
Uig, IV51 9XP
01470 542 477
www.skyebrewery.co.uk

LANARKSHIRE

Strathaven Ales
Craigmill Brewery, Strathaven, ML10 6PB
01357 520 419
www.strathavenales.co.uk

The Clockwork Beer Co
1153-1155 Cathcart Road,
Glasgow, G42 9HB
0141 649 0184
www.clockworkbeerco.com

ORKNEY

Highland Brewery Co Ltd
Swannay Brewery, Swannay By Evie,
Birsay, KW17 2NP
01856 721 700
www.highlandbrewingcompany.co.uk

Orkney Brewery
Quoyloo, Stromness, KW16 3LT
01667 404 555
www.sinclairbreweries.co.uk

PERTHSHIRE & KINROSS

Moulin Inn & Brewery
Baledmund Road, Moulin,
Pitlochry, PH16 5EH
01796 472 196
www.moulininn.co.uk

The Inveralmond Brewery Ltd
1 Inveralmond Way, Inveralmond,
Perth, PH1 3UQ
01738 449 448
www.inveralmond-brewery.co.uk

RENFREWSHIRE

Houston Brewing Company
South Street, Houston,
Johnstone, PA6 7EN
01505 614 528
www.houston-brewing.co.uk

SHETLAND

Valhalla Brewery
Baltasound,
Unst, ZE2 9DX
01957 711 658
www.valhallabrewery.co.uk

SOUTH LANARKSHIRE

Broughton Ales Ltd
Broughton, Biggar, ML12 6HQ
01899 830 345
www.broughtonales.co.uk

STIRLING

Bridge of Allan Brewery
Queens Lane,
Bridge of Allan, FK9 4NY
01786 834 555
www.bridgeofallan.co.uk

Eglesbrech Brewing Company
Behind The Wall, 14 Melville Street,
Falkirk, FK1 1HZ
01324 633 338
www.behindthewall.co.uk

Tryst Brewery
Lorne Road,
Larbert, FK5 4AT
01324 554 000
www.trystbrewery.co.uk

WALES

CARMARTHENSHIRE

Black Mountain Brewery
Telegraph Inn, Station Road,
Llangadog, SA19 9LS
01550 777 727

Coles Family Brewery
White Hart Inn,
Llanddarog, SA32 8NT
01267 275 395

Ffos y FFin Brewery
Ffos y Ffin Fawr, Capel Dewi,
Carmarthen, SA32 8AG
07838 384 868
www.ffosyffinbrewery.co.uk

The Jacobi Brewery of Caio
Penlanwen, Pumsaint,
Llanwrda, SA19 8RR
01558 650 605
www.jacobibrewery.co.uk

William Evan-Evans Brewery
The New Brewery, 1 Rhosmaen Street,
Llandeilo, SA19 6LU
01558 824 455
www.evan-evans.com

CEREDIGION

Bragdy Gwynant
Tynllidiart Arms, Capel Bangor,
Aberystwyth, SY23 3LR
01970 880 248

Penlon Cottage Brewery
Penlon, Pencae,
Llanarth, SA47 0QN
01545 580 022
www.penlon.biz

CLWYD

Jolly Brewer
Kingston Villa, 27 Poplar Road,
Wrexham, LL13 7DG
01978 261 884
www.jollybrewer.co.uk

Plassey Brewery
The Plassey, Eyton,
Wrexham, LL13 0SP
01978 781 111
www.plasseybrewery.co.uk

CONWAY

North Wales Brewery
Ty Tan-y-Mynydd, Moelfre,
Abergele, LL22 9RF
01745 832 966
www.northwalesbrewery.net

DENBIGHSHIRE

**Great Orme Brewery Ltd
(Bracdy Y Gogarth)**
Y Bracdy, Nant-Y-Cywarch,
Glan Conwy, Colwyn Bay, LL28 5PP
01492 580 548
www.greatormebrewery.co.uk

Sandstone Brewery llp
Unit 5 Preston Road,
Wrexham Industrial Estate,
Wrexham, LL13 9JT
07851 001 118
www.sandstonebrewery.co.uk

FLINTSHIRE

Facer's Brewery
c/o Tan Y Coed, Bryn y Garreg,
Flint Mountain, Flint, CH6 5QT
07713 566 370
www.facers.co.uk

GLAMORGAN

Artisan Brewing Co Ltd
183 Kings Road,
Cardiff, CF11 9DF
07505 401 939
www.artisanbeer.co.uk

Bryncelyn Brewery
Wern Fawr Inn, 47 Wern Road,
Ystalyfera, SA9 2LX
01639 843 625
www.bryncelynbrewery.co.uk

Bullmastiff Brewery
14 Bessemer Close,
Cardiff, CD1 8DL
029 2066 5292

Dare Brewery Ltd
The Falcon Inn, 1 Incline Row,
Godreaman, Aberdare, CF44 6LU
07812 366 369
www.darebrewery.co.uk

Newman's Brewery
The Celt Experience Brewery,
Unit 2e Former Hill Buildings,
Pontygwindy Industrial Estate,
Caerphilly, CF83 3HU
08708 033 876
www.newmansbrewery.com

Otley Brewing Company Ltd
Unit 42 Albion Industrial Estate, Cilfynydd
Road, Pontypridd, CF37 4NX
01443 480 555
www.otleybrewing.co.uk
The Otley Brewing Company producing real
ales with the finest malts hops and
Breconshire water since August 2005. A
micro-brewery dedicated to the craft of
producing Welsh ale with a difference. Fresh,
modern, easy to drink, with an image to
stand out from the crowd.

OTLEY
BREWING
COMPANY

Rhymney Brewery Ltd
Unit A2 Valley Enterprise Centre,
Pant Industrial Estate, Dowlais,
Merthyr Tydfil, CF48 2SR
01685 722 253
www.rhymneybreweryltd.com

Swansea Brewing Company
Joiners Arms, 50 Bishopston Road,
Bishopston, Swansea, SA3 3EJ
01792 290 197

The Cardiff Brewery
Crawshay Street,
Cardiff, CF10 1SP
029 2040 2060
www.sabrain.com

The Hurns Brewing Co Ltd
Phoenix Brewery, Unit 3 Century Park,
Swansea Enterprise Park,
Swansea, SA6 8RP
01792 797 300
www.hurnsbeer.co.uk

The Vale of Glamorgan Brewery Ltd
Unit 8a Atlantic Trading Estate,
Barry, CF63 3RF
01446 730 757
www.vogbrewery.co.uk

Zerodegrees Cardiff
27 Westgate Street,
Cardiff, CF10 1DD
029 2022 9494
www.zerodegrees.co.uk

GWENT

Warcop Country Ales
c/o 9 Nellive Park,
St. Brides Wentlooge,
Newport, NP10 8SE
01633 680 058
www.warcopales.com

GWYNEDD

Conwy Brewery Limited
Unit 3 Morfa Conwy Enterprise Park,
Parc Caer Selon,
Conwy, LL32 8FA
01492 585 287
www.conwybrewery.co.uk

Purple Moose Brewery Ltd
Madoc Street, Porth Madog, LL49 9DB
01766 515 571
www.purplemoose.co.uk

Snowdonia Brewery
Snowdonia Park Hotel, Waunfawr,
Caernarfon, LL55 4AQ
01286 650 218
www.snowdonia-park.co.uk

MONMOUTHSHIRE

Carter's Brewery
White Hart Inn, White Hart Lane, Machen,
Caerphilly, CF83 8QQ
01633 441 005

Cwmbran Brewery
Gorse Cottage, Craig Lane,
Upper Cwmbran, Cwmbran, NP44 5AS
01633 485 233
www.cwmbranbrewery.co.uk

Kingstone Brewery
Tintern, NP16 7NX
01291 680 111
www.kingstonebrewery.co.uk

Tudor Brewery
29 Nevill Street,
Abergavenny, NP7 5AA
01873 855 074
www.kingsarmsabergavenny.co.uk

PEMBROKESHIRE

Nags Head Brewery
Abercych, Boncath, SA37 0HJ
01239 841 200

POWYS

Breconshire Brewery Ltd
Ffrwdgrech Industrial Estate,
Brecon, LD3 8LA
01874 623 731
www.breconshirebrewery.com

Heart of Wales Brewery
Stable Yard, Zion Street,
Llanwrtyd Wells, LD5 4RD
01591 610 236
www.heartofwalesbrewery.co.uk

Monty's Brewery Ltd
Castle Works, Hen-Domen,
Montgomery, SY15 6HA
01686 668 933
www.montysbrewery.co.uk

Appendix: Customs and Duty

know of two microbrewers who have been jailed for failing to pay their duty and VAT bills. (I also know of one who was jailed for taking part in one of those fake export scams, but that's another story.) Two out of the 1,000 or so people who have set up microbreweries in the last 40 years may not seem all that many. But neither of them set out to commit fraud: cash-flow and other problems simply overwhelmed them. The harshness of their sentences shows, nevertheless, that Her Majesty's Revenue & Customs (HMRC) is not to be trifled with.

Fortunately, the world wide web makes HMRC much easier to understand and therefore satisfy. These days you no longer have to send away for copies of the various rules and regulations, or search them out in the public library and then spend hours and a small fortune photocopying them. All you have to do is visit **www.hmrc.gov.uk** and look up Notice 226 (December 2005) by clicking first on the "Excise & Other" link, then on "Information & Guides", then on "Alcohols", then on "A guide to alcohol duties & procedures", and finally on "Beer duty". This covers everything any brewer or group of breweries or packager or importer needs to know and even includes downloadable copies of all the forms you will need to fill in. It also gives access to all the relevant bits of legislation in their unintelligible full version. Unfortunately, Notice 226 runs to over 90 pages and is almost unreadable. What follows is therefore an attempt to condense and, to an extent, to translate (although not to interpret) its relevant sections. I have left out sections relating to importers, contract packagers and "connected" breweries; but I have presented my précis in the same order as the Notice (illogical though it often seems) to make it easier for you to check my version against the original.

Before we plunge in, though, to find out the actual rate of duty currently payable go back to "A guide to alcohol duties & procedures" and click on "Rates of duty on alcohol". This will tell you that the standard rate brought in by the 2009 budget is £16.47 per percentage point of alcohol by volume per hectolitre, or "Hl%". It changes every year, though, so keep up to date!

The Basics

In the Alcoholic Liquor Duties Act 1979, beer is defined as including ale, porter, stout and any other description of beer, and "any liquor which is made or sold as a description of beer or as a substitute for beer" whose alcoholic strength exceeds 0.5 per cent alcohol by volume (although no duty is chargeable on beer that does not exceed 1.2 per cent). This includes mixtures such as shandy. Also classified as beer for duty purposes are certain mixtures of beer with alcoholic liquors or "other substances" of less than 5.5 per cent.

Brewers and their production premises must be registered with HMRC's National Registration Unit (address below).

Duty is charged on the quantity and alcoholic strength by volume (see HI% above) and is normally calculated by reference to the quantity and alcoholic strength stated on the package label or invoice. It becomes payable when the beer is released from or consumed in registered premises or excise warehouses but may also be paid on the constructive removal of beer from "duty suspense" (that is, when it is held on or moved between registered premises or to excise warehouses on registered premises).

To calculate and pay the duty, you must:

- Keep records of all beer produced.
- Keep records of all beer leaving registered premises, or otherwise passing the "duty point".
- Keep a beer duty account.
- Complete a beer duty return and send it to the Beer Duty Accounting Centre; and
- Pay the duty by direct debit unless HMRC has agreed otherwise.

If you qualify for small brewery relief, you must keep records in a beer production account as above, and records of all "small brewery beer" you handle in duty suspension.

Customs officers will make visits to ensure duty is being correctly assessed and accounted for, based on audits of your commercial, accounting and management control systems and on physical checks. Officers will also carry out physical checks on production, stock and movements of beer in duty suspension. They will normally make an appointment, and if they visit without one the attending officer must explain why. You have to grant officers access to any area of the registered premises provided the visit is "at a reasonable time". Your staff must be aware that officers showing the correct ID may visit without appointment.

If you fail to comply with the law or do not account for the correct amount of excise duty, HMRC's options include the issue of assessments and/or civil penalties. These are explained in Notice 208 "Excise assessments" and Notice 209 "Civil penalties: fixed, geared and daily". In many cases you will have the right to appeal. Full details of the appeals procedure are set out in Notice 990 "Excise and customs appeals".

Registration: General

The proprietor, partnership or company intending to brew beer must apply for registration at least 14 days before it starts brewing unless it is covered by one of the exemptions listed below. A separate registration is required for each premises in which beer is produced. Once any queries on the application are settled HMRC will send you a certificate of registration, which will confirm the date of registration and advise you of any conditions which are applicable. You should keep the certificate on the premises to which it refers as officers may ask to see it. Your registration will last until you stop production at the premises. You must notify HMRC in writing both if you intend to cease production and when you have actually ceased.

Except where registration is not required (if you are brewing for personal consumption or for research purposes), production of beer by an unregistered person or on unregistered premises is an offence for which there are severe penalties.

Conditions affecting registration may include:

- Limitation of the extent of registered premises
- Restriction of the classes of beer which may be received or held on registered premises
- Financial security for the duty on beer in duty suspension

If you need temporary additional storage space (for instance, due to seasonal demand) you can apply for temporary registration of any premises under your control within 5km of your registered premises.

To apply for registration, complete the form in Section 32 with a detailed plan of the proposed registered premises. If the whole site is to be registered premises, the plan need only show details of its perimeter. Send them together with a direct debit mandate to the:

National Registration Unit (Alcohol and Tobacco)
HM Revenue & Customs
Portcullis House
21 India Street

Glasgow G2 4PZ
Tel 0141 555 3369, Fax 0141 555 3555
If you have an enquiry once your application form has been sent, contact the NRU. For enquiries before this stage, contact our National Advice Service.
To obtain a direct debit mandate form, contact the:
Beer Duty Accounting Centre
HM Revenue & Customs
Queens Dock
Liverpool L74 4AA
Tel 0151 703 1375

You must make a reasonable estimate of the volume of beer that will be produced in the current calendar year in your brewery and enter details in question 9 of the application form. You must note in your business records how you have made the estimate.

If any changes affect your registration particulars you must write to the NRU giving details. The following changes would require a new application to be completed:

- Change of legal entity, for example, formation of a limited company or
- Change in the ownership or control of your business (in the case of a sole proprietor or partnership)

Other changes that must also be notified in writing

- Change of address of your registered and/or adjacent premises
- Change of name of the registered person, for example, change of company name
- Change of bank account details
- Change of your duty guarantor
- Cessation of production
- The production of other excisable goods on your registered premises;
- Financial difficulties/impending insolvency; or
- You become VAT registered or de-registered

You must apply in writing to make any changes to the classes of beer you are registered to hold

Financial Security

The financial security that may be required as a condition of registration is a guarantee by an approved guarantor who undertakes to pay HMRC in the event of an irregularity. HMRC requires financial security to safeguard the duty on all duty-suspended intra-EU movements of beer and may also require guarantees:

- For beer held in duty suspension on registered premises
- For movement of beer within the UK
- To cover beer that has passed the duty point but upon which duty has not been paid. Further information can be obtained from our National Advice Service.

To arranging financial security, contact the Financial Securities Centre (FSC) at the NRU. Guarantees are the only form of security acceptable to HMRC, which will issue the draft wording to you when you have agreed your level of security. Only HMRC-approved companies may act as guarantors: most banks and insurance companies have this approval, but if you want to check a particular company please ask the Financial Securities Centre.

Duty Liability

Beer becomes liable to duty at the point of production, normally when the earliest of any of the following events takes place: The beer

- Is put into any package.
- Is removed from the brewery.
- Is consumed.
- Is lost (*see* Section 10)
- Reaches that state of maturity at which it is fit for consumption.

However, duty only becomes payable when the beer passes the duty point: that is, when it leaves duty suspension. Duty ceases to be suspended when:

- The beer leaves registered premises, unless it is delivered to other registered premises, to an excise warehouse; for export or shipment as stores, or to entitled diplomats or members of visiting forces
- The beer is received by registered premises not entitled on their registered holder certificate to hold that class or description of beer
- The beer is constructively removed

- The beer is consumed
- The beer is lost
- The beer is irregularly diverted
- You are no longer registered
- The premises on which you are holding the beer cease to be registered or
- The beer is produced and you are not registered to hold beer in duty suspense.

Normally, the duty should be paid by the 25th of the month following the calendar month in which the beer passed the duty point. But if it would help your business to account for duty on duty-suspended beer in advance of delivery from registered premises, you may do so. This is known as "constructive removal". The duty should be paid by the 25th of the month following the calendar month in which the beer was constructively removed.

To work out the duty at the end of the accounting period:

- Total the quantity of beer, at each particular strength, which has passed the duty point in the accounting period.
- Convert the quantity to hectolitres (hl) to two decimal places.
- Multiply the result by the strength of the beer to arrive at the hectolitre percentage (hl%).
- Add together all the hl% totals for the beers of different strengths.
- Multiply the total hl% by the applicable duty rate to find the duty figure.

If in doubt, contact the National Advice Service.

Small Brewery Relief

Small brewery relief applies to beer, other than that brewed under licence, produced by eligible breweries whether in the UK or overseas. Beer produced under licence is always liable to the standard rate of duty.

A brewer with a single brewery not connected with other breweries must satisfy all of the following conditions for its beer to qualify as small brewery beer:

- No more than 60,000hl of beer may have been produced in the brewery in the previous calendar year.
- Less than half of the beer produced in the last calendar year may have

been produced under licence.

- You must reasonably estimate that in the current calendar year your brewery will produce no more than 60,000hl.

These conditions are the same if your brewery is "connected to" other small breweries. The definition of "connected breweries" is determined by Section 839 of the Income and Corporation Taxes Act 1988. The definition of "connection" is very wide; but examples of the circumstances in which people are connected include individuals connected by marriage, family relationships and the like, and companies under the same effective control. This is to prevent, for example, a large business being artificially split into a number of small breweries, each of which would be below the 60,000hl limit.

Estimating the Current Calendar Year's Production

An acceptable estimate must take all relevant factors into account including existing contracts to supply beer and expansion plans. It is important that you make this estimate honestly. If you make an untrue estimate by stating the brewery will produce 50,000 hectolitres in the current calendar year when you know that a reasonable estimate would be 70,000 hectolitres, HMRC can recover all the underpaid duty. You only have to inform HMRC of your estimate when you apply for registration. You don't need to notify subsequent estimates but you must note in your business records each calendar year's estimate at the time you make it, together with details of how you arrived at the estimate. This information must be kept in the form of a beer production account, which you must keep under Schedule 3(a) of the Beer Regulations 1993.

Beer Production Account

Your beer production account must show your estimate of the current year's production with details of how you arrived at it; the previous calendar year's actual production, to be recorded each month; and the total quantity (in bulk hectolitres to two decimal places) of beer that you have produced in that calendar month, split if appropriate between your own beer and beer produced under licence. The quantity should not be reduced to take account of beer you subsequently determine to be spoilt or unfit for use or for any returned spoilt beer.

At the end of each calendar year, your annual production totals shown in the beer production account will determine your continued eligibility for small brewery relief scheme and the reduced rate for the following year. To be eligible for relief you must use the previous calendar year's production and your estimated production in the current year. Neither production total may exceed 60,000hl.

To qualify for small brewery relief, a new brewer must make a reasonable estimate of the amount of beer that will be produced in the current year which, where appropriate, must be grossed up to arrive at a full calendar year's figure using the formula $E \div (365-N) \times 365$ where E = the amount of your estimate and N = the number of days in the calendar year before the brewery started production. For example, if you intend to start brewing on 1 August and you estimate, based on the size of the plant, business plans and workforce, that in the five months to 31 December the brewery will produce 6,400hl, the grossed-up estimate is 15,268hl.

Provided that you reasonably estimated that production would not exceed 60,000hl in the current year, then the first 60,000hl will be small brewery beer and subject to a reduced rate of duty. Any beer over that amount will not be small brewery beer and will be subject to the standard rate of duty.

If you share a brewery, the production figure for the purposes of small brewery relief will be the total production within the brewery in that year.

Calculating Duty Relief

If your actual or honestly estimated annual production figure is less than 5,000hl, the reduced rate is quite simply 50 per cent of the standard rate, rounded up to the nearest penny. (**Remember, though, that any beer you brew under licence from a third party is charged at the full rate; if beer produced under licence exceeds half of your output you lose your eligibility for relief altogether.**)

If your production figure or estimate (P) is between 5,000hl and 30,000hl, you can calculate the duty per hectolitre as follows: (P–2,500) over P times the standard rate. If your production figure is, say 7,500hl then the calculation is: 7,500 – 2,500 = 5,000; divided by 7,500 = 0.6 recurring; multiplied by £16.15 = £10.96 per hectolitre times the % ABV.

The calculation for production of 30,000-60,000hl is more complicated still. You will find it expressed as a proper equation on the HMRC website; translated into step-by-step sums, it goes like this.

First, subtract 30,000 from your production figure or estimate P. Let's say P = 45,000hl. Divide the result (15,000) by 100 and multiply by 8.33 to get

1,249.5. Subtract 1,249.5 from 2,500 to get 1,250.5. Subtract 1,250.5 from P (45,000hl, remember?) and get 43,749.5. Divide 43,749.5 by P and you get 0.97221; which multiplied by the standard rate of £16.47 gives you a duty payable figure of £16 per hectolitre, a saving of 47p per hectolitre or, assuming the average strength of your output is about 4 per cent ABV, nearly £85,000 for the year. And even if you're useless at sums, £85,000 is well worth a few minutes' struggle with a calculator.

Irregularities, Losses and Deficiencies

As a registered brewer, you are responsible for the control of beer in your premises. You must have the necessary systems to control and safeguard your stocks and examine critically all losses and deficiencies.

Your records of production and processing should indicate how much beer you lose during routine operations, for example, the losses you normally incur during packaging. For accidental losses, regulation 14(3) of the Beer Regulations 1993 requires you to record the date and time the loss occurred; a description (product name) and the volume of beer lost, and the alcoholic strength if the loss occurred after production has been completed; and the reason why the accidental loss occurred. If beer cannot be accounted for after the start of production and there is no acceptable explanation, you are liable for duty on the missing beer. You cannot normally offset stock losses against production surpluses.

Normally there is no duty relief of beer that is lost after it has passed the duty point. But if duty suspended beer is spoilt, you do not have to pay the duty providing HMRC is satisfied that it was unintentionally spoilt, contaminated or otherwise rendered unfit for consumption in the registered premises and has not been consumed.

Measurement of Quantity

HMRC can require duty to be paid on the actual quantity of beer in each container as it passes the duty point. However most brewers do not measure the quantity in each container, but use the "average system" common throughout Europe.

Under this arrangement, the average contents of packages must not be less than the declared contents marked on the can, bottle or label or, in the case of draught beer, on the invoice or delivery note. Within limits the actual contents of each container may be more or less than the declared contents.

Packagers using the system must conform to weights and measures codes of practice issued by the British Beer & Pub Association and agreed with Trading Standards. SIBA has a similar code of practice on the contents of kegs and casks. Packagers are obliged to monitor and record the actual quantity of beer in a proportion of packages to ensure they fulfil the code's requirement.

Small Packages

Under the average system of quantity control, duty will normally be charged on the quantity declared on the container for beer delivered in small packages such as cans and bottles. Evidence of compliance with weights and measures legislation will be sufficient to accept the labelled contents as the duty base, unless there are grounds for believing that deliberate duty avoidance is involved. Packagers should exercise "due diligence" to ensure not only that the can or bottle contains on average at least the amount of beer stated on its label, but also that volume in excess of the declared contents is minimised.

To demonstrate that "due diligence" has been observed, you must monitor the filling process to ensure that the quantity put into the package does not regularly or excessively exceed the amount declared on the container. You should record these checks and provide an adequate audit trail to satisfy our officer that due diligence is being exercised. Where there is evidence of consistent excessive overfilling, additional duty will be due.

Large Pack

To ascertain the quantity in large pack – containers from 10–400 litre capacity such as kegs and casks – packagers customarily fill the containers in accordance with the average contents rules. The quantity of beer in a container will be treated as the average of the samples taken for the purpose of complying with these rules, which permit some latitude in the sampling regime adopted. However, in determining volume for duty purposes, packagers will be expected to maintain a minimum sampling rate of one container per filling head per operating day or 0.1 per cent of a production run of 4,000 containers or more; the samples to be representative of the mix of containers filled. A copy of the sampling protocol you intend to use to assure compliance with average contents rules and for duty purposes should be sent to HM Revenue & Customs.

Some smaller packagers do not take samples but use their containers as capacity measures. To meet HMRC's tolerance requirements, they should ensure that the average capacity of their containers is such that they are operating within the set limits.

Sediment in Cask-conditioned Beer

Duty need not be charged on undrinkable sediment in cask-conditioned beer provided the customer (for example, the publican) is made fully aware in writing, at or before the time of receipt, of the quantity of beer on which duty has been charged. If, for example, a barrel (163.7 litres) is likely to contain 2.3 litres of sediment, the customer must be made aware by a statement on the label, delivery note or price list etc. that duty has been charged on 161.4 litres (a copy of the notification to customers must be retained). Any sediment on which duty has not been charged cannot be included in any subsequent claims for relief on spoilt beer.

There is no prescribed method for calculating the proportion of undrinkable sediment, but you must be able to satisfy HMRC that the method you use gives equitable results. Sediment levels for each quality of beer and container size must be regularly monitored by brewers and reviewed/amended (as necessary) at least annually and agreed with HMRC. Any changes to recipes/ingredients etc. during the year, that would significantly affect sediment levels must be notified to HMRC and the allowance adjusted accordingly.

There is no undrinkable sediment allowance for polypins and mini-pins sold by brewers to the public or on bottle-conditioned beer.

Alcoholic Strength

For duty purposes alcoholic strength is the percentage of alcohol by volume (ABV) in the beer expressed to one decimal place, for example, 4.19 per cent ABV becomes 4.1 per cent ABV. Ignore figures after the first decimal place.

You may use any method you wish to measure the strength of beer as long as it produces results that agree with those that would be achieved using one of HMRC's preferred reference methods (described below). Additionally, if using these or any other methods not based on laboratory analysis, an independent analyst must test the ABV of each of your products at least annually to ensure consistency with calculated results. The results of the independent analyses must be held in your business records.

You must continuously monitor and record your ABV results, which should normally fall randomly on either side of the target strength. The average of your results should equate closely with the declared strength.

It is recognised that ABV may occasionally vary, but provided appropriate action is taken quickly to return the strength of the beer to within its normal specification, due diligence will have been demonstrated. You must keep records of action taken to maintain product strength within control limits.

You must establish the strength of each batch for each of your products. Where beer from one batch is packaged into different container types, for example, cans and bottles, you may combine the results. If you can demonstrate to HMRC that based on available information and experience, due care was taken when deciding target ABVs for new and/or infrequently brewed products (and that all decisions, actions etc were properly recorded), HMRC will accept the label/invoice/delivery note strength for duty purposes. Customs officers will examine your results and your record of actions taken. Where the results have consistently fallen above your target, they will wish to confirm that action was taken as soon as the problem was identified to bring the process back into control or to change the declared ABV. If you have failed to take such action, an assessment will be raised for the additional duty due. If there is a dispute over the strength, officers may take samples of beer to be analysed to establish the actual dutiable strength of the beer.

Cask and bottle conditioned beers will continue to ferment after removal from registered premises, resulting in an increase in strength. You must account for duty on the strength at which you expect the beer to be when it is consumed. This is also the strength that must be shown on the label/invoice/delivery note. And in addition to procedures to establish the ABV at packaging, you must regularly monitor and record the actual strength of each quality of cask and bottled conditioned beer at the expected time of consumption, to establish its alcoholic strength. The precise method and frequency of checking is a matter for you, but you must be able to satisfy HMRC of the accuracy of your results.

Beer Duty Account

A beer duty account is a summary of the beer duty due in each accounting period and must contain the following information:

- The amount of duty due on all beer which leaves duty suspension
- The amount of duty reclaimed on spoilt beer which has been reprocessed or destroyed
- The amount of duty reclaimed on drawback.

- The amount of any underdeclarations and overdeclarations from previous periods
- The net amount of duty due for the period and the date and method of payment.

You should keep the beer duty account in a specific book or ledger opening or on computer, providing you can print a satisfactory legible copy of the account when required.

Records

As a revenue trader you need to keep and preserve certain records and accounts as evidence of your business activities (Revenue Traders (Accounts and Records.) Regulations 1992). You also have to allow HMRC access to all your business records.

You have to keep a record of:

- Production
- Stock
- Handling
- Buying
- Selling
- Importation
- Exportation of beer

You must normally keep your records for six years. If, however, this causes problems, ask our National Advice Service if you can keep some records for a shorter period. You must get HMRC's agreement before destroying any business records that are less than six years old. You can keep your records on any form of storage technology, provided that copies can be easily produced and there are adequate facilities for allowing a Customs officer to view them when required. Obtain agreement from the National Advice Service before transferring records. You may be required to operate the old and new systems side by side for a limited period, and HMRC may refuse or withdraw approval if its requirements are not met.

You can keep your records on a computer provided they can be readily converted into a satisfactory form and made available to HMRC when required. If you do keep your records on a computer HMRC requires access to it.

Beer Duty Returns

The beer duty return (EX46) is the form on which you declare your liability for beer duty in each accounting period. You must make a return of your beer duty liability each accounting period, which will normally be a calendar month. If your duty liability for the month is nil you must still send a return. If you fail to submit a return on time you will be liable to penalties. HMRC may estimate the duty which would have been due and to pursue the debt through the civil courts.

If you foresee any problems, you should immediately contact the Beer Duty Accounting Centre (see page 175.)

EX46s are routinely sent out to all registered brewers and packers. If you do not receive a return, you should contact the Beer Duty Accounting Centre.

Each copy of the form has full instructions on how to complete it. You must complete all boxes, writing "none" where necessary. Returns must be completed in ink and any changes must be initialled and dated by the person who signs the declaration – the proprietor, a partner, the company secretary, a director of the company, or any other authorised person.

You must ensure that beer duty returns are completed accurately. Failure to exercise due care in completing returns may result in civil penalties. If you deliberately make a false beer duty return you may face prosecution for the offence and incur heavy penalties. You must submit your return so that it arrives not later than the 15th of the month following the accounting period. When the 15th falls at a weekend or on a public holiday the return must be received by the previous working day.

Mixing Beers from Different Brews and of Different Strengths

- Beer that is not in duty suspension may not be mixed with duty-suspended beer.
- Beers of different strengths that have passed the duty point may not be mixed until they are sold to the consumer.
- You may mix duty-suspended beers only on registered premises or in an excise warehouse.
- There are no restrictions on the mixing of beers of the same strength that have passed the duty point.
- You may mix small brewery beer with beer of a different rate of duty in duty suspension.

- The mixture will not be small brewery beer and therefore will be liable to the standard rate of duty.

Additions to Beer

Beer can be primed with sugar to boost its alcohol content on registered premises. A registered brewer planning to prime beer on unregistered premises must seek HMRC approval and keep a record of any such premises at which priming takes place. If you are not a registered brewer or registered holder you may not prime beer unless HMRC has approved the arrangements. For approval write to the National Advice Service stating the address of the premises at which you wish to undertake priming; the addresses of registered premises from which the beer will be received; estimated annual quantities of the beer to be primed; and the destination of the primed beer. Your records must include the date and time of the priming; the type of beer (product name) that is primed; the quantity and strength of beer that is primed; the type and quantity of primings added; and the quantity and expected strength of the resulting product. These records should be kept on the premises where priming is carried out and made available to Customs officers when requested.

Beer in duty suspension on registered premises can be diluted with water. If you wish to add water to beer elsewhere, before it is sold or supplied to the consumer, you must obtain approval by writing to the National Advice Service. However, if you add water to small brewery beer after it has left the registered premises where it was produced, it will no longer be small brewery beer.

You can add finings (provided they do not contain alcohol) to beer on any premises.

If you wish to mix beer with any substance, including non-alcoholic beverages, after the duty point, you must seek prior approval from the National Advice Service. However, if you only intend to produce drinks whose alcoholic strength is not more than 1.2 per cent ABV, you do not need approval. Shandy of more than 1.2 per cent and its variants are classified as beer. These include shandy made with lemonade, lemon cordial, lemon flavourings, lemon juice,or lemon squash; lager and lime made with lime cordial, lime flavouring, lime juice, lime squash or limeade; ginger beer shandy, shandygaff or a mixture of beer and ginger, ginger cordial, ginger, ginger flavouring, ginger squash or unfermented ginger beer; beer and fruit cordial, fruit flavourings, fruit-flavoured carbonated water, fruit juice or fruit squash; or beer and any alcoholic liquor or substance other than spirits.

Mixtures containing alcohol other than spirits – for instance, alcopops based on beer – where the end strength is 5.5 per cent or more are liable at the appropriate made-wine rate of duty. Beer mixed with spirits is liable to the spirits rate of duty. This applies even if the majority of the product is beer rather than spirit. There are only two instances where an element of spirit may be used without incurring the spirits rate. These are where there are no spirits in the final product – for example, the spirits are used as a carrier for a flavouring added at an early stage of production – or where the spirits are added in such a small quantity they do not increase in the alcoholic strength of the beer.

If you are unsure of the duty category that will apply to any blend or mixture you intend to produce, you should consult the National Advice Service beforehand. It will also advise you of any additional approvals you may need (for example, a made-wine producer's licence.)

Duty Relief of Duty on Beer that has been Spoilt or is Otherwise Unfit for Use

You can claim duty relief on any beer that has been charged with duty and has subsequently been spoilt or is otherwise unfit for use, provided it is presented for duty reclaim in the same container in which it left duty suspension (unless delivered in bulk). However, where this is not possible for health and safety or other practical reasons, and subject to prior approval from HMRC, the beer may be transferred to other containers.

If a registered brewer buys duty-paid beer that becomes spoilt and he wishes to destroy it and claim spoilt beer relief, he must apply to HMRC for approval to do so. In the case of beer imported on payment of duty, only the person who accounted for the duty on importation will normally be entitled to claim relief, but the National Advice Service will be able to provide further information in these circumstances. NB: spoilt beer does not have to be destroyed if duty relief is to be claimed. It can also be reprocessed – mixed with other beer on registered premises or filtered and/or repasteurised.

You can only claim for the actual quantity of beer destroyed or reprocessed on which duty has been charged. This will depend on whether you use a spoilt beer vessel; destroy directly from cask, keg or other package; or a combination of both. If you wish to decant beer to determine the volume for relief, you must use a gauged and tabulated spoilt beer vessel or establish the volume by using a properly calibrated meter. If you use a spoilt beer vessel to claim relief, you must take a sample for laboratory testing to establish its alcoholic strength. This must be recorded in support of your claim. If you destroy or decant for reprocessing directly from cask, keg or other containers, you can only claim for the actual quantity of beer returned on which duty has been charged. In the case of unbroached containers, you should use the declared contents. Broached containers and depot leakers, which may be unbroached, should have their actual contents measured for duty reclaim purposes. Remember to exclude any undrinkable sediment allowance from the quantity claimed.

To make a claim, total the entries in the spoilt beer record (including those for destructions and reprocessings of spoilt beer) and at the end of the accounting period transfer the total to your beer duty account. To claim relief, enter this total (that is, the spoilt beer relief claimed) in box 12 of your beer duty return.

The following are ineligible for relief:

- Unconsumable beer (for example, sediment in cask conditioned beer) on which duty was not charged
- Diluted beer (unless HMRC approved the addition of water)
- Adulterated beer (beer containing additions which HMRC did not approve)
- Where no satisfactory audit trail is available.

Destroying Spoilt Beer

You must destroy the beer in a way acceptable to HMRC and which makes it unsaleable as a beverage. A Customs officer will advise you if you need to give notice; otherwise you can destroy spoilt beer whenever you wish provided that the following conditions are met:

- A full audit trail is maintained.
- The requirements of other regulatory authorities (e.g. the Environment Agency) are observed; and
- Proper control practices are maintained, including appropriate action at management and supervisory levels.

If you are destroying the beer away from your registered premises, the operation must be supervised by a representative of the brewery.

Repayment of the duty will normally require evidence of a full credit of the duty paid value, or replacement of the goods to your customer (or owner of the goods at the time they became spoilt). In cases where an abatement is made to the amount of credit given, you must be able to demonstrate that the abatement is not due to accidental loss, adulteration, dilution after the duty point or similar circumstances.

The minimum amount of relief that you can claim in any accounting period is £50. If you destroy beer on which the amount of relief is less than £50 during an accounting period, wait until the total amount of relief reaches at least £50 before making a claim. This means that one claim may cover beer destroyed during several accounting periods. If the accounting periods cover a change in duty rates, separate entries must be made in the spoilt beer record for beer charged with duty at the old and new rates.

HMRC does not object to bulking of beer at two rates in one destruction, so long as a system to apportion the total has been agreed in advance.

When beer is either returned to the brewery for destruction or destroyed remotely, Regulation 33(1) of the Beer Regulations 1993 requires you to enter the following details in the destruction section of your spoilt beer record:

- The total volume of spoilt beer destroyed
- The strength of the spoilt beer destroyed
- The date and time of the destruction
- The volume and strength of the beer in each container from which the spoilt beer was directly destroyed
- Evidence of duty charged or paid
- The amount of remission or repayment claimed
- The description of the beer returned by each purchaser for which a claim is made
- The name and address of each purchaser
- The numbers and sizes of each container in which the beer was returned by each purchaser returning the beer.

When beer is returned for reprocessing, enter the following particulars in a reprocessing section of your spoilt beer record:

- The date and time the beer was returned for reprocessing
- The volume and strength of the beer, in each container, in which it was returned for processing

- The total volume and strength of the beer reprocessed
- Evidence of the duty charged or paid
- The amount of remission or repayment claimed
- The description of the beer returned by each purchaser for which a claim is made
- The name and address of each purchaser
- The numbers and sizes of each container in which the beer was returned by each purchaser returning the beer.

Unless HMRC allows a longer period, the spoilt beer record must be completed within one hour of reprocessing taking place.

Returning Duty-paid Beer to Duty Suspenison

Duty-paid beer cannot be returned to duty suspension unless it is spoilt and comes back for reprocessing. If duty-paid beer is returned to registered premises because of a failed delivery, e.g. because a customer is unwilling or unable to accept a delivery or an erroneous delivery has been made, the beer must be separately identified from duty-suspended stock in your records, for example in a failed delivery account.

Beer on which duty has been paid can, subject to certain conditions, be stored with duty suspended beer in your registered premises. No physical segregation of duty suspended and duty-paid beer is necessary. The change of status of any beer from duty suspended to duty paid must be recorded and the product(s) clearly identified in your records.

Exports to EU Member States

You may remove either duty-suspended beer or duty-paid beer to other member states, but you must follow the detailed procedures set out in Notice 197 "Excise goods: holding and movement". These include the following requirements:

- You must have a minimum level of financial security (guarantee) of £20,000 in place.
- You must ensure that you are sending the beer to a warehouse which the fiscal authorities have approved to receive that type of beer.
- You must use specific documentation
- You must receive a valid certificate of receipt confirming that the consignee received the beer.

If you despatch duty-paid beer to the EU and want to reclaim the duty, you must observe the conditions of the drawback system contained in Notice 207, "Excise duty: drawback". (Drawback is a relief for the repayment of duty paid on goods that have not and will not be consumed in the UK.) You should offset the amount of drawback claimed during the accounting period by completing Box 13 on duty return (EX46). The claim should be for completed movements only and supported by the necessary documentary evidence as required by Notice 207.

You may send duty-suspended beer to a non-registered trader, but before you send the beer you must ensure that the consignee has paid or secured the destination member state's duty on the goods. You must hold original evidence before you despatch the beer and you must ensure that the evidence of payment travels with the consignment.

Exports of Beer to Non-EU Countries

To export duty-suspended beer to non-EU countries, you must follow the procedures set out in Notice 502, "A brief guide to export procedures". You must use the Single Administrative Document (SAD/Form C88). Information and guidance on completion of the SAD is contained in the Tariff, Volume 3, parts 1 and 2.

HMRC expects you to produce commercial evidence of exportation for any beer you have removed from your registered premises for export in duty suspension to non-EU countries. Detailed guidance on the type of export evidence it accepts is in Notice 703, "Exports and removals of goods from the UK". Guidance on the documents to be completed is in Notice 197 "Excise goods holding and movement".

You may export duty-paid beer to non-EU countries, but to reclaim the duty you must observe the conditions of the drawback system contained in Notice 207 "Excise duty: drawback".

Unless you can produce evidence that the beer left the EU, you will be liable for duty and VAT at the appropriate rates.

Determining the Strength of Beer

Method One

(a) A representative sample is to be taken and, after first being cleared of sediment and gas by filtration in an approved manner, a definite quantity thereof by measure at the temperature of 20° C shall be distilled.

(b) The distillate shall be made up at the temperature of 20° C with distilled water to the original measure of the quantity before distillation.

(c) The strength of the distillate made up in accordance with paragraph (b) shall be ascertained by determining its density in air at the temperature of 20° C by means of an approved pycnometer used in an approved manner; and

(d) The strength of beer shall be taken to be the percentage of alcohol by volume in the table entitled "Laboratory Alcohol Table" which corresponds to the density determined in accordance with paragraph (c), except that where the density so determined is between two consecutive numbers in the table aforesaid the strength shall be determined by linear interpolation.

NB: Where the result ascertained by the method specified above is rendered inaccurate by the presence of substances other than alcohol, that method shall be adjusted in such manner as may be approved for the purpose of producing an accurate result.

Method Two

If you have no or minimal laboratory facilities, you may calculate the alcoholic strength of your beer by multiplying the number of degrees by which the beer has attenuated by a factor. In order to ensure that your calculations are accurate, it is essential that the original gravity be established as soon as possible after collection and before fermentation commences, which will normally be within one hour of filling the fermenting vessel.

NB: If you add priming sugar to promote secondary fermentation you will need to calculate the alcoholic strength of the finished product as outlined below.

Step action:

1. Measure the original gravity (OG) within one hour of collection

2. Wait until fermentation is completed – for cask-conditioned beer this will be after secondary fermentation in the casks; then

3. Measure the present gravity (PG - also known as the specific or final gravity)

4. When you have taken your readings, calculate the alcoholic strength using the formula:

(OG – PG) x f = a% ABV where:

- OG is the original gravity of the beer.
- PG is the present gravity of the beer.

- a is the beer's alcoholic strength; and
- f is the factor connecting the change in gravity to alcoholic strength.

The value of f is not constant because the yield of alcohol is not constant for all fermentations. In lower-strength beers, more of the sugars available for fermentation are consumed in yeast reproduction than in producing alcohol.

Complaints and Suggestions

If you have a complaint you cannot resolve it on the spot with the Customs officer, or have a suggestion about how HMRC can improve its service, contact one of its Regional Complaints Units. You will find the telephone number under Revenue & Customs or Customs & Excise in your local telephone book. Ask for a copy of the code of practice "Complaints and putting things right" (Notice 1000). You will find further information on the HMRC website, **www.hmrc.gov.uk**. If HMRC is unable to resolve your complaint to your satisfaction you can ask the Adjudicator to look into it. The Adjudicator, whose services are free, is a fair and unbiased referee whose recommendations are independent of HMRC.

You can contact the Adjudicator at:

The Adjudicator's Office
Haymarket House
28 Haymarket
LONDON
SW1Y 4SP
Tel (020) 7930 2292 Fax: (020) 7930 2298
E-mail: adjudicators@gtnet.gov.uk
Internet: **www.adjudicatorsoffices.gov.uk**

Further Information

The British Beer & Pub Association has a series of Guidelines offering advice to brewers and packagers. Copies from: Brewing Publications Ltd, Market Towers, 1 Nine Elms Lane, London SW8 5NQ Tel 0207 627 9191 Fax 0207 627 9123, or visit **www.beerandpub.com**.

Further Help and Advice

If you need general advice or more copies of HM Revenue & Customs notices, ring the National Advice Service on 0845 010 9000, 8am-8pm Mon-Fri.

If you have hearing difficulties, please ring the Textphone service on 0845 000 0200.

To speak to someone in Welsh, Tel 0845 010 0300, 8am-6pm, Mon-Fri.

Directory of Services and Supplies

Please note: the following list is as complete as we could make it but not exhaustive, and we apologise to any providers of supplies and services that have been missed out. Many of the firms listed offer services and supplies in more than one category, but space prevents us from listing each company more than once. It is therefore always worth a thorough check of their websites to see just how wide and varied their activities are.

Bottling machines and sundries

Carlson Filtration, Butts Mill, Barnoldswick, Lancs BB18 5HP
Tel 01282 811000.
www.carlson.co.uk
Email sales@carlson.co.uk

Darley Labels, Wellington Rd, Burton-on-Trent DE14 2ED
Tel 01283 564936
www.darleylabels.co.uk
Email labels@darleylimited.co.uk

Enterprise Tondelli, Unit 7, College Farm Buildings, Barton Rd, Pulloxhill, Beds MK45 5HP
Tel 01525 718288
www.enterprisetondelli.com
Email craig.wilson@enterprisetondelli.com

Garthwest Corrugated Cardboard, Rotterdam Rd, Sutton Fields, Hull HU7 0XA
Tel 01482 825121
www.garthwest.com
Email enquiries@garthwest.com

Gavin Watson Labels, 93 Saracen St, Glasgow G22 5HZ
Tel 0141 336 8233
Email sales@gavinwatson.co.uk

Graphic Packaging International, Filwood Rd, Fishponds, Bristol BS16 3SB
Tel 07771 901493
www.graphicpkg.com
Email keith.brimble@graphicpkg.com

Krones UK, Westregen, Great Bank Rd, Wingates Industrial Estate, Westhoughton, Lancs BL5 3XB
Tel 01942 845000.
www.krones.de
Email sales@krones.co.uk

Leek Bottling Supplies, Unit 12 Churnet Court, Churnetside Business Park, Cheddleton, Leek ST13 7EF
Tel 01538 361919
Email leekbrewery@hotmail.com

Linpac Materials Handling, Newfield Close, Green Lane, Walsall WS2 7PB
Tel 01922 726060.
www.lmh.global.com
Email lmhsolutions@lmhglobal.com

Prolight, Endeavour Park, Crow Arch Lane, Ringwood BH24 1SF
Tel 01425 473500
www.prolightlabel.co.uk
Email enquiries@prolightlabel.co.uk

OPM, Speedprint House, Halifax Rd, Crossroads, Keighley BD22 9DH
Tel 01535 642528
www.opmlabels.com
Email sales@opmlabels.com

StockBox, 2 The Cottages, Home Farm, Barnsdale Rd, Allerton Bywater, Castleford WF10 2AX
Tel 01977 510888
www.stockbox.co.uk

Brewing Consultancy and Installation

Abbott & Co, Northern Rd, Newark NG24 2EJ
Tel 01636 704208
www.mashtuns.com
email info@air-receivers.co.uk

AB UK, Brealey Works, Station St, Misterton, Notts DN10 4DD
Tel 01427 890099
www.abuk.co.uk
Email info@abuk.co.uk

Brewing Design Services, 81-82 Akeman St, Tring, Herts HP23 6AF
Tel 01442 890721/679.
Email info@tringbrewery.com

Iceni Brewery, Foulden Rd, Ickburgh, Norfolk IP26 5BJ.
Tel 01842 878922.
www.icenibrewery.co.uk
Email icenibrewe@aol.com

Mossbrew, 9 Trafalgar St, Burnley BB11 1TQ. Tel 01282 830909
www.mossbrew.co.uk

David Porter, Griffin Inn, Haslingden, Lancs BB4 5AF. Tel 01706 214021
www.pbcbreweryinstallation.com

David Smith, 6 Church St, Copmanthorpe, York YO2 3SE
Tel 01904 706778
www.brewingservices.co.uk
Email david.smith999@ntelworld.com

Brewing plant & equipment

Alan Ruddock Engineering, Unit 6, Shepherds Grove Est., Stanton, Bury St Edmunds IP31 2AR
Tel 01359 250989
www.brewing-equipment.co.uk
Email sales@brewing-equipment.co.uk

Axflow, Orion Park, Northfield Ave, London W13 9SJ. Tel 020 8579 2111.
www.axflow.co.uk
Email tony.peters@axflow.co.uk

Bedford Stainless Engineering, Unit 1, Enterprise Park, Brunel Industrial Estate, Harworth, Doncaster DN11 8NE
Tel 01302 752003
www.bedford-stainless.co.uk
Email bedford@btconnect.com

Brupaks, Unit 12 Honley Business Centre, New Mill Rd, Honley, Holmfirth HD9 6QB
Tel 01484 660008
www.brupaks.com
Email brupaks@brupaks.com

Bühler Ltd, Bühler House, Centennial Park, Elstree WD6 3SX
Tel 0208 238 6666
www.buhlergroup.com
Email buhler.london@buhlergroup.com

Central Bottling International, Plumtree Farm Industrial Estate, Bircotes, Doncaster DN11 8EW
Tel 01302 711056
www.centralbottling.com

Dixon Group Europe, Dixon House, 350 Walton Summit Centre, Preston PR5 8AR.
Tel 01772 323529
www.dixoneurope.co.uk
Email marketing@dixoneurope.co.uk

Don Valley Engineering, Sandalls Stone Rd, Kirk Sandall, Doncaster DN3 1QR
Tel 01302 881188
www.donvalleyeng.com
Email sales@donvalleyeng.com

Eastfield Process Equipment, Eastfield Farm, Tickhill, Doncaster DN11 9JD. Tel 01302 751444
www.eastfieldprocessequipment.co.uk
Email sales@eastfieldprocessequipment.co.uk

Fulton Boiler Works, 210 Broomhill Rd,

Brislington, Bristol BS4 4TU
Tel 0117 972 3322
www.fulton.com
Email uk-info@fulton.com

J&E Hall, Hansard Gate, West Meadows,
Derby DE21 6JN
Tel 01332 253400
www.jehall.co.uk
Email marketing@jehall.co.uk

Hi-Line Services Ltd, 56 Britannia Way,
Lichfield WS14 9UY
Tel 01543 258741
Email info@hilineservices.co.uk

Johnson Brewing, Unit 10 Canalside
Industrial Estate, Woodbine St East,
Rochdale OL16 5LB
Tel 01706 715107
www.johnsonbrewing.com
Email info@johnsonbrewing.com

MDM Pumps, Spring Lane, Malvern WR14
1BP
Tel 01684 892678
www.mdmpumps.co.uk
Email info@mdmpumps.co.uk

Moeschle UK, The Quadrant, 99 Parkway
Ave, Parkway Business Park, Sheffield S9
4WG
Tel 08700 493455
www.moeschle.co.uk
Email sales@moeschle.co.uk

Samson Controls, Perrywood Business
Park, Honeycrock Lane, Redhill RH1 5QJ
Tel 01737 766391
www.samsoncontrols.co.uk
Email sales@samsoncontrols.co.uk

Seepex UK, 3 Armtech Rd, Houndstone
Business Park, Yeovil BA22 8RW
Tel 01935 472376
www.seepex.com
Email sales@seepex.co.uk

Verder Ltd, Whitehouse St, Hunslet, Leeds

LS10 1AD. Tel 0113 222 0250.
www.verder.co.uk
Email info@verder.co.uk

Vigo Ltd, Dunkeswell, Devon EX14 4LF
Tel 01404 890262
www.vigoltd.com
Email info@vigoltd.com

Windsor Fabrications, Park Works, Park Rd,
Dukinfield, Cheshire SK16 5LX
Tel 0161 330 5471
www.windsorfab.plus.com
Email sales@windsor-fabrications.co.uk

York Refrigeration, 14 Cross Lane
Industrial Estate, Wallasey CH45 8RH
Tel 0151 630 1800
www.jci.com
Email martin.barrow@jci.com

Casks, Cask Washing, Ancillary Supplies

CypherCo, Twyford Rd, Rotherwas
Industrial Estate, Hereford HR2 6JR
Tel 01432 34340
www.cypherco.com
Email info@cypherco.com

Eurobung, Roe Head Mill, Far Common Rd,
Mirfield WF14 0DG
Tel 01924 496671
www.eurobung.co.uk
Email sales@eurobung.co.uk

Kammac plc, Brewery Support Services
Container Management Division, Suite 39,
Anglesey House, Anglesey Rd, Burton-on-
Trent DE14 3NT
Tel 01283 743743
www.kammac.com
Email justin.raines@kammac.com

Logopak International, Grovewood House,
Kettlestring Lane, Clifton Moor, York YO30
4XF
Tel 01904 692333

www.logopak.com
Email sales@logopak.net

Rotech (Swindon) Ltd, Units 10-11, Blackworth Industrial Park, Highworth, Swindon SN6 7NA
Tel 01793 764700
www.rotech.com
Email enquiries@rotechkeg.com

Computer Services

Chatsworth Computers, Chatsworth House, Millennium Way, Chesterfield S41 8ND
Tel 01246 457150
www.chatsworth.co.uk
Email info@chatsworth.co.uk

Durham Brewery Ltd, Unit 5a, Bowburn North Industrial Estate, Bowburn DH6 5PF
Tel 0191 3771991
www.durham-brewery.co.uk
Email gibbs@durham-brewery.co.uk

Premier Systems, Whitesides Farm, Fritham, Lyndhurst, Hants SO43 7HH
Tel 02380 811100
www.premiersystems.ltd.uk
Email sales@premiersystems.ltd.uk

Dispense Systems

Alumasc Dispense, Standard Works, Stirling Way, Borehamwood WD6 2AJ
Tel 020 8953 4191
www.alumascdispense.com
Email sales@alumaschdispense.com

Drinks Dispense Group, Lakeside House, Turnoaks Park, Burley Close, Chesterfield S40 2UB
Tel 01246 273166
www.drinksdg.com
Email enquiries@drinksdg.com

England Worthside, Hope Mills, Hope Place, Keighley BD21 5LJ

Tel 01535 682222
www.worthside.co.uk
Email enquiries@worthside.co.uk

John Guest Ltd, Horton Rd, West Drayton UB7 8JL.
Tel 01895 449233.
www.johnguest.com

Hallamshire Brewery Services, Liverpool St, Sheffield S9 2PU
Tel 0114 243 1721
www.hallamshire.co.uk
Email sales@hallamshire.u-net.com

IMI Cornelius UK, Tything Rd, Alcester, Warks B49 6EU
Tel 01789 763101
www.cornelius.com
Email abigailm@corneliusuk.com

Engineering Services, Process Management, CIP Systems

ABM Ltd, Pitt St, Widnes WA8 0TG
Tel 0151 420 2829
www.abm.ltd.uk
Email andrew.r@abm.ltd.uk

Alfa Laval, 7 Doman Rd, Camberley GU15 3DN
Tel 01276 63383
www.alfalaval.co.uk
Email general.uk@alfalaval.co.uk

Beverage Process, PO Box 25, Ledbury, Herefs HR8 1YL
Tel 01531 631948
www.beverageprocess.com
Email info@beverageprocess.com

Endress & Hauser Ltd, Floats Rd, Manchester M23 9NF
Tel 0161 286 5000
www.uk.endress.com
Email info@uk.endress.com

FKI Logistex, Trowel House, Kettering Parkway, Kettering NN15 6XR

Tel 0870 350 3055
www.fkilogistex.com
Email david.stock@eu.fkilogistex.com
FMA Process Engineering, Three Spires
House, Station Rd, Lichfield WS13 6HX
Tel 01543 255152
www.fma.uk.com
Email info@fma.uk.com
GEA Process Engineering Ltd, Leacroft Rd,
Warrington WA3 6JF
Tel 01925 855702
www.tuchenshagen.co.uk
Email n.jones@tuchenhagen.co.uk
Gimson Engineering, 30 Boston Rd,
Beaumont Leys, Leicseter LE4 1AU
Tel 0116 236 8688
www.gimsoneng.co.uk
Gramos Applied Chemicals, Spring Rd,
Smethwick B66 1PT
Tel 0121 525 4000
www.gramos-applied.com
Email info@gramos-applied.com
Hanovia Ltd, 145 Farnham Rd, Slough SL1
4XB
Tel 01753 515300
www.hanovia.com
Email sales@hanovia.com.
Inoxpa Realm Ltd, Gladstone Rd, Croydon
CR20 2BQ
Tel 0208 689 5521
www.inoxpa-realm.com
Email inoxpa-realm@inoxpa.com
Lorien Engineering Solutions, Trent
House, Fradley Park, Lichfield WS13 8RZ
Tel 01543 444244
www.lorienengineering.com
Email engineering.solutions@lorien.co.uk
Microdat, Lowfields Rd, Leeds LS12 6BS
Tel 0113 244 5225
www.microdat.co.uk
Email enquiries@microdat.co.uk

Moody plc, West Carr Rd Industrial Estate,
Retford DN22 7SN
Tel 01777 701141
www.moodyplc.com
Email info@moodyplc.com
Pall Food & Beverage, Europa House,
Havant St, Portsmouth PO1 3PD
Tel 02392 302269
www.pall.com/foodandbev
Email processuk@pall.com
Parker Hannafin, Tachbrook Park Drive,
Tachbrook Park, Warwick CV34 6TU
Tel 01926 317878
www.parker.com
Penborn Technical Services, Garrett
House, Windmill Rd, Brentford TW8 0QA
Tel 020 8569 7979
www.penborn.com
Email enquiries@penborn.com
Veolia Water Solutions, Whittle Rd, Meir,
Stoke-on-Trent ST3 7QD
Tel 01782 599000
www.veoliawaterst.co.uk
Email enquiries@veoliawaterst.co.uk

Hop Merchants

Botanix Ltd, Hop Pocket Lane, Paddock
Wood TN12 6DQ
Tel 01892 833415
www.botanix.co.uk
Email intray@botanix.co.uk
Charles Faram & Co, The Hop Store,
Monksfield Lane, Newland, Malvern WR13
5BB
Tel 01905 830734
www.charlesfaram.co.uk
Email paulcorbett@charlesfaram.co.uk
Lupofresh/Morris Hanbury International,
Benover Rd, Yalding, Maidstone ME18 6ET
Tel 01622 815720/700
Email admin@lupofresh.com or admin@
morrishanbury.com

Steiner Hops, 319 High St, Epping CM16 4DA
Tel 01992 572331
www.hopsteiner.com
Email enquiries@hopsteiner.co.uk

Institutions

Brewing, Food & Beverages Industry Suppliers Association, PO Box 4563, Wolverhampton WV1 9BX
Tel 01902 422303
www.bfbi.org.uk Email info@bfbi.org.uk

Brewing Research International, Coopers Hill Rd, Nutfield, Surrey RH1 4HY
Tel 01737 822272
www.brewingresearch.co.uk
Email bri@brewingresearch.co.uk

Brewlab, Darwin Annexe, University of Sunderland, Chester Rd, Sunderland SR1 3SD
Tel 0191 515 2535
www.brewlab.co.uk
Email info@brewlab.co.uk

Campaign for Real Ale (CAMRA), 230 Hatfield Rd, St Albans AL1 4LW
Tel 01727 867201
www.camra.org.uk
Email camra@camra.org.uk

Institute of Brewing & Distilling, 33 Clarges St, London W1J 7EE
Tel 0207 499 8144
www.ibd.org.uk
Email enquiries@ibd.org.uk

International Centre for Brewing & Distilling, Heriot-Watt University, Riccarton, Edinburgh EH14 4AS
Tel 0131 451 3183
www.bio.hw.ac.uk/icbd

Society of Independent Brewers (SIBA), PO Box 101, Thirsk YO7 4WA
Tel 0845 337 9158
www.siba.co.uk
Email secretariat@siba.co.uk

Laboratory, Analysis, and Technical Support

Anton Paar Ltd, 13 Harforde Court, John Tate Rd, Hertford SG13 7NW
Tel 01992 514730
www.anton-paar.com
Email paul.jiggens@anton-paar.com

Bellingham & Stanley Ltd, Longfield Rd, North Farm Instrial Estate, Tunbridge Wells TN2 3EY
Tel 01892 500400
www.bs-ltd.com
Email sales@bellinghamstanley.co.uk

Cara Technology, Leatherhead Enterprise Centre, Randalls Rd, Leatherhead KT22 7RY
Tel 01372 822218
www.cara-online.com
Email hilary.flockhart@cara-online.com

Gas Measurement Instruments Ltd, Inchinnan Business Park, Renfrew PA4 9RG.
Tel 0141 812 3211
www.gmiuk.com
Email sales@gmiuk.com

GSPK, GSPK Technology Park, Manse Lane, Knaresborough HG5 8LF
Tel 01423 865641
www.gspk.co.uk
Email enquiries@gspk.co.uk

Hach Ultra Analytics, Unit 4, Holmewood Business Park, Chesterfield Rd, Holmewood, Chesterfield S42 5US
Tel 01246 599760
www.hachultra.com
Email uksales@hachultra.com

Integrated Scientific Ltd, 3 Aspen Court, Rotherham S60 1FB
Tel 01709 830493
www.integsci.com
Email sales@integsci.com

Skalar UK Ltd, Breda House, Millfield Industrial Estate, Wheldrake, York YO19 6NA

Tel 01904 444800
www.skalar.com
Email r.hill@skalar.co.uk

Stevenson Reeves, 40 Potterow, Edinburgh
EH8 9BT
Tel 0131 667 9225
www.stevenson-reeves.co.uk
Email sales@stevenson-reeves.co.uk

Strathkelvin Instruments, Rowantree
Avenue, Newhouse Industrial Estate,
Motherwell ML1 5RX
Tel 01698 730400
www.strathkelvin.com
Email info@strathkelvin.com

Malt, sugars, adjuncts

Bairds, Station Maltings, Witham, Essex
CM8 2DU
Tel 01376 513566
www.bairds-malt.co.uk
Email sales@bairds-malt.co.uk

BOCM Pauls Ltd, Lidum Mill, Ashby Rd,
Shepshed, Loughborough LE12 9BS
Tel 0870 0500 306
www.bocmpauls.co.uk
Email richard.leigh@bocmpauls.co.uk

Crisp Malting Group, Great Ryburgh,
Fakenham, Norfolk NR21 7AS
Tel 01328 829391
www.crispmalt.com
Email info@crispmalt.com

Thomas Fawcett & Sons, Eastfield Lane,
Castleford WF10 4LE
Tel 01997 552490
www.fawcett-maltsters.co.uk
Email james@fawcett-maltsters.co.uk

French & Jupps, Stanstead Abbots, Ware
SG12 8HG
Tel 01920 870015
www.frenchandjupps.co.uk
Email info@frenshandjupps.co.uk

Greencore Group, 24 Eastern Way, Bury St
Edmunds IP32 7AD
Tel 01284 772000
www.greencoremalt.com
Email greencoremalt@greencoremalt.com

Micronized Food Products, Standard Way,
Northallerton DL6 2XA.
Tel 01609 751000
Email colin.miller@
micronizedfoodproducts.co.uk

Muntons, Cedars Maltings, Stowmarket
IP14 2AG
Tel 01449 618300
Email sales@muntons.com

Ragus Sugars Ltd, 139 Bedford Avenue
Trading Estate, Slough SL1 4RT
Tel 01753 575353
www.ragus.co.uk
Email sales@ragus.co.uk

Simpsons Malt, Tweed Valley Maltings,
Tweedside Trading Estate, Berwick-upon-
Tweed TD15 2UZ
Tel 01289 330033
www.simpsonsmalt.co.uk
Email malt@simpsonsmalt.co.uk

Edwin Tucker & Sons, The Maltings, Teign
Rd, Newton Abbot TQ12 4AA
Tel 01626 334002
Email malt@tuckersmaltings.com

Warminster Maltings, 39 Pound St,
Warminster BA12 8NN
Tel 01985 212014
www.warminster-malt.co.uk
Email chris.garratt@warminster-malt.co.uk

DD Williamson (UK), Trafford Park Rd,
Manchester M17 1PA
Tel 0161 886 3345
www.ddwilliamson.co.uk
Email info@ddwmson.com

Process Aids

Ineos Silicas Ltd, 4 Liverpool Rd,
Warrington WA5 1AB
Tel 01925 416100
www.ineossilicas.com
Email john.leake@ineossilicas.com

ISP Europe, Waterfield, Tadworth KT20 5HQ
Tel 01737 377103
www.ispcorp.com
Email gbushell@ispcorp.com

Murphy & Son, Alpine St, Old Basford,
Nottingham NG6 0HQ
Tel 0115 978 5494
www.murphyandson.co.uk
Email info@murphyandson.co.uk

Promotional and Marketing

The Beer Mat Corporation, Cariocca
Business Park, Sawley Rd, Manchester M40
8BB
Tel 0871 264 3439
www.thebeermatcorporation.co.uk
Email info@beermatcompany.co.uk

Burton Beer Mats, Moor St Works, Moor
St, Burton-on-Trent DE14 3TA
Tel 01283 564769
www.burtonbeermatsltd.co.uk
Email sales@burtonbeermats.co.uk

Festival Glasses, Calderdale Business Park,
Club Lane, Ovenden, Halifax HX2 8DB
Tel 01422 382696
www.festivalglass.co.uk
Email info@festivalglass.co.uk

Invicta Plastics, Harborough Rd, Oadby,
Leicester LE2 4PH
Tel 0116 272 8330
www.invictagroup.co.uk
Email p_crossland@invictagroup.co.uk

Mosaic Board Printers, 1 Pytchley Lodge
Rd, Pytchley Lodge Industrial Estate,
Kettering NN15 6JQ

Tel 01536 312500
www.mosaic-boardprint.com
Email mosaicboard@btconnect.com

Promotional Marketing & Design,
Wellswood House, Birchfield Rd, Wavertree,
Liverpool L7 9LY
Tel 0845 257 0274
www.promo-uk.com
Email talk2us@promo.com

Quarmby Promotions Ltd, Britannia Rd,
Milnsbridge, Huddersfield HD3 4QE
Tel 01484 653011
www.quarmby.com
Email email@quarmbystudio.com

Index